Keeping Bees
With a Smile

for:

Michael John.

" *Keeping Bees With a Smile* is a valuable guide for independent-minded beekeepers who are seeking ways to keep bees without treating them with chemicals, disrupting their homes, and otherwise intruding on their lives. Fedor Lazutin, one of Russia's foremost natural beekeepers, describes a beekeeping system based on a trust of a bee colony as a living being capable of solving life's challenges without human assistance. Beginner-friendly and complete with fascinating photographs, it is a special book, and one that I expect will 'shake up' the thinking of the independent-minded beekeepers in North America and Europe. "

— Dr. Thomas D. Seeley
Professor and Department Chair, Cornell University
Author of *Honeybee Democracy* and *The Wisdom of the Hive*

GARDENING WITH A SMILE SERIES · BOOK 3

Keeping Bees With a Smile

A Vision and Practice of Natural Apiculture

Fedor Lazutin

Translated by Mark Pettus, Ph.D.
Edited by Leonid Sharashkin, Ph.D.

DEEP SNOW PRESS

Ithaca • New York

Gardening With a Smile Series
Book 3

Keeping Bees With a Smile
by Fedor Lazutin

Translated from the Russian by Mark Pettus
Edited by Leonid Sharashkin

Artist: Andrey Andreev
Technical drawings: Alexander Razboinikov
Cover photograph: Alexey Kirillov

ISBN: 978-0-9842873-5-2
Library of Congress Control Number: 2013944067

Text printed on 100% post-consumer recycled paper.

Published by Deep Snow Press
www.DeepSnowPress.com

Contents

Acknowledgements

I'd like to express my sincere appreciation to Zhenya Chuklova and Lena Lazutina, as well as Dmitry Vatolin and Maxim Sidorov, who offered all kinds of invaluable observations regarding the text.

I am infinitely grateful to Dr. Leonid Sharashkin for his dedicated effort and meticulous care in preparing the English edition, to Dr. Mark Pettus for the exquisite translation, and to Andrey Andreev for the truly wonderful illustrations.

Furthermore, this book would likely never have come about without the involvement of many friends and neighbors, who have so actively contributed to developing the natural approach to beekeeping. Thanks to all of you!

Part I

A Path to Natural Apiculture

A Brief Introduction

Dear reader, the book you have before you is anything but another run-of-the-mill beekeeping manual. It's not a textbook and doesn't pretend to say anything radically new about apiculture. Rather, I simply felt the irresistible urge to share the experiences and observations that inspired me, some time ago, to adopt a particular approach in working with these remarkable insects.

What I have in mind is a natural beekeeping method that keeps human intervention into the life of bees to a minimum: no feeding them sugar, no changing the size of the nest with brood boxes and supers, no subjecting the bee colony to chemical agents of any kind, and no artificial propagation. In short, a natural beekeeper gives his bees the maximum degree of freedom to live their life as they see fit.

But is this even possible?

Of course it is! Even as I type this, looking up from my computer screen, I can see a modestly sized beeyard outside my window. I only inspect my bee nests twice a year, in the spring and late summer; the rest of the time I'm simply an onlooker, admiring the finely choreographed work of these amazing insects. And despite the fact that our hives are populated by European dark bees, known for their grumpiness, my wife and son and I work all summer on our grounds, passing near the hives repeatedly every day. All of our guests (of which we have plenty!) also make a point of visiting our beeyard, to take a look at our beautiful hives and their inhabitants, without the least fear of being stung (Photograph 14, p. 333).

Without exception, no one can believe, at first, that everything could possibly be so simple. And no wonder, since the engrained stereotype paints beekeeping as a labor-intensive day-in-and-day-out chore that is all but incompatible with any other activity. On top of that, beekeeping is portrayed as an extremely complex profession, one that requires years of training.

It is precisely this stereotype that has dealt such a heavy blow to modern beekeeping. The results are simply ludicrous: 3.5 million bee colonies in all of Russia!* In a country seemingly designed by nature herself to host hundreds of times more bee colonies and feed the nations of the world with its honey! And all of this without harming nature—in fact, by benefiting nature immensely.

Does this all sound like a fantasy? Not in the least. Only a fraction of a percent of the nectar supply in Central Russia's temperate zone (about which I'm writing primarily, since I'm most familiar with it) is being taken advantage of. Just spend some time in a village! You'll be lucky to find an apiary with ten bee colonies. In fact, you'll be hard pressed to find even a couple of apiaries with a hundred or more colonies in an entire district. How can this be?

I've done a lot of thinking on this topic, sifted through mountains of literature, and spoken with both professional and amateur beekeepers. And I've come to understand that the root of the problem lies in the approach to nature in general, and to bees in particular.

---

* For comparison, the European Union, with a land area four times smaller than Russia's, has some 15 million bee colonies. The United States, with 40% less land area, has some 2.7 million colonies (down from almost 6 million in the 1940s). *Ed.*

Once upon a time, man—fancying himself the ruler of the natural world—granted himself the right to interfere in the most delicate of the mechanisms that govern the life of a bee colony. And those mechanisms began to break down. Ever since, apiculture has been struggling with the consequences of this breakdown, sinking ever deeper into the mire.

However, in the 19th century and the crazy 20th, a good number of people have kept their bees naturally, striving to honor nature's laws to the fullest possible extent. Even today, many such people remain. For a variety of reasons, they rarely trumpet their existence, and their voices are seldom heard in print or in beekeeping forums on the Internet.

At one time, when I began keeping bees on an extra-deep frame, I almost felt as if I'd invented an entirely new hive. But not for long! When I looked back through all the available literature (around 70 books and a large number of journals), I suddenly discovered exactly the same kind of hives, and highly similar systems for keeping bees in them. The first such hive was that of Georges de Layens (described in more detail below, pp. 103 and 134–135). Invented in 1864, his hive became very popular in Russia in the early 1900s. Until, that is, the forced introduction of industrialized collective-farm apiculture...

So over the past several years I've been asked regularly to share my beekeeping experience and to speak of the difference between the natural and industrial approaches, of the global history of beekeeping, and of what it has led to. It turns out that a great number of people are interested in bees!

Many people dream of adding a few beehives to their garden, and in such a way as to have as little fuss with them as possible, to have them look pretty and not ruin the view, and without the bees bothering the family members and neighbors. That is, they have the same dream that I once had. It is for people like these that this book was written—as well as for those who sincerely love these wise little insects and keep them in "traditional" Dadant or Langstroth hives, but have long suspected that something isn't quite right!

Meanwhile, I am overjoyed at the sight of the beautiful horizontal hives with extra-deep frames popping up at the homes of many of my friends. After all, having bees as neighbors makes people kinder, wiser and happier.

How It All Got Started

Back in the day, when I decided to set up two or three beehives on my land, I was absolutely certain that apiculture was a long-established branch of knowledge and that the only thing left for me to do was to arm myself with its conclusions and recommendations and competently put its theories into practice.

This certainty was reinforced by the ten or so booklets I managed to buy or borrow from friends, which, with a neophyte's zeal, I read through voraciously, and in good faith.

They all contained highly similar descriptions of the bee colony and its life cycle, the products of beekeeping and nectar plants, and bee enemies and diseases. They all had completely identical drawings of hives designed by Dadant, Langstroth, and a few others, along with some basic recommendations for using them.

And while I made sense of the first part rather quickly, attaining a solid understanding of the basics of bee colony life, the second part—the practical side of things—left me more or less stumped. Why?

First of all, I very much wanted to understand the train of thought that motivated these hives' creators to build them as they did; I wanted to tease out the logic behind the methods applied in working with bees, and to see some kind of comparative analysis that spelled out the pluses and minuses of various beekeeping systems.

But the books only contained ready-made plans, without further explanation or commentary. Do this, that and the other, they said—this is the right way, the scientifically justified way, of doing things. And there were no answers to the many questions that had arisen during my reading. Not only were no answers forthcoming from the literature—my seasoned beekeeping friends had no answers either.

At any rate, I brushed all of this aside for the time being and got down to business. All of the colorful stories detailing beginners' bungling forays into beekeeping, of which I'd heard quite a few by that time, I attributed exclusively to a failure to follow the specialists' recommendations.

I, of course, did everything with absolute perfection: I built three solid Dadant hives and populated them with colonies of Carpathian bees I'd bought from a commercial beekeeper I knew. And, as I started working with them,

I began to understand very quickly that something was wrong...

Or, more accurately, everything was!

I sensed with all of my being how much bees abhorred any intrusion into their homes—for example, when a bee-keeper lifts the top off the hive and pulls out the frames, one after another, into broad daylight, with their fragile brood and busily working bees. When, all summer long, he constantly smokes the bees, sweeps them off the frames, and adds and removes the supers.

I greatly disliked artificial propagation methods, swarming prevention, and other procedures the beekeeper is forced to perform on an almost daily basis. Meanwhile, as all of this went on, questions continued to pile up that neither books nor beekeeping friends could provide sensible answers for.

Over the course of the following winter, I delved much more deeply into the topic of beekeeping. When spring arrived, based on the conclusions I'd drawn, I transferred my bees into warm, solid horizontal hives consisting of twenty-five extra-deep frames. One year later, I bought around ten bee colonies of the local race, as closely related to the European dark bee as possible, and installed them in the same kind of hive. Ever since then, I've continuously been filled with joy at the sight of my bees, living and working peaceably not far from our house.

But the question remains:

WHAT'S WRONG WITH MODERN BEEKEEPING?

Why does beekeeping continue to decline further and further, despite all of the scientific developments? Why, despite being so clearly healthful and beneficial, has beekeeping not become a popular, widespread activity? Why are bees everywhere falling ill and dying?

I eventually began to compare modern beekeeping with someone who, having set out for another town, made a wrong turn long, long ago. And despite everything, he keeps plodding along, crossing rivers and mountains, enduring cold and hunger. He senses that he's going the wrong way, but refuses to admit it to himself, because he's afraid to.

And yet, there's simply no denying it!

Through studying the literature, watching my bees, and speaking with many people, I came to understand that a natural approach to beekeeping is a healthy alternative to the industrial approach that still dominates the world's apiaries. This understanding gave rise to a beekeeping system based on deep respect and complete trust of a bee colony as an intelligent and highly advanced living being capable of independently governing its life and solving all of life's challenges.

This system makes it possible to keep bees while expending a minimum of effort and labor, practically without interfering in their lives, without disturbing them unnecessarily, and without doing them any injustice. And the bees respond with gratitude: they work peacefully, without bothering family members or neighbors—all while providing you with the most healthful and tasty product in the world—honey.

Yet the greatest joy for me was to realize that I hadn't discovered anything new. All I'd done is arrive, after considerable independent thought, at the same conclusions that many others had reached long before I did. It was only after finding numerous confirmations of my thoughts and conclusions in the literature that I decided to publish this book.

A small side note. I must hasten to add that the natural approach to beekeeping, whose principles are described in this book, may prove interesting and useful to anyone and everyone. However, the practical recommendations directly regard only those living in the deciduous forest zone of European Russia. And this is very important! This area enjoys an abundance of nectar plants, and forests and meadows filled with wildflowers, and its natural environment has not been as damaged by human activity as it has been in many areas farther south.

This region is very well suited to hosting large stationary apiaries. At the same time, it has a short summer, an extended period with no honeyflow whatsoever, and long winters that require a warm hive and substantial winter reserves.

All that being said, by relying on natural beekeeping principles, anyone can develop a system for any locale and climate, as long as they're serious about it.

The Industrial and Natural Approaches

No book that expresses the viewpoint of one or several people can claim to be entirely free of subjectivity. For my sometimes excessively sharp tone, I apologize in advance to those who keep bees in Dadant or Langstroth hives and do so with the best of intentions, like so many beekeepers in the past. That is, they leave up to 50 pounds (25 kg) of honey for the winter, keep an emergency supply of capped honey, use no feeds other than honey, avoid disturbing their bees unnecessarily, and only keep bees of the local race.

Furthermore, I do not dispute the fact that one can indeed apply various scientific methods (a two-queen system, uniting colonies, and others) to encourage the bees to produce record-setting honey harvests, as certain apicultural shock-workers managed to do during the Soviet period. If anyone has the time and desire for this and enjoys constantly fiddling around with their bees, testing all sorts of approaches and theories on them—be my guest!

Just don't think that there's no other way to do things! After all, thanks precisely to unrelenting and even aggressive propaganda advocating industrial methods as the only methods possible, millions of people have been deprived of the possibility of keeping just a few bee colonies in their gardens, as they did in the old days, exclusively for their own use and enjoyment.

And what a joy it is! My wife and I (and our six-year-old son) have already gotten so used to our little bees that we simply can't imagine life without their friendly buzzing, their unflaggingly energetic vibe, and their delectable honey on our table.

In short, it is a verified and indisputable fact that one can keep bees naturally, with a minimal expenditure of time and labor; thousands of years' worth of experience with tree hives* and log hives prove it. As if that weren't enough, we also have a century-and-a-half's worth of experience keeping bees in hives with extra-deep frames—experience that is conspicuously absent from the pages of books and journals on beekeeping.

Reminding everyone of this method is one of the goals of this book.

---

* *Tree hives* (Russian: *bort'*)—artificial tree hollows in living trees, often at considerable height, made for attracting and housing bee colonies. After natural tree hollows, tree hives are Russia's most ancient form of beekeeping. *Ed.*

The Bee Colony's Intelligence

Observing a bee colony, striving to understand what motivates its particular actions, will inevitably leave you asking some deep philosophical questions. In the end, how you answer these questions will prove decisive in choosing your own approach to beekeeping.

In my view, a willingness to make splits,* force-feed bees with sugar, or artificially impregnate queens speaks to a certain approach to life, or rather a lack of any approach whatsoever—that is, doing things "the way everyone else does," without a second thought.

For me, it became clear long ago that every life form is governed by intelligence. Just take a careful look at any insect! An ant crawls along a blade of grass. It stops, wiggles its antennae, pauses for a moment (in thought?), then hurries on about its business. Its every action is carefully thought out and aimed at achieving a goal. And what's true of insects is all the more true of higher animals.

The behavior of any living creature, even the very smallest ones, is so complex and multifaceted that no science can hope to explain it fully. After the most complicated studies, the only thing scientific learning has learned (forgive the tautology!) is to describe the processes taking place in living

---

* *Making splits*—artificially propagating bees by dividing a colony into several parts. This and other beekeeping terms can be found in the Glossary at the end of the book. *Ed.*

tissues—but the question of what stands behind these processes remains unanswered. The only possible answer requires us to assume that everything that lives is intelligent.

Personally, I am convinced that a Higher Intelligence exists that governs all of Life, and that every little plant and every little creature possesses its own individual intelligence. It's just that their intelligence doesn't resemble ours; it lies in other dimensions, beyond the reach of modern man's "vision."

I say "modern" man intentionally, since, it seems to me, there was a time—the so-called Golden Age of humanity—when humans still sensed their connection with this Universal Intelligence and recognized every creature's right to live. These humans understood the purpose of their existence and lived in peace with all other beings. They were filled with energy and joy.

When was this exactly? I don't know. But accounts have survived of ancient Egyptians' ability to use certain sounds to cajole a colony of bees into leaving its hive (most likely in order to harvest the honey), or, on the other hand, to draw a swarm of bees into a new home prepared just for it.

As for the bee colony, all of its actions, the entire rhythm of its life, may only be understood if we acknowledge the fact that bees possess a collective intelligence. When they team up, bees give rise to a kind of overarching "field of thought" and work in unison to resolve highly complicated tasks, such as building a brood nest or maintaining the hive's microclimate.

Judge for yourself. There was a certain researcher studying how honeycomb is constructed. He compelled some bees to build comb under conditions they would never encounter in nature—and each and every time, they hit upon the ideal solution to the problem. He spun the hives in a centrifuge, altered the magnetic field—and eventually was even able to obtain a spherical comb that he dragged around to various forums and exhibitions for many years afterward.

By this researcher's own account, the bees built this comb in several stages: they went to work, stopped, "thought," destroyed what they'd built, and began anew—and they did this multiple times until they found the proper solution. I repeat: such actions cannot be chalked up to mere instinct,

since this challenge was likely being encountered for the first time in the entire history of bees' existence.

Another researcher began moving a sugar feeder a certain fixed distance each day, in the same direction, until the bees (three days later) managed to anticipate where the feeder would show up next. That is, when he brought the feeder to its new location, the bees were already waiting for him!

Are these not convincing examples of a bee colony's intelligence? And there are a lot more where these came from!

Now comes the surprising part. Almost all beekeepers know about all this; in practice, they've encountered the highly complex and often inexplicable behavior of their bees. And yet, willy-nilly, they're forced to turn a blind eye to it, since otherwise they'd have to abandon all of the methods they've grown so accustomed to. And that's a very hard thing to do. As a result, an industrial beekeeper will praise bees to the sky for their amazing intelligence, even while treating them like stupid, senseless little bugs.

Am I wrong?

If you think so, I recommend that you read the literature on methods for artificially inseminating queen bees—or, better yet, watch an instructional video. Personally, I've read the literature, but I couldn't bring myself to sit through the entire video—watching it was downright painful.

And the bees? They'd like nothing better than to escape and fly away, but, like puppets on strings, they can't stray too far. A beekeeper has a full arsenal of tools for forcing them to live in his hive: he can cut out queen cells, split up the colony, remove the brood, or change the queen. Take a look at Shimanovsky's classic work on beekeeping,* and you'll find hundreds of methods for preventing swarming!

---

* Vsevolod Shimanovsky, *Beekeeping Methods*, 1916 (in Russian). *Ed.*

The bees, meanwhile, are left with only one option: to respond with aggression and outbreaks of disease.

Where does this leave us? Well, we're left with the fact that if people have various approaches to a certain subject, then arguing with them or trying to persuade them is useless! It's been proven many times in practice: despite appearing to have a conversation with someone, you always seem to be talking past each other.

This work was written from the viewpoint of the natural approach, and therefore simply can't be understood from any other angle. Consequently, anyone who can't accept the position laid out above *internally* shouldn't bother reading any further.

Those who remain, however, I invite to join me, as we march on together!

The Goals of This Book

This book's primary goal is to gather and systematize the scattered bits of information concerning the natural approach, found in practically any publications dealing with this topic.

The second goal is to present the minimum amount of knowledge about the life of bees and the principles of beekeeping that is absolutely essential for anyone who has decided to set up even a couple of bee colonies for the first time.

The third goal is to make life easier by answering, once and for all, numerous questions asked by those interested in the natural approach.

Finally, the fourth goal is to promote a return to apiculture's former glories, when everyone, young and old, knew how to get along with bees, when every yard was home to numerous beehouses, when people ate their fill of honey and lived to be a hundred!

In my presentation, I hope to avoid, as much as possible, commonly known or easily accessible information, emphasizing instead information you're unlikely to find in a standard text on beekeeping.

So, let's get down to business!

The Tree Hollow as the Bees' Natural Home

The tree hollow, as the bees' natural home, has been studied and written about repeatedly. Information of a tree nest's structure provides a wealth of inspiration for reflecting and drawing the practical conclusions necessary when building hives. After all, bees (especially our local northern bees) have adapted their entire life cycle to life in a tree nest.

What are the primary features of a tree hollow that should be kept in mind?

- A tree hollow has thick walls—4 inches (10 cm) and beyond—that ensure solid insulation, protecting it from the cold during winter and the heat during summer.

- The tree hollow is especially well "insulated" from the top by several yards' worth of tree trunk, situated directly above the bees' nest.

- As a rule, a tree hollow has only one "entrance," formed by a knot in the wood that has rotted out. The bees attempt to seal off any other gaps or openings.

- Bees are especially fond of tree nests whose entrance is situated halfway up the hollow—at least 10–12 inches (22–25 cm) from the top—that is, the upper portion of the bees' nest should always consist of an *extremely warm vault with no air vents whatsoever.*

• Moreover, the tree nest can have a considerable depth, sometimes exceeding even 6 feet (2 m). That is, as long as there's a warm vault at the top, the bees aren't bothered by a large empty space toward the bottom. This may even be advantageous, since extra moisture can accumulate at the bottom of the nest during the wintering period, which then escapes during the summer.

• Bees like a nest that is as least 20 inches (50 cm) tall.

• And, to state the obvious, the tree nest is never moved from one place to another, nor does the location of its entrance ever change!

A falling tree might, I suppose, be an exception to the final rule—after all, such things do happen. So beekeepers know that, when removing from a tree a swarm trap in which bees have been living for several days, one can move it a bit lower, or a bit to the side, and the bees will still find it. But if it's moved much farther, they'll continue to congregate where the swarm trap was hanging previously. That is to say that bees have a strong sense of place, and become very accustomed to the location of the entrance to their home; any and all changes are a source of distress. For example, if, on a horizontal hive, one round entrance is sealed and another one opened, the hive's bees, upon returning home after foraging, continue to beat their heads against the closed entrance, without immediately locating the new one, for a very long time (more than a week).

Here's another interesting point. A tree nest located in a live tree may sway slightly in the wind, along with the tree trunk itself. Could this explain why bees, starting at a certain depth, join individual combs with brace comb?

One especially important matter is a tree nest's diameter, since this topic has given rise to widely conflicting data.

Some time ago (the mid-19th century), the renowned Polish beekeeper Kazimierz Lewicki, following an exhaustive study of the tree nests available to him, made his deep frames 10 inches (24 cm) long. He took this length (or just over it) to be the diameter of the standard, statistically average tree nest (see Figure 7, p. 114, and Figure 5, p. 104).

But what, then, are we to make of more ancient testimony? Below is a well-known quotation, taken from Nikolay Krivtsov's book, *European Dark Bees* (St. Petersburg: Lenizdat, 1995):

> On the Russian forests, Iovii Novocomensis* wrote that "the most dependable harvest is of wax and honey, for the land is full of honeybees. Here, in the forests and the thick tree groves, one often comes upon extraordinary swarms of bees settled in the trees; one often finds tremendous masses of honeycomb hidden away in the trees; and the tree stumps, some of incredible thickness, sometimes harbor veritable lakes of honey."

A very simple explanation presents itself: at one point, there were virgin forests where oaks or linden trees of more than 3 feet (1 m) in diameter—far from being giants—were

---

* *Iovii Novocomensis*—reference to Paolo Giovio (1483–1552), an Italian humanist whose 1525 book contains a description of Russia's geography. *Ed.*

the norm, as were hollows of more than 20 inches (50 cm) in diameter. By the late 19th century, however, such forests no longer existed in Russia's temperate zone, much less in Europe. Trees growing in regions settled by modern man simply aren't allowed to live to see a hundred...

So it turns out that bees aren't at all intimidated by the size of a hollow; during the winter, the bee cluster gets along fine in a spacious hollow with fresh air circulating on all sides, as long as there's honey stored up top, a nice warm vault above the nest entrance, and moderate ventilation.

By way of confirmation I'll give an example from my own experience. One spring, when I was inspecting one of my colonies, I discovered that I'd forgotten to place an insulated division board to one side of the nest, and that the bees had wintered on ten extra-deep frames, across the full 25-frame volume. And they'd had an excellent winter: the hive was completely dry and contained very few dead bees.

Meanwhile, in the summer, strong honey-producing colonies can develop in high-volume tree nets with a large comb area.

Some Useful Facts About Comb

A tree hollow, log, or hive merely provides the outer walls for the bees' home—or, to use some construction lingo, its "frame." They provide a convenient container for the waxen combs where the entire life of a bee colony plays out. In the comb's wax cells, reserve "provisions" are stored away, the queen bee lays her eggs, the larvae develop, and young bees are hatched.

Bees dedicate a great deal of energy to building their comb; therefore, the comb is used repeatedly, until it becomes completely unusable. For this reason, a swarm of bees "loves" to settle on some old, empty comb (frames from which the honey has been extracted), preferring it to an empty box or a swarm trap with some foundation.*

Detailed descriptions of comb, including its structure, dimensions and uses, can be found in any classical text on beekeeping, so there's no need to repeat them here. However, I'd like to draw your attention to a few important points that will prove useful to us down the road.

So here goes:

Each individual comb is attached to the top of the hollow and drawn straight downward. Bees begin by building a central comb, on two sides of which (at the expected distance!) two more combs quickly appear and begin to grow,

---

* *Foundation*—a sheet of wax stamped with the bases of honeycomb cells.

and more and more combs beyond them, until no room remains in the hollow.

A small colony will successfully overwinter on six combs, and a larger one on eight. An especially strong colony needs all of twelve combs for wintering (and growing in spring), but this is the limit. The famous French beekeeper Charles Dadant stopped at this number— twelve—when developing his hive model.

Young combs are semicircular in shape. Hanging nicely from the top of the hollow, they look something like slices of cheese, with the larger "slice" in the center, and the slices to each side of it growing progressively smaller (Photograph 19, p. 336). When the combs reach the vertical walls of the hollow or the log hive, the bees begin to fasten them to the walls as well—not along their entire length, but here and there, leaving vertical gaps. These gaps create popholes from one comb to another; they are also essential for properly ventilating the bees' dwelling.

After all, bees maintain a temperature of around 95°F (35°C) in areas where their brood is located, as well as a certain humidity, "turning on" the heat or the ventilation as necessary.

These are the purposes (popholes and ventilation) served by the openings and vertical gaps in the combs themselves; they are especially vital for wintering successfully. Winter, of course, is a critical period; bees spend all summer preparing their home for it! Once winter comes, they're no longer able to drill an extra hole or shift honey around.

A newly constructed bees' nest is quite a captivating sight! From the top of the hollow hang delicately fashioned combs, completely teaming with bees. Somewhere, in the thick of the crowd, the queen is on the move, surrounded by her retinue; the sluggish drones slouch about; the worker bees toil away, each occupied with her own particular task. Some store and process the nectar; some feed the brood; some clean the cells; and others, dangling like a cluster of grapes, are drawing fresh comb.

A bee colony doesn't fill in its dwelling with comb without rhyme or reason, but rather according to a very specific "general plan," developed in each instance based on the dimensions and shape of the hollow, the location of the entrance, and other factors. The bees leave popholes in some combs; some are built with undulations, like a wave; and some are even curved to one side and fused with neighboring combs.

Many people attribute all of this to sheer caprice, believing that comb is "cobbled together" haphazardly. But this is a major misconception—one that speaks to that human lack of intelligence that distinguishes him from an intelligent Nature!

But here's a contradiction: when we place a frame with foundation into a hive, we're forcing that hive's inhabitants to build their comb in a certain way, in a way they'd never build it if left to their own devices—that is, from the very start, we're working against nature!

Yes, this is indeed the case. And therein lies the fundamental drawback of a movable-frame hive. However, we do have two ways of compensating for it.

First, we can build a hive and fill it with frames in a way that approximates, as much as possible, the way bees would fill it themselves in a natural setting. And, secondly, following the springtime inspection, we can refrain from disturbing the nest portion of the hive. The bees themselves, in response to the task presented to them, will create the best possible conditions for raising their young and wintering successfully!

Here and there, they won't draw their comb to the bar of the frame, leaving a vertical gap; here and there, they'll leave openings in the comb. Experienced beekeepers know that bees are especially prone to "botching" comb in this fashion in the nest portion of the hive. And, "winterizing their bees," these same beekeepers will try to replace these botched combs with better ones, leaving the winter cluster without popholes or ventilation!

By the way, more than once I've read and heard about beekeepers who do not winterize bees—that is, they do not rearrange frames in the nest portion of the hive, leaving everything as is. They are quite successful, except for one little problem: the depth of the frames! Bees are incapable of wintering successfully on a standard Dadant frame 11 $^{13}/_{16}$ inches (300 mm) deep!* That is, if they do winter on one, it's at the very limits of their abilities, under abnormal, unnatural conditions—with all of the expected consequences.

But we'll return to this question later. For now, let's get back to honeycombs, and to the following issue, one very important for us: the life cycle of the bee colony.

* In Russia, the standard Dadant brood frame is 17 $^{1}/_{8}$ inches (435 mm) long and 11 $^{13}/_{16}$ inches (300 mm) deep. This is the "Dadant frame" referred to in this book. In the United States, the standard Dadant brood frame dimensions are slightly different: 17 $^{5}/_{8}$ inches long by 11 $^{1}/_{4}$ inches deep. *Ed.*

The Bee Colony's Developmental Cycle

We now see that a large amount of fresh, clean comb gives a bee colony the room it needs for growth, while a shortage of comb can slow or even completely halt it. This fact gives rise to a natural cycle in a bee colony's development, whose timetable depends on the size of the living space at its disposal and on the vitality of the colony itself.

Understanding this natural cycle is probably the most important element of a natural approach to beekeeping. By relying on this understanding, we can decide how to deal with the bees in our care, and work out the few operations that must be carried out in the hive during the course of the year.

This understanding allows us to grasp why the keeper of a multi-story hive must constantly struggle with swarming, and how to ensure that the bees in our hives continue working calmly all summer, gathering honey and preparing for winter.

So, your attention please! Here are the main facts about comb:

- Bees expend a great amount of effort on building comb. Calculations show that a bee will consume at least 8 g of honey in order to build just 1 g of comb. Over one summer, a strong colony is capable of drawing up to 15 Dadant frames (or 10 extra-deep frames*) of comb, but it can fill many times more frames with honey!

• Bees use comb multiple times; that is, in a given cell, multiple generations of bees will be hatched, and reserves of honey and beebread** will be stored on multiple occasions.

• Comb in which bee brood is raised gradually darkens and eventually turns completely black. The cell walls thicken and the cell diameter is reduced.

• Bees do not use old (black) comb, abandoning it in favor of fresh comb.

• Bees are unable to break down black comb in order to build new comb in its place. Or perhaps they simply choose not to? In any case, it's just not done.

• A bee colony rarely uses old (last year's) honey reserves; assuming that foraging is available, they prefer nectar or fresh honey from the current season. Old, partially crystallized honey builds up in the hive as a kind of "dead weight," luring any number of hungry creatures.

Thus, the big picture of bees' life in a tree nest looks something like this: the bees are constantly building new comb, taking full advantage of whatever empty space is available. The queen deserts the old comb to work on the new, and the black, exhausted comb, with its reserves of old honey,

---

* *Extra-deep frame*—standard-length frame that is at least 17 $^1/_2$ inches deep. *Ed.*

** *Beebread*—fermented pollen stored in comb cells; it is used for feeding brood and the queen. *Ed.*

remains unused. And the result? The result is that a strong colony can fill a modestly sized hollow in a single season, and, having wintered in it, is in the mood to swarm come spring. This is perfectly understandable: when the flow* begins, all available cells quickly fill with nectar; the queen has nowhere left to lay her eggs; the young bees have nowhere to build; and, on top of everything, the overpopulated nest begins to overheat.

In a large hollow, bees will build additional comb, expanding downward and out to the sides, and gradually moving away from the black, exhausted layers. During the second and, perhaps, third years the bees are unlikely to swarm, as they grow their large and powerful colony (I'm speaking of the European dark bee). In time, however, having filled the entire space inside the hollow, they will begin to cast one powerful swarm after the other.

Consequently, the life of a bee colony in a tree hollow follows the same law of cyclicity seen in the Universe in general, and in the world of living nature in particular. At the end of the cycle, whose length depends on the size of the hollow, the strength of the swarm that occupies it, the volume of the summer's flow, and other factors, the colony will abandon the nest, leaving its contents to the numerous fanciers of apian delicacies, from wax moths to bears. Thanks to their efforts, the hollow will be cleared out within a very short time, and ready for a new swarm to move in.

Such, as I understand it, is the overall life cycle of a bee colony. But within this larger cycle is a smaller one that is no less important for our practice: the cycle a bee colony lives through over a given year, which brings us to our next topic.

---

* *Flow* or *honeyflow*—the availability of nectar in nature. *Ed.*

A Year in the Life
Of a Bee Colony

We all know that each individual worker bee has a relatively short lifespan: around 40 days. During that time, it manages to live a full, productive, and vivid life, whose stages are described in detail in the professional literature. During various periods of its existence, it will be charged with cleaning cells, feeding the young, drawing (that is, building) comb, foraging, guarding the nest, and performing many other tasks, all to the benefit of its apian clan.

A worker bee dives right into its complicated and multifarious labor almost immediately following its "birth." And here's the amazing part: no one teaches it what to do. It doesn't take any final exams and isn't assigned some work quota. At every moment, the bee itself knows exactly what it needs to do and how to do it.

This topic, of course, exceeds the scope of scientific research. Bee behavior has traditionally been explained by invoking all-powerful *instinct*—which is to say that it hasn't been explained at all. Of course, this is all to be expected, since here we've come to the threshold of the *spirit*, beyond which materialistic science is rendered completely impotent.

Meanwhile, if one looks carefully, one can see this spirit shining through in the life of any living creature, if one can only stop dismissing everything we've grown used to as being simple and obvious. But this is another topic for another day, somewhat tangential to our present study.

I'll refrain, as usual, from providing a full-blown description of the life of an individual bee, referring the reader instead to the traditional literature. Instead, we'll focus our attention on information that can only be assembled bit by bit, from various far-flung sources.

The idea that a beehive is a kind of box containing a certain number of bees is fundamentally flawed. The life of a bee colony is always in flux. The number of bees in that colony depends on the queen's laying rate and can fluctuate dramatically over the course of the year. In the spring, there are very few bees; they behave lethargically and allow the beekeeper to calmly carry out his inspection of their nest. During this period, the winter bee still predominates; its task is simply to survive the winter and raise the new brood that will replace it once spring arrives.

The queen already begins to lay her eggs in late winter, but lays very little at first, gradually increasing her egg production. However, as soon as the first flow begins, her laying rate rises dramatically, and some time later a large number of young bees begin to appear in the hive. This is easily seen: each day the youngsters emerge and take flight—forager bees, marked by the bright spots of their pollen pellets, are constantly swerving into the hive entrance, and a friendly, joyous buzz is heard throughout the beeyard.

In Russia's deciduous forest belt, the springtime buildup stretches from mid-April to mid-May, and this is the time to tackle your spring inspection—the only operation in the entire year that requires you to disassemble the nest. The best time for it is early May, when the early flow has already stabilized, but the bees haven't yet reached their peak of strength. If you wait until the end of the month, you'll be making your life more difficult!

But we're getting ahead of ourselves. So by late May (don't forget to adjust the timeframe based on your latitude) the bee colony has gained considerable strength. Around this time, it will face a fairly short period with almost no flow, when the springtime nectar plants have finished blossoming, and the major ones haven't started yet. During this period, a colony with sufficient space in its hive will continue to grow, and those who are feeling a bit cramped may cast a swarm.

A natural beekeeper who is looking to expand his apiary may easily take advantage of this natural mechanism. Following the spring inspection, he can stop adding frames to the hive (or, in order to produce the very earliest swarms, not inspect the hive at all) and seal the gap beneath the division board walling off the empty space (details on hive structure will be provided later), thereby limiting the colony's ability to grow. Once they've cast a swarm, you'll need to reopen the gap, move the division board, and add some frames.

This simple procedure can generate as many swarms as necessary, and at the best time for swarming—early summer. Robust swarms installed during this period will not only have time to prepare adequately for winter, but will also manage to yield at least some honey.

If you don't need any swarms, then all you need to do is make sure that the colony always has some fresh foundation to build on, and room for growth. If that's the case, then there's an 80–90% probability that the European dark bee will not begin swarming, preferring instead to grow, over the course of the summer, by filling out the entire space at its disposal.

That is, each spring we put the bees in a situation resembling a large, empty tree hollow (of which we spoke earlier) free of old honey reserves and old black empty comb, and with plenty of space and possibilities for growth.

This is what taking advantage of natural mechanisms is all about.

The primary honeyflow comes in June and early July. Anyone who's been in a beeyard during that time knows what an unforgettable spectacle it can be. The entire yard hums like a single, giant hive. In an uninterrupted line, the bees fly headlong from the hive entrance and, returning with their heavy load, alight laboriously on the landing board. When darkness falls, the flights come to a halt, but some bees remain stationed on the landing board, fanning—driving out of the hive warm air filled with the wonderful aroma of honey.

During August, the colony's activity level gradually falls, and the number of bees in the hive dwindles. Here again, a question occurs to the curious observer: how does the queen, during the thick of such a bountiful harvest, realize that the honeyflow will soon decline? After all, she has to know this ahead of time (by three weeks) in order to reduce her egg production! Science claims that the bees, conspiring among themselves, begin feeding her less. But remember that a worker bee only lives for a little over a month—how, then, could it be aware of annual natural cycles, especially since these cycles may shift by a week or two in any given year?

My sense is that a bee colony that has lived for generations in a particular area constitutes a small part of that area's natural environment, and therefore simply "knows" what the weather will be like by at least half a year in advance. Not that there's anything surprising about that—after all, scientists have discovered many plants that prepare for winter differently based on whether or not the winter will be harsh or mild.

This observation directly regards a later chapter that will deal with bee races; it also relates to certain recommendations found in beekeeping publications.

One such recommendation calls for "helping" the bees grow their colony in time for the main honeyflow. To this end, one is advised to insert electric heaters in the hives in early spring, or to engage in stimulative feeding, or to take other such steps. There's no shortage of methods! As for the results—you'll hear about them from time to time, from practicing beekeepers who aren't embarrassed to admit their mistakes.

For example, let's say you artificially increase the bee population. Then you have a protracted spring, or rains set in. The major honeyflow is postponed by two weeks or so, the bees are in a bad way—and the polemics rage in the beekeeping magazines: what went wrong? Yes, you should have increased the population, but you should have done so a bit later, and using some other method! Beekeepers read the magazines and resume their experiments. Does it sound like I'm exaggerating? I'm not. Just read some old issues of *Beekeeping* magazine—it's all there.

So by late August or mid-September (the time always varies!) the queen stops laying eggs, and three weeks after that, the final brood emerges.

Bees that are "born" in the fall no longer participate in the work. Their task is to survive the winter and raise the spring brood. They live several times longer than summer bees because they move very little and don't work themselves to death by foraging.

When the daytime temperature outside falls to 50°F (10°C), the bees all but halt their flights and begin to gradually form a cluster. Just ahead is the most difficult time of the year: winter.

A Word or Two on Wintering

Strange as it may sound, fairly little is known about the life of a bee cluster during winter. If you walk up to a hive during winter (needless to say, my bees spend the winter outdoors) and press your ear up to the entrance, you'll be able to hear the humming of the bees—the colder it is outside, the louder the humming becomes. By causing their chest muscles to vibrate, the bees closest to the cluster core help raise the temperature inside it. Based on this humming sound, one can judge how the colony is wintering.

In order to generate the energy necessary for heating, the bees slowly consume the honey set aside for the winter. The classical literature claims that the bees are constantly changing their positions within the cluster, moving from the periphery to the center, or upward toward the honey (to replenish the reserves in their honey stomachs), and back again. Today, these ideas are changing a bit. It turns out that the wintering process begins with bees of various ages, and that the older bees—better adapted to lower temperatures— form the "crust" and protect those inside the cluster from the cold. Once the weather warms up, the crust bees die off rather quickly, while those in the core remain able to work for a while longer.

That's the picture, more or less. How accurate is it? I don't know. After all, the devil's in the details. For example, a bee cluster is intersected by combs—how do they cope with it? How does the queen behave? Does she keep her retinue during the winter? And so on and so forth. But let's leave these questions for the researchers, and take a moment to thank them for what they have managed to learn—all of which is of great interest to us.

As usual, we'll stick to a few points of special importance. After all, we have our own agenda: to avoid interfering with the bees' preparations for the most difficult stage in their lives.

So without further ado, *here's the important stuff:*

• Bees do not hibernate during winter. Even during the harshest cold, a cluster's interior maintains a temperature of at least 68°F (20°C), and as much as 95°F (35°C) in late February to early March, when the brood begins to appear.

• Bees obtain the energy needed for heating by consuming the honey located directly above the cluster (Figure 1). In the process, the cluster moves gradually upward at a rate of approximately 1 mm every 24 hours.

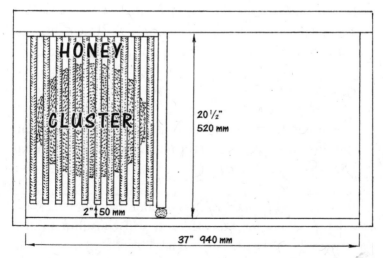

Figure 1. Position of the winter cluster in a horizontal hive

• Bees are unable to use the honey stored in the outer combs. It is only of use in the spring, when the weather outside grows warm and the cluster breaks up.

• The cluster forms in the fall on empty (!) comb, near the lower part of the hive, leaving as many honey reserves as possible "up top."

• Since the cluster takes the shape of a sphere, the least amount of honey will be left in the central comb, a bit more on the adjacent combs, and so on. And, surrounding the cluster, there will remain good frames full of honey and beebread that will fuel springtime growth.

• The preceding point, which reflects the classical understanding of the distribution of winter reserves, needs some qualification. The fact is that bees, as practicing beekeepers have observed, may leave a share of their reserves in the back of the hive (far from the entrance), or leave a comb filled with honey in the center, or leave a portion of beebread inside. They have their own idiosyncratic considerations—more complicated than ours.

• A cluster can be up to 10 inches (25 cm) in diameter.

• In order to pass from one comb to another from within the cluster during winter, the bees leave gaps and round openings in the comb.

• At least 50 pounds (25 kg) of honey should be left for a large colony for the winter. It will consume around 30 pounds (15 kg), leaving 20 pounds (10 kg) in reserves, without which the bees will grow terribly anxious.

• Honey gathered during the main honeyflow is best suited for use during wintering. During the dearth period, bees will "manufacture" honeydew honey that could lead to their deaths during winter. Therefore, the bees ready their winter reserves ahead of time, at the peak of summer—a fact exploited by industrial beekeepers as they add and later remove a super.

• During the winter, the bees are unable to chew a hole through the comb, move honey, or seal any gaps that appear with propolis. All of these things must be done ahead of time.

To summarize:

Wintering is the most serious trial for a bee colony over the course of the year—a trial they spend all summer preparing for. They build a nest, arrange for ventilation and passageways between the combs, and stock up their reserves in their own particular manner. And, if they aren't interfered with, they'll survive the winter splendidly!

Even many industrial beekeepers are beginning to understand this, and no longer rearrange the nest in preparation for winter. However, this very reasonable move doesn't necessarily lead to success, since the very structure of popular industrial hives doesn't allow bees to build their winter nest the way they'd like to.

The Ideal Comb:
How Deep Is Deep Enough?

Now let's calculate how tall the comb should be to allow bees to winter successfully. A cluster is 10 inches (25 cm) in diameter. The bees remain in the cluster for 5–6 months (the dearth period extends even longer). One millimeter of movement per day brings us to 7 inches (18 cm) total. So, the required comb depth is 18 inches (45 cm), including a 1-inch (2-cm) margin. As we mentioned before, this is why bees prefer a hollow of at least 20 inches (50 cm) in depth.

This is also why a large bee colony wintering on a 12-inch-deep Dadant frame (30 cm deep) must be inspected between January and February, and, more often than not, given supplemental food—even if they spend the winter indoors. Since this frame is the most widely used in Russia, we'll have more to say about it later.

But let's get back to spring. As it empties the cells of their honey, the bee cluster has gradually moved upwards over the course of the winter. Here, in the upper portion of the hive, the queen begins to lay eggs, gradually working her way downward as spring progresses. In nature, everything is entirely rational: in the spring, it's warmer in the upper portion of the hive, so less energy is required to heat the brood. A month later, the upper cells are freed up (as the young bees hatch), and can now be filled with honey, thus beginning the preparations for the following winter.

One peculiar feature of the European dark bee is its tendency to store reserves in the upper portion of its nest combs first; only when sufficient reserves have been set aside for winter does it move on to fill the combs to the immediate right and left of the nest, and then those farther away.

This is very important! The farther south the bee originates, the less pronounced this instinct is. Bees living in warmer climates, that enjoy a moderate honeyflow throughout the year, don't prepare for winter at all and "scatter" the honey all over the comb. More northerly latitudes provide for a flow that is brief (just three months), but intense; the bees' top priority is to set aside around 8 inches (20 cm) of honey "up top." Once that's done, they can enjoy the rest of the summer.

You and I should find this perfectly understandable— after all, isn't it the same way with humans? And not only humans! Ever tried taking the last bone from a dog?

At the height of summer, when it's hot outside, and when the hive has enough bees to care properly for their young, the queen will lay eggs in any available comb, although she'll prefer the combs that are closest to the entrance. Worker bees, having filled the upper portion of the nest combs with honey (that is, the winter reserves), will store any surplus honey in empty combs located farther from the entrance. Everything proceeds in perfect harmony.

I'm probably painting an overly simplified picture; in reality, things are much more complex. But, generally speaking, this is what we're looking at.

Now for one more topic—small, perhaps, but no less important.

Winter Ventilation of the Beehive

In both summer and winter, bees have to ventilate their hive. In the summer, this is simple enough: some bees sit in front of the entrance and push air out of the hive by vigorously fanning their wings.

During the winter, of course, there is much less need for air circulation, but the need is still there. During this time of the year, the bees are consuming honey, and exhaling, along with their breath, water vapor and carbon dioxide. And while a certain increase in the carbon dioxide concentration is perfectly acceptable, an excess of water vapors can lead to potentially harmful dampness.

As we know, a tree hollow typically has only one entrance, near the middle of the nest. By itself, this would hardly be enough to allow for hive ventilation, but a tree hollow has its own special features. In a hollow, the bee cluster usually has a large amount of empty space beneath it, and a mouldering, moisture-retentive bottom capable of absorbing excess humidity.

In a hive, there's rarely a lot of space beneath the comb, so for ventilation two entrances are provided: an upper and a lower entrance. In this case, thanks to the heat differential, air will constantly circulate through the entrances. The bees can simply and easily regulate the airflow using the laws of physics—by changing the size of the upper entrance.

You can easily convince yourself of this by peeking into the top (round) entrance during the winter. You'll see that some colonies leave it fully open, while others narrow it with propolis, leaving only a tiny hole for ventilation. What does this depend on? On the colony's size, most likely, and, perhaps, on other factors as well.

Interestingly enough, bees have another way of regulating air circulation during the summer: during a cool spell, they'll crowd the upper entrance, using their own bodies to decrease its size.

This system of two open entrances is standard practice for bees wintering outdoors. Yet we're left with two questions. First: at what width should the lower entrance be left open? And second: shouldn't we go back to the natural system with just one entrance, leaving the bees to deal with it, without the beekeeper's having to worry about when to expand it and when to narrow it? We'll explore this issue in greater detail in Part III. For now, I'll offer a few observations on the topic.

Why is one entrance preferable? Because bees are forced with some frequency to defend their nests from various creatures who crave their stockpiles of honey. Usually, that means wasps, not to mention their own kind—bees from other hives. Large colonies can easily handle this problem, but smaller ones face a struggle. On the one hand, we know that the robbing of weak colonies—and it's a regular occurrence at any apiary—is a natural process; yet, on the other hand, surely we should give even weaker colonies every opportunity to defend themselves.

The literature claims that bees have a harder time protecting their hive with two openings than with one. Why is that? Most likely, it's because bees tend to use one or the other entrance—the top or the bottom—for their flights at various periods of their life, so whatever entrance is left unused is also left unguarded, or less guarded. In a small colony, the bees primarily work in the upper section of the hive and fly through the upper entrance, neglecting the lower one—just take a look at it and you'll see for yourself. And this is where unwanted guests may drop by and peek inside. And once they've peeked, they can point the way for their friends. If, however, there's only one entrance, then that's where the bees will fly, and they'll be able to guard it adequately.

My other observation regards wintering. As we've already learned, in order to winter successfully in the open air, bees need a heat-insulating dome above their clusters, and they need their humid, "used" air replaced by fresh air. When there are two entrances, one above the other, the warm air exits the upper entrance, and the cooler outside air enters through the lower one. Evidence of this is the hoarfrost that develops around the upper entrance on clear, frosty days. Moreover, if the lower entrance is left just slightly ajar (by just a couple inches), then the air circulation will only pass through the central portion of the hive, while the sides will become damp and stagnant—I know this from repeated experience. If the lower entrance is kept a bit wider during the winter (around 6 inches or 15 cm), then the colony will winter much more successfully.

So that's what I usually do—although things would be even better if the lower entrance were left wide open, all the way to the division board.

These measures are reasonable enough, but they do have one downside: you have to take them. Narrowing the lower entrance in late summer to prevent robbing, and widening it before winter to allow for ventilation. Can't we avoid this somehow? Indeed, this is possible (see Part III).

I've heard and read repeatedly of beekeepers who winterize as follows: using a Dadant brood box, they leave a super with honey (enough to last the winter), seal all the entrances, remove the bottom completely and replace it with an empty box. To defend against mice, they wall off the nest box from the empty box with some wire mesh. And the bees winter swimmingly!

The principle at work here is this: a sealed, heat-insulating top and an open space at the bottom. The cold, humid air falls downward, and is replaced by fresh air from the bottom. The bees keep warm, and there's no humidity.

It is possible, in a horizontal hive with extra-deep frames, to completely shut the top entrance while leaving the bottom one wide open. That should leave enough ventilation for the summer (in our region, there's rarely much heat to speak of), and the bees themselves can decide how much to seal up the opening in preparation for winter. Robbing would be no cause for concern, either—having just one entrance makes guarding the hive easier. In extreme cases (if, say, the bees are "bearding"—clustering outside the hive entrance during a spell of extreme heat), there's always the possibility of opening the upper entrance during the main flow period, but I doubt it would ever come to this.

All things considered, there's still plenty to think about regarding the location and sizes of the entrances. Certainly, if we simply allowed the bees to arrange the interior of the hive themselves, without frames, they'd independently devise the most sensible ventilation system. But, given the fact that we're already meddling with their lives, using sheets of foundation to define certain comb sizes and orientation, we should also understand where and how the entrances should be set up in light of the comb arrangement.

But here's the interesting thing. All else being equal (if this is even possible), some colonies winter splendidly, greeting spring with a completely dry hive and a little die-off, while other hives may have a few moldy combs and more dead bees.

Furthermore, every beekeeper will see some number of his colonies perish each winter, often for no apparent reason: there's honey in place, the nest is dry—but the bottom is covered with dead bees. Why?

Having thought quite a bit about this question, and chatting with more experienced beekeepers and consulting the literature, I personally have arrived at a firm conclusion: all of this can be traced exclusively to the race of the bees.

And this is a key issue when it comes to a natural approach to beekeeping.

Bee Races

My friends and I have been the frequent guests of a highly experienced beekeeper in the region of Ryazan. He's kept bees for over forty years, doesn't feed them sugar, only propagates using his own swarms, and doesn't winterize his hives. Simply put, he does everything he can to let the bees lead their lives as they see fit. He's long since stopped keeping count of his colonies—they number somewhere around a hundred and forty. His sturdy little hives stand in the yard behind his house, with its vegetable garden and berry patches, with its ever-bickering chickens, its imperiously strutting geese, and his boisterous grandsons running around. And bees everywhere!

We've spent hours discussing various beekeeping matters, and each time Vladimir Dmitrievich (as our friend is called) keeps returning to the same topic, a topic that pains him deeply: how beekeepers have managed to destroy the European dark bee.

Vladimir Dmitrievich remembers that when he was a child (both his father and grandfather kept bees), the bees even *looked* different! Big, dark and furry, "like little monkeys" (his words!). There were never problems with wintering, not to mention disease.

Around that time, the Soviet authorities began importing bees from more southerly regions, and the genuine European dark bee became a thing of the past. After all, even if one only kept the local race in one's apiary, its offspring wouldn't remain full-blooded—because a queen attracts drones from all around during her mating flight, and all of the surrounding apiaries have Carpathian bees, Caucasian bees, and possibly even Italian bees.

Vladimir Dmitrievich sees the consequences at his apiary on a daily basis. The majority of his bees are almost black in color, while a few have yellow or bluish-gray stripes. Such is the "fruit" of the foreign drones' labors.

At some point, I began seriously studying the subject of bee races, to which I hadn't ascribed much importance at first. And it turned out that this was the most important subject of all!

You simply can't imagine the scale on which, in the not-too-distant past, southern bee races were introduced throughout the Soviet Union. A single queen-rearing apiary in Krasnodar could produce 150 thousand purebred queens per year, and there was no lack of such apiaries! They were primarily "replicating" the mountain grey Caucasian bee, which was "discovered" in the late 19th century by the Russian researcher Konstantin Gorbachev. His discovery was met with such enthusiasm that I simply can't refrain from discussing it here—particularly since today everyone is swept up by the fad for Carpathian bees, and is gradually forgetting the mountain grey Caucasian, whose praises were sung for an entire century.

The mountain grey Caucasian won everyone over with its surprisingly docile disposition, first and foremost. Mountain-dwelling folk had dealt with this bee since the dawn of time, without using smokers or even facemasks; they would always take their bees with them as they moved nomadically from place to place—unafraid, of course, to place the bees near their own dwellings.

The mountain dwellers viewed their wicker skeps, along with the bees inside them, to be part and parcel of any self-respecting household, and never failed to make wedding gifts of them, in order to bring the newlyweds prosperity and fertility.

In contrast to the yellow bees of the Caucasian valleys, the mountain grey Caucasian bee is capable of surviving in harsh high-altitude conditions, often enduring extremely severe weather—and it was this endurance that served as the main argument for the mass colonization of this bee across the central Russian flatlands.

So help me, I simply can't understand why the intelligent, educated people who hatched this entire colonization effort failed to consider a number of completely obvious factors!

First, despite the harsh winters, the non-flight period in the Caucasus is much shorter than it is even in the Black Earth Belt a hundred miles north. In the mountain regions, both at the start and end of winter (I've seen it firsthand!),

there are days when the sun warms things up considerably—even enough for the bees to emerge for a short flight and purge their bowels. At our latitudes, such a thing is impossible for six long months. And that's a crucial difference!

Second, the climate is completely different. The mountain grey bee has no tolerance for humidity. So, when Russian beekeepers put their Caucasian bees in wintering sheds (insufficiently ventilated to boot), nosema,* if not worse, is all but guaranteed.

Third, the nectar resources are entirely different as well—the species of flowers, and the timing and duration of the nectar plants' blossoming season. After all, even in the Caucasus, every distinct region has its own unique bee population, as even the earliest researchers recognized. Because even though the conditions may differ only slightly, differ they do—and a bee is an integral part of its natural environment.

We, meanwhile, without a moment's thought, go and transplant this bee not into some neighboring Caucasian valley, but all the way to Vologda in the north! And we expect stupendous results!

One additional argument for colonizing the mountain grey Caucasian was its long proboscis,** which was a real sensation in its day. But surely if nature endowed the Caucasian bee with such an outstanding feature, then it was precisely in the Caucasian mountains that this feature was needed, and not in the Russian north.

---

* *Nosema* or *nosemosis*—a disease affecting adult honeybees. It is caused by a microscopic fungus and manifests with diarrhea, bees' inability to fly, and other symptoms. *Ed.*

** *Proboscis*—bees' straw-like tongue, which they use for sucking nectar. *Ed.*

Researchers who have studied bee races give similar accounts of the global process of bee colonization. As bees populated ever newer territories, they gradually adapted to the various local conditions and gave rise to local races and populations. As they moved northward, they grew accustomed to the lengthy winters and took maximal advantage of the brief summer, while in the south they learned to withstand heat and drought.

Researchers have shown that, as we have noted, bee populations vary from one neighboring area to another within a single region; the bees from these various populations even differ on a phenotypic level: in terms of the length of their legs and wings, the dimensions of dorsal and ventral plates covering their abdomen, and so on.

Yet we humans have the audacity (what a piece of work is man!) to take a bee colony living in the Caucasian foothills and transplant it to the East European Plain. What could possibly come of this? Let's consider.

Let's say that the colony in question is accustomed to falling dormant in December. Then, all of a sudden in early November—freezing weather! The colony's nest isn't ready and its brood hasn't entirely emerged. These bees usually begin flying in mid-March, but when March finally arrives, the snow is still piled higher than the roof! Their intestinal tract is designed to store up fecal matter (bees don't defecate during winter) for only four months, and now they can't so much as stick their nose out of the hive for half a year!

When to expect the honeyflow, how to combat enemies, what sort of temperatures to expect during the winter—the bees have no idea. What's left for them to do? Get sick and die.

Yet the stubborn beekeeper, armed with his panoply of modern scientific methods, fights his way through all these problems and gives the bees a chance to survive! He drags the hives into a shed (thus sparing them the full brunt of winter), treats the bees for diseases of all description throughout the season, and makes splits from those colonies that do survive, in order to restore the "headcount" of bees in the aftermath of a less-than-stellar winter. And he views all of this as the norm.

Still have your doubts? Am I mistaken? Perhaps I've gone a bit overboard? By no means! In the winter of 2006–2007, 80% of the bees in North America died in what might well be dubbed a national disaster, considering the fact that these busy little bees are responsible not only for the honey harvest, but also for pollinating many agricultural crops. And rest assured that American apiculture is firmly grounded in the most cutting-edge science!

Of course, many imported (non-local) bees continue to do their thing, hauling in the honey and allowing themselves to be manipulated in any way you please—there's no denying the truth. But this way of keeping bees will never be sustainable; years of abundant honeyflow and financial success will always be interspersed with years of large-scale bee die-off, when beekeepers—having tried every last medicine and method at their disposal—start calling supply companies in search of inexpensive package bees.

I wish I could find the words to write even more convincingly, but I can't. To me, the degeneration (through miscegenation with southern races) of our local bee races is a tremendous calamity!

Judge for yourselves: at a local regional beekeepers' society, I inquired once about whether there were any apiaries in the area that housed the local bee race. Everyone shrugged their shoulders: fat chance!

And indeed, the Oka population of the European dark bee—the bee indigenous to our region—is no longer to be found in nature. Is this not a national disaster? Almost all the local beekeepers buy "Carpathians" and "Caucasians" from southern apiaries. Meanwhile, at the local beekeeping shop, treatments for bee diseases are flying off the shelves...

Did you know that disease-inducing microorganisms adapt very quickly to any medical treatment? And once they've adapted, they unleash a new wave of disease—which, in turn, can only be suppressed with new and more powerful treatments.

For example, numerous observers now claim that amitraz and thymol (treatments against Varroa mites) have become all but ineffective. Luckily, new, more powerful, and more expensive treatments are already in stores—all for you, our beloved little bees!

That's the situation. We've gone far astray in our senseless striving to remake nature according to our whim; it's high time we took a break and reconsidered.

There's a way out of this mess, and only one: gradually returning to the local race, the European dark bee. Otherwise,

even industrial beekeeping is doomed to gradual decline, and natural beekeeping is simply unthinkable!

Some beekeepers I know recently hit upon a large website of German enthusiasts who are joining forces to restore populations of the indigenous European dark bee. And although the situation in Europe is even more dire than in Russia, at least someone has started the ball rolling!

Now, I must say a few words about our local Russian populations of the European dark bee.

The European Dark Bee

Previously, great expanses of Russian territory were home to large populations of a single race of bee, the European dark bee. This race's primary features are described in the literature and are directly linked to the unique features of its range and habitat. Let's list them:

- The European dark bee has a pronounced instinct to defend its home. This is perfectly understandable: the long period without any honeyflow forces it to guard its precious reserves assertively.

Make no mistake: the local bees will take none too kindly to anyone who busts into their nest during the summer: they'll crawl all over you, and even if they don't manage to sting you, they'll chase you far, far away.

But why intrude at all? In my household, we don't disturb our bees (adding frames on one side doesn't bother them), and live alongside them all summer long, in peace and harmony. That is, we walk around them, work next to the hives, entertain our guests—and have no problems whatsoever. And in the spring, when the colony hasn't gained full strength yet, taking the nest apart goes very smoothly. In the fall, we can also easily remove the side frames full of surplus honey—the bees have already abandoned them.

By the way, I've heard many beekeepers tell of exceedingly "angry" colonies that, despite all the anger, work harder and produce more honey than other colonies. And, if there's trouble, they'll defend themselves!

That's why I personally don't get too worked up when I detect a "bad attitude" in one of my new (swarm) colonies. In fact, quite the opposite. However, whenever I work with Carpathians (that is, when someone asks me for help), I'm always befuddled: I can *really* take off my gloves, my mask, and forget all about the smoker! Is this a real bee we're dealing with??? (I'm joking, of course.)

• When a frame is removed from a hive, European dark bees who happen to be working on it become extremely agitated and run downward, forming a kind of beard that dangles from the bottom frame bar.

• A European dark bee colony's strength peaks in time for the main flow in order to make maximum use of it. As discussed above, the bees are a small part of nature (an absolutely essential part at that) and live in accordance with its cycles. And they can sense these cycles, adjusting their own lives accordingly throughout the year. The southern bee—as I understand from those who work with it—is capable of "not noticing" the abundant blossoming of the linden tree, preferring instead to forage leisurely among various wildflowers. Of course, it simply "doesn't know" that summer will soon end, and a long, harsh winter will set in.

• As we have noted, the European dark bee stores its reserves near the top of the nest, and only then moves to the other corners of its home.

• The European dark bee caps its comb with a "dry" snow-white seal.

• The European dark bee can fly at lower temperatures than the southern bee. It appears that this quality is due to its greater "furriness," which allows it to retain the heat generated by the movement of its muscles during flight.

• The European dark bee is winter-hardy—that is, it prepares its nest properly for the lengthy winter and easily weathers it (this much is obvious to me and others who keep European dark bees).

• Researchers claim that European dark bee drones are considerably more active than southern ones, which means that a European dark bee queen, all else being equal, is more likely to couple with them during her mating flight.

These two features leave the door open for us to gradually restore the European dark bee, provided that we stop constantly importing other races. And that's a joyous prospect!

One question—already mentioned above—still remains unanswered: why, given the obvious advantages of the local race, did people begin keeping southern bees at their apiaries?

There are several answers.

First, let's take a look around us and ask: do all of modern man's activities really benefit him—not to mention the world around him? Can we really call all of his actions reasonable? Personally, I am highly doubtful. My doubts are based on the water we drink and the air we breathe, not to mention the hospitals, pharmacies, and dental clinics on every corner.

Second (and most importantly), as we've already noted, the European dark bee is much more active in defending its nest. From the point of view of modern industrial apiculture, this creates a big hassle for the beekeeper, who has to break into the hive constantly to carry out all kinds of routine procedures.

Third, modern man, feeling the constant need to invent and experiment, all too often fails to consider the consequences of his actions. And these consequences—that is, not the short-term, but the long-term result of our actions—are the main criteria for assessing their value.

Let's say I've gone and bought some "purebred" Carpathian bees (by the way, this is easier said than done—today, more often than not, you'll find some kind of imitation of the popular brand of the day), and the summer goes great. But what next? Next is a difficult winter (this isn't the bees' native climate). Then, if you're lucky, a good year or two before you'll have to buy a new queen from a queen-rearing apiary. And so on. Why? Few people realize that a Carpathian queen's first generation of offspring (provided that she's mating with local drones) can often manage to get by, while the second is very likely to be unviable.

And since the so-called Carpathians offered for sale are in fact of the first generation produced by miscegenation with local drones, the very next generation has little chance of survival. Many people know this from personal experience, including me.

So by buying foreign (non-local) bees or queens, you're dooming yourself to constantly buying new purebred queens down the road, along with treatments for numerous diseases. That means that your apiary will keep costing you money and will remain dependent on queen breeders, stores, and cash on hand. And if at any point you lose control (which can happen for any number of reasons), you'll be bee-less before you know it. And that's very sad.

I assure you that such incidents are far more common than people usually suppose.

And what do you get in return? The ability to take apart the brood nest with impunity, whenever you want—and that's all! All of the southern races' other advantages are dubious at best.

If, on the other hand, your apiary houses bees that are of the local race, more or less (I repeat, pure races are a thing of the past), then as long as you treat them "humanely," they'll remain healthy and winter successfully. And even if some colonies don't make it, it's no catastrophe—there'll be swarms in the summer, and the apiary will restore itself. By the way, it's the weaker, less disease-resistant colonies that perish, and the ones that do survive will produce strong, healthy offspring. It's natural selection at work.

Have I managed to convince you? If I haven't, I can only hope someone else will. Because the European dark bee's advocates keep increasing in number!

Bee Diseases

This topic follows logically from the former, although deciding to tackle it wasn't easy. Why?

I suspect that my approach to bee diseases may inspire especially sharp criticism from the professionals. But there's nothing I can do about that.

As you may have guessed, I have no intention here of listing every last bee disease and the methods for fighting them; such information can be found in any book on industrial beekeeping. And if you're left wanting more, look at the specialist literature—for example, a guidebook entitled *Honeybee Diseases and Pests* (by Oleg Grobov, Anatoly Smirnov, and Evgeny Popov, published in 1987 by Agropromizdat).

My task is considerably simpler: to articulate the problem from the viewpoint of the natural approach.

I've got this dog named Chara. She's a mix of German shepherd and mutt. She spends most her time in her doghouse, occasionally taking leave for a short stroll through the neighboring fields and forests.

She'll swim in the creek, hunt some mice, and try (for the sport of it) to run down a rabbit. She gnaws on some grasses, and doesn't neglect to shower her favors on the neighbors' compost piles. And then she goes back to her doghouse for a day or two.

What illnesses has she suffered during the eight years of her life? None. And it has never entered my mind to study canine diseases or to give her, say, some kind of preventative vaccinations (other than her rabies shot, since that's officially required). What's more, whenever we go into town and take her walking on a leash, someone, without fail, walks up and says: what a nice dog you've got—she's got a gorgeous coat!

Nor do I know a single dog owner in the countryside who gets mixed up in treating or preventing possible diseases. Why is that, you ask?

It's no different with humans. Imagine a normal, healthy, vibrant human being. Does someone like that need to peruse thick volumes of medical encyclopedias (unless they're in medical school)? I doubt it. They're getting along just fine without them.

But what if we throw a person like that into some unnatural circumstances? What if, for example, he's forced to live in a cellar and eat nothing but microwavable pasta dishes? I can assure you that, in time, he (or his relatives) would need to bone up on their medical knowledge!

You can already see what I'm driving at.

I'm driving at the fact that bees—so immeasurably closer to nature than modern man—simply should not get sick! And the fact that they do get sick should tell us that the way we treat them is fundamentally flawed.

To be more precise, they may well get sick, but they'll usually manage to cope with their problems as long as we don't get in their way. And I'm constantly coming across proof of this in articles written by amateur beekeepers, as well as in classical beekeeping literature.

It's worth mentioning that such well-known diseases as nosema and foulbrood were encountered way back in the early 19th century by the apiculturist Petro Prokopovych; but the majority of bee diseases were only noted around the turn of the 20th century, and today the list continues to grow.

I'll provide a couple of quotations regarding these diseases, taken from A.I. Root's famous encyclopedia *The ABC and XYZ of Bee Culture*:

> Nosema has received little serious attention in this country. It has been accepted as a troublesome disease of minor importance, minimized by good beekeeping practice. Strong colonies in the fall that are provided with an abundance of pollen and honey are usually capable of remaining strong. ...
>
> It should be stated that good beekeeping makes it very difficult for European foulbrood to get a start. Colonies should be strong in the spring. In order to have such colonies it means good wintering; and good wintering in the northern states at least, implies an abundance of natural stores, natural pollen and protection. In the milder climates it requires a larger amount of stores to the colony.

And now, a quotation from the newspaper *Beekeeping in Yaroslavl Province*, issue 40, 1910.

According to D.V. Ushakov's 1899 study entitled *Beekeeping in Yaroslavl Province and Basic Measures for Improving It*, the province was home to 3,523 apiaries with 21,152 bee colonies... 98.5% of colonies were wintering in cellars, and, at the time, were enduring misfortunes of every description. Foulbrood was prevalent in every district; 6,666 colonies were known to have perished, of which 89.8% were in peasant apiaries.

I would like to point out that the majority of authors, both in that time and today, tend to view wintering outdoors as healthier and more natural. After all, it's well known that it's the humidity that bothers bees in winter, not the cold. But wintering outside requires warm hives, preferably double-walled, and adequate reserves.

Speaking of food reserves: are bees today provided with high-quality winter food? The answer is an emphatic no.

In modern beekeeping practice, honey is extracted throughout the season. That means that the beekeeper pulls the best reserves, prepared especially for wintering (this is so important that it bears repeating!)—and then, lest the bees head into the winter with nothing but honeydew honey, or no honey at all, he force-feeds them sugar. He may even give them sugar in the middle of summer—during an extended rainy period, for example—since the honey the colony had gathered up to that point has already been pulled!

And note that the beekeeper we've described means well, by modern standards. And there are so many of them out there who supplement their bees with sugar throughout the entire summer! The honey generated in this fashion may, in the laboratory, be barely distinguishable from the real thing, but it's still not the Honey with a capital "H" that we so love and value! Nevertheless, it does generate a good profit for the commercial beekeeper.

But what's truly fascinating is that *all* the modern literature on scientific beekeeping recommends feeding bees sugar, with various additives! At one point it was even considered a proven fact that sugar was better for bees than honey! Eventually everyone had second thoughts, and now it's recommended to feed bees sugar, but not excessively. Of course, it's perfectly clear that honey differs from sugar syrup in any number of ways; in particular, syrup lacks crucial vitamins and trace minerals.

What's the result, when these things are missing from the diet? Ask anyone in the medical field! An overall weakening of the organism, reduced immunity, and lower resistance to disease. So, what's there to be surprised about?

The fact that bees are able to winter on sugar speaks merely to their tremendous vitality—of their natural health and endurance.

Let's move on. We've already mentioned how beekeepers refuse to allow their bees to ready their own nests for the winter, forcing them to live on too shallow a frame, and all but eliminating the cushion of air beneath the wintering bee cluster.

Are there any positive counterexamples? Absolutely, and in great abundance. In my study of the experiences of amateur beekeepers, I'm always coming across genuine paragons of intelligent apicultural practices. When, for example, keepers with Dadant hives put a few capped super frames into storage during the primary flow period, and then, in the fall, without disassembling the nest, add them back to the super for the coming wintering period. When keepers properly insulate their hives and leave them outdoors for the winter. When they refuse to feed their bees sugar and only propagate them by swarming.

Beekeepers who operate their apiaries in this fashion do without medicines, because their bees don't need them.

But at industrial apiaries, everything's aimed at the quick return. Just do the math: how much extra honey can you get from a hundred hives by feeding them with just 20 pounds (10 kg) of sugar each? That's correct—a ton. Which means 200 thousand roubles ($6,500), at current prices. It's hard to hold back. Although one certainly can.

Daniil Naichukov could. Despite the harsh conditions in the Siberian city of Tomsk, he managed to pull 170 pounds (78 kg) of honey per colony (on average over a 10-year period) simply by keeping strong colonies, and leaving around 65–75 pounds (30–35 kg) of honey for each colony, in the hive and in reserves. And the bees repaid him in spades!

Truth be told, he did feed the bees up to 20 pounds (10 kg) of sugar per colony in the fall (on top of the honey reserves!), but this seems to have been dictated by the "powers that be"—he worked at a Soviet collective farm.

You can find the details in his book *An Experience of Generating Large Honey Harvests in Siberia*, published in Tyumen in 1960. By the way, there's not a word in the book about diseases.

Now, to wrap up the topic of supplemental feeding, let's yield the floor to Ivan Shabarshov, speaking of the works of Anatoly Butkevich (1859–1942), a prominent researcher into the life of bees. The quotation is taken from the book *Russia's Apiculturists* (Agropromizdat, 1986).

Anatoly Butkevich conducted many experiments in supplemental spring and fall feeding to boost brood production. Comparing his results, he demonstrated that the role of supplemental feeding is greatly exaggerated. If a nest contains large food reserves, then stimulative feeding is utterly useless. "The effect of stimulative feeding when reserves are available in the hive is purely psychological," he wrote. "If they have reserves, strong colonies will grow successfully without stimulative feeding, once the hives are removed from winter storage." Thus, plentiful food reserves are needed in a nest. Butkevich was one of the first to speak of this fact.

American beekeepers also thought at one time that stimulative feeding was beneficial. Later, they turned their back on this approach in favor of another one. They began providing their colonies with plentiful food starting in the fall, with boxes full of honey. As Dr. Miller, a famous American beekeeper, said on the subject: "The best time for spring feeding is the previous fall." In other words, bees need large winter reserves. A shortage of food in the spring will limit bees' ability to multiply. Butkevich has noted that feeding bees with low-quality feed—for example, with beet sugar—has a markedly negative effect on the quality of the young bees; and, as he said, "it's not just the quantity of bees that's important, it's their quality as well"—that is, their energy, productivity, and longevity. Prior to Anatoly Butkevich, no one in the Russian beekeeping literature had said so much about the negative impact of sugar feeding on bees. Research conducted by subsequent generations of biologists confirmed the observations of this prominent apiculturist.

The spring growth of a colony is conditioned by its strength, and its strength depends on the queen's fertility near the end of the previous summer. According to Anatoly Butkevich's observations, stimulative fall feeding leads to an unnatural increase in egg-laying at a time when, if left to its natural seasonal rhythm, it would already have

begun to ebb, and therefore causes the queen to become exhausted. During the winter, she is then unable to regain her strength, to store up her reserves of nutrients, to restore the cells in her reproductive glands. "This shows us once again," said the beekeeper, "of how carefully we must approach the natural course of the life of bees. If we ask too much of a normal queen, then we're mortgaging our future." His experiments showed that colonies subjected to stimulative feeding in the fall were less profitable than those that were not. The bees themselves said "no" to the question asked of them. Modern beekeepers also believe that the major factor in allowing a queen to reach her maximum egg-laying capacity is keeping the colony abundantly fed throughout the entire year. Food reserves, when abundant, tend to stimulate the queen's activity, or to limit it if they are insufficient.

But let's get back to bee diseases.

We've already established the main idea: if we don't run roughshod over the laws of nature, and leave the bees as much room as possible to live their own lives, then we can stop worrying about their health. True, we won't entirely eliminate disease; weak colonies will fall ill and die off, but there won't be many of them.

And that's how things were 200 years ago, when humans were aware of the existence of bee diseases, but didn't ascribe much importance to them. Today, it's totally different—and not because of the polluted environment, but rather because of us, modern man. This view is further supported by the fact that even today some people still keep bees "the way their grandfather did," without trying to turn them into something they're not, and without running back and forth to the store for medicine.

That's the principle I follow at my apiary; I don't treat bees for diseases and don't take any preventative measures. And the honey only gets better as a result—it no longer contains those poisonous substances that are intended to eliminate disease-causing microorganisms and parasites, but whose effects on human health have not been fully accounted for.

For my part, I have no evidence to offer on this score; but I might mention that there are data showing that amitraz and thymol, for example, impair not only the Varroa mite, but also the organism of the bee itself.

I do have some fascinating thoughts to share regarding' this most feared scourge of every apiary, Varroa mites. Allow me to cite the book *500 Questions and Answers About Beekeeping* (by G.N. Kotova, I.D. Lysov, and V.P. Korolev, published in 1992 by Prometei). Let's take question No. 466:

Is it possible to entirely cure bee colonies of Varroa?

In theory, it is possible, if all beekeepers would apply their treatments responsibly and heed the medicines' usage recommendations. In practice, the infestation rate can be reduced to 2–3%, which will allow the bees to produce a marketable output.

So where does that leave us? Completely eliminating the mites is impossible. A certain number of them (by the way, not only the Varroa—there are other kinds of bee parasites as well) will always be present in a hive. That's the first thing.

Second, if the number of mites doesn't exceed a certain level, then the colony is considered healthy. If the mites multiply, however, then the colony "gets sick." Interesting, huh?

Inevitably, the question arises: what prevents the mites from multiplying in every colony and destroying it completely? Answer: a strong and healthy bee colony somehow suppresses the mite, keeping its number at an insignificant level. Another question, then: why does a bee colony armed with some mite-suppressing mechanism not go ahead and eliminate them entirely?

Answer: the mite is a clever, mischievous little creature! It somehow contrives to outwit the gentle, gullible bee.

I'm joking, of course. But, to speak seriously about this matter, we'll have to embark on a minor digression and continue our deliberations on nature's intelligence in general.

Symbiosis in Nature
(A Philosophical Digression)

It's quite obvious that human beings tend to take two extreme approaches when it comes to the coexistence of all living things on Planet Earth.

Some view life as a constant struggle for a place in the sun, fought between all of life's various forms; during that struggle, they destroy and devour each other. In the process, the stronger (or better adapted) individuals win.

Others view life as a colossal symbiosis, involving all life's forms and manifestations. Predators and their prey, parasites and their hosts, plant-eaters and plants—all of them play their small but unique role in life's great symphony. As the offspring of a single Universal Intelligence, they cannot but do their part in carrying out the great task that is common to them all.

There's a ton of interesting literature on this question. And although I happen to be an ardent advocate of the second point of view, I don't aim to foist it on anyone else.

But it would be hard for me to explain to those who believe in nothing but struggle why I can regard this mite with such equanimity, without resenting its very existence. After all, surely this mite has its own special function—one that is not without some global significance. If this were not so, why would nature ever have produced it in the first place? This is definitely food for thought.

Bees and Their Enemies

It seems to me that the mite may help to cull weak, unviable bees. It precipitates their ruin in order to prevent an even greater harm threatening the bee colony. And the bees, "knowing" all of this, do not eliminate the mite entirely.

And I do believe that they have a way of getting rid of the mites. This parasite is known to attach itself to the scruff of the bee's neck, and the bee can't remove it on its own. But bees, of course, habitually lick and clean each other. Why wouldn't they use their paws and jaws to remove mites from their buddies' backs? I believe they do remove them. But not always.

How do you like that?

Of course, the wicked mite, multiplying wildly, may destroy an entire colony! You already know the explanation: all of that colony's bees were weak, for reasons we've already explained sufficiently.

By the way, around the time when the Varroa mite began running riot in Russia (the date is known precisely: 1964), entire apiaries died out. Or, more precisely, almost died out—a portion of the colonies always survived in the end. Some colonies, meanwhile, were left completely unaffected by the mite. Why?

On the one hand, this was in the Soviet period, when almost all bees were kept on large collective farms or state-owned apiaries, in accordance with the requirements of official apiculture. Southern queens were distributed throughout the country by the hundreds of thousands, the Dadant hive and the corresponding frame were adopted as the standard and produced on an industrial scale, and any and all deviations were frowned upon.

But, on the other hand, beekeepers of the older, prerevolutionary school were still alive, and were doing things as they saw fit (preferring, for example, the European dark bee). Perhaps bees today owe their very lives to these beekeepers?

Even now, large industrial apiaries subject their bees to year-round preventative treatments against various diseases. The majority of amateur beekeepers follow suit. In the process, special attention is paid to fighting the Varroa mite, which is considered the most dangerous parasite.

Even our friend Vladimir Dmitrievich, who never once in his life medicated his bees, does take preventative measures against the Varroa each fall—just in case. That's how powerful the fear of this parasite is.

Everyone did their darndest to convince me to do the same. The argument is simple: unless you treat your bees with amitraz and thymol (the mite medication) in the fall, they'll all die. Of course, such words inspired a certain fear, but despite it all I never once treated my bees. Nor do I have any intention of doing so.

After all, if I'm keeping my bees (the local race, of course) naturally, then they'll deal with any diseases themselves. And if one colony dies, then another colony, a healthy one, will yield stronger offspring and the apiary will be restored.

On the other hand, if I bail out my bees in their fight against a given disease, then their descendents will be deprived of their mechanism for fighting it. And if one considers the fact that disease-causing microorganisms easily adapt to any treatment that targets them, then where will this all lead? Particularly when the bees themselves no longer know how to cope with the disease independently? It's all perfectly clear.

And what if we take into account the widespread practice of selling knockoff (or very low-quality) treatments? Or the well-known fact that an improper dosage of a medicine can lead to the very opposite of its intended effect? That these medicines are harmful for the bees themselves?

All of this makes the life of the industrial beekeeper very difficult! It turns into that same kind of endless struggle I spoke of earlier. Is this the kind of life you want? I doubt it. That's why the number of beekeepers continues to dwindle.

Not long ago, we were paid a visit by a good friend, a beekeeper from the Tula region. He and his wife have 15 years of beekeeping experience under their belts, and more than 100 bee colonies. You'll rarely meet such kind, life-loving and hard-working people. But it's hard to envy them! There's all kinds of work to be done at their apiary, from early spring to late fall. Requeening, supplemental feeding, disease prevention, adding second boxes and supers, preventing swarms, making splits, and repeatedly inspecting the nests.

Sergey and Tanya (as our friends from Tula are called) are very attached to their bees and are unlikely to ever stop keeping them—and yet, seeing them work and listening to their stories is enough to dissuade one from ever keeping even a single bee colony!

But then, we've already dealt with the topic of bee diseases, and I have no desire to delve back into it. So I propose moving further. Let's take a quick look at the history of beekeeping in general.

A Bit of History

Humans have been keeping bees since ancient times. In the northern latitudes of Russia, they used natural and artificial tree hollows and log hives; to the south, they used skeps and clay vessels. How did they do it? It's an interesting question, but, to my deep regret, it remains murky. The literature boasts hundreds of descriptions of how a Dadant hive is built, but not a single detailed description of ancient methods for working with a log hive. Nothing beyond a few vague words about how the comb was cut once a year (in the fall), and the bees were often smoked to death using sulfur. If anyone has come across any other details, please let me know! I'm certain that things weren't so simple. The beekeepers of old must certainly have possessed special knowledge and skills that were passed down from one generation to the next.

The difficulties associated with keeping bees in a log hive are entirely obvious: quickly aging combs in the nest area and the need to replace them; pulling honey along with comb that could have been used again, etc. One can imagine how hard it must have been to cut out the comb—the comb would break, and the honey would flow down the walls of the log, upsetting the bees and inciting robbing.

It's not hard to guess where the beekeepers' imagination led them: they needed to invent a kind of bee nest that would make it easy to remove the comb and put it back again. So top-bar hives appeared first, followed by movable-frame hives. But this didn't solve the problem; more inventions and discoveries had to be made first:

> 1851: bee space—Lorenzo Lorraine Langstroth*
> 1857: artificial foundation—Johannes Mehring
> 1865: the centrifugal honey extractor—Fransesco de Hruschka

Thus appeared the frame with foundation embedded in it. Foundation is a sheet of wax imprinted with the bases of comb cells—that is, in essence, the partitions between the individual cells, facing in opposite directions.

Bees have two basic instincts when it comes to building comb: building them "from scratch" and repairing (restoring) damaged layers. This second instinct leads them to "draw" the cells traced on the wax foundation, which results in a nicely fashioned frame containing comb.

And since there's a gap between the walls of the hive and the side bars of the frame measuring between $^1/_4$–$^3/_8$ inch (6.5–9.5 mm)—a discovery of Langstroth!—which the bees don't close up, a keeper can simply remove the frame and put it back. A dream come true!

So, the invention of the movable-frame hive gave beekeepers the following advantages:

• Adding fresh foundation into the nest portion of the hive, gradually removing old, blackened comb.

---

* In Europe, Johann Dzierzon's 1848 hive model was already using the correct bee space. L.L. Langstroth was aware of Dzierzon's work when designing his own hive. *Ed.*

- Easily removing comb with honey from the hive, extracting honey, and returning the high-quality empty comb back into the hive.

However, in addition to all of this, beekeepers also won the ability to manipulate their colonies in various ways: transferring frames from one hive to another, splitting up colonies, creating nucs, and much, much more.

And this was the end of everything!

Today, there are many people advocating a return to the log hive. I've got nothing against that! Let's think more about it and give it a try.* But personally, for the time being, I'm going with a movable-frame hive—keeping in mind a *smart* hive and a natural approach to beekeeping—since I don't view the invention of foundation and frames as a bad thing. By no means!

So, what *is* bad, then?

What's bad is to abuse one's powers by neglecting the lives of living creatures we consider beneath us, by giving priority to our own petty business interests over the universal interests of all of humanity and the planet we live on.

History has repeatedly seen a good invention gradually dragged into the realm of the absurd, until eventually it begins to have effects that are the complete opposite of what was initially expected. The foundation frame has become a vivid illustration of this pattern.

---

* Unlike Russia, some jurisdictions, including many US states, require combs to be easily removable for inspection. The enforcement of these laws, as well as available exceptions (e.g., for research purposes) varies depending on the state. *Ed.*

The History of the Frame

Today, when, thanks to the work of many generations of smart and dedicated researchers, we have a highly detailed picture of the life of a bee colony, it can be hard to understand what was going through the minds of 19th-century beekeepers. What did they rely on when proposing one type of hive or another, or a certain size frame? And there were many variants of each (see Figures 3–7, pp. 103–114)!

The pages of beekeeping encyclopedias contain pictures and photographs of hundreds of highly varied and often outlandish structures. But the train of thought of their inventors often remains closed to us. And how interesting it would be to understand them! I would be thrilled to see republications of original beekeeping sources—for example, the works of Prokopovych, Huber, Quinby, and de Layens.

But then, a detailed account of the history of industrial beekeeping exceeds the scope of this book; at the present moment, we're more interested in the results.

As of today, the results look like this. Of the great variety of hive systems and methods for keeping bees in them (and these two things are closely related), just a few have won out and gained global supremacy. And it's absolutely essential to know them.

But even more important is to understand the principles of working with them—and this is something the traditional literature never emphasizes. Let's try to fill in this gap.

Modern Systems of Industrial Beekeeping

The Langstroth Hive

Today, the world's most common hive is the Langstroth hive. It was invented in America by the Protestant pastor L.L. Langstroth in 1851, then modified and mass-produced by the industrial beekeeper A.I. Root.

The hive consists of boxes (usually up to 6) which are set one atop the other. Brood frames measure 17 $^5/_8$ by 9 $^1/_8$ inches (448 x 232 mm),* with 10 frames to a box. Boxes 9 $^9/_{16}$ inches (243 mm) deep are called *bodies*, and those 6 $^5/_8$ inches (170 mm) deep or less are called *supers*.

On its surface, the system for keeping bees in a Langstroth hive appears exceedingly simple and streamlined, which attracts the attention of many beekeepers, especially newbies. What does it involve? Traditional recommendations go as follows:

In the spring, a second box, filled with frames holding foundation and empty comb, is set atop the box in which the colony wintered. Some time later, the queen moves into the new box (it's warmer there, and there's more free space); at some point thereafter, the boxes are reversed, and a third box is inserted between them or above them.

---

* In Russia, the standard length of both Langstroth and Dadant frames is slightly less: 17 $^1/_8$ inches (435 mm). *Ed.*

Two or three weeks later, when the colony has assimilated its new box and gained strength, this procedure is repeated. That is, the two bottom boxes again swap places, and yet another box is inserted between them and the top box.* And so on and so forth (Figure 2). And since industrial beekeepers pull honey throughout the summer, the queen must be confined to a brood box using a screen partition (queen excluder) through which the worker bees can pass, but the queen cannot, due to her size.

Everyone who's first introduced to this system always asks the same question: why all this shuffling of the boxes? Wouldn't it be simpler just to "toss" another one on top, and let the bees have at it? Many have tried this, and it doesn't always work out. Why?

Let's recall that in nature bees draw comb exclusively from the top down, and a tree hollow could never expand upward! Therefore, they sometimes ignore a new box that was simply set on top of the nest, and go about their business as if it wasn't even there. But if you separate the two halves of the hive and insert a box in between them, then the bees will feel compelled to fill in the "hole"—they simply can't help themselves.

Why then, you ask, do the bees take to the very first box added in the spring? The thought goes something like this: after a winter and early spring spent in tight quarters, the bees are happy to find such vitally important space, without which they'd simply be unable to grow at all. On top of that, the total

---

* This sequence is called "bottom supering with brood box reversal." It is one of the many available techniques. Today, many beekeepers refrain from reversing brood boxes and prefer "top supering" (adding honey supers one on top the other) to the bottom supering method. *Ed.*

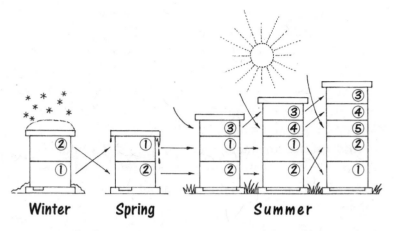

Figure 2. The bottom supering sequence with brood box reversal

depth of a two-box nest is around 18 ¹/₂ inches (470 mm), which is ideal for preparing for the coming winter.

But this is only true of the first box, set on top of the winter box. The same little stunt won't necessarily work with the following boxes (if they're simply set on top); in the end, you'd be forced to resort to shuffling.

Since bees won't manage to prepare a nest for winter if it's constantly being rearranged, a conscientious beekeeper would do well to save a honey box and set it atop the nest portion of the hive come fall. Some amateur beekeepers do exactly that, but it's a big hassle and cuts into your bottom line—and so, as a rule, the bees are allowed to gorge themselves on sugar in preparation for winter.

At gigantic industrial apiaries in Canada, for example, the following system is used: a feeder is set atop the nest box, filled with around 50 pounds (25 kg) of molasses. The bees haul off the molasses and live on it during the winter.

So there's the basic arrangement (I've just described its major principles, without getting into the details). Wow, you say, everything really is so extraordinarily streamlined; there's a step-by-step description of everything you have to do—so just do it! It's like the instructions to some household appliance!

But appearances can be deceiving. After all, bees aren't a bicycle or a coffeemaker—they're intelligent living beings! And they want to build their own lives, not follow schemes foisted on them by us humans.

And yet the technology certainly works! Hundreds of thousands of beekeepers use it, millions of bee colonies live in Langstroth hives, and they pump out the honey and earn their keeper money!

Yes, it's true. But what principle is it based on? Let's formulate it in all honesty.

The system of keeping bees in a Langstroth hive with a bottom supering sequence and brood box reversal is based on the periodic (approximately once every two weeks) destruction of the bee's home, and relies on the bees' instinct to restore the integrity of their nest.

Is that OK? Is this natural for the bees? Judge for yourselves. More will be said below regarding how the bees react to his approach by their keeper.

For now, let's say a few words about another industrial hive—the Dadant hive.

The Dadant-Blatt Hive

The Langstroth hive is better suited for industrial beekeeping in warm and hot climate zones, where there is less danger of the nest becoming too cold as a result of shuffling entire boxes, and where, as a result, the bees are better able to cope with the constant havoc visited upon their home. For this reason, many Russian beekeepers who have attempted to transition to the Langstroth hive have abandoned the idea and gone back to the Dadant hive, for lack of any lesser evils to choose from.

So, what's the major difference between the Dadant hive and the Langstroth hive? Well, working with a Dadant hive is based on a completely different principle. *It consists in periodically pulling the honey that the bees store away for the coming winter.*

Remember what we've said about the European dark bee: that it grows extremely anxious if there's not at least 6 inches (15 cm) of honey "up top," and that it does everything it can to ensure that this reserve is there.

It is this behavior that keepers of Dadant hives take advantage of. The hive is built like this: a 12-frame brood box with frames 11 $^{13}/_{16}$ inches (300 mm) deep and 17 $^{1}/_{8}$ inches (435 mm) long,* and supers with frames 17 $^{1}/_{8}$ by 5 $^{3}/_{4}$ inches (435 x 145 mm). The beekeeping system is as follows.

The colony typically winters in one brood box (without a super). At the end of the winter, the bees are usually fed sugar; then, in the spring, the keeper inspects the brood nest and, once a stable flow has been established, he adds frames with fresh foundation into the nest. After that, he leaves the nest alone for a while; then, when the colony has more or less gained full strength (and this moment can't be missed—which requires experience and flair), he adds a super on top of the brood box.

The bees raise no objections: ample room has suddenly appeared for them to store their winter reserves, since the total depth of the nest has now reached 18 inches (455 mm), including the $^{3}/_{8}$ inch (10 mm) distance between the frames of the brood box and those in the super. The super isn't very deep, so no excessive cooling of the nest occurs.

But then the super fills up. What is to be done? Well, the hive's inventors (it seems to me) saw fit to simply remove the entire super and replace it with an empty one. And let the bees go on working!

In practice, every beekeeper has his own way of doing things. Some, for example, don't remove the full super; instead, they lift it up and insert an empty one in between it and the brood box ("bottom supering"). Some have completely abandoned the supers and only work with boxes, and some use both boxes and supers. But these are all just

---

* In the United States, the standard Dadant brood frame dimensions are slightly different: 17 $^{5}/_{8}$ inches long by 11 $^{1}/_{4}$ inches deep. *Ed.*

details; for us, it's the principle of the thing that's important: *the periodic seizure (or separation from the nest portion) of the honey reserves that the bees have prepared for the winter.*

We'll see later how the bees react to all this. For now, let's try to understand why the Dadant hive is so common in Russia.

After all, it's certainly a peculiar idea to force a bee colony to winter on comb just 12 inches (30 cm) deep! Let's recall that a winter cluster of bees takes up 8–10 inches (20–25 cm), leaving around 2–4 inches (5–10 cm) of reserves above the cluster (including the super, it would be 8–10 inches or 20–25 cm). That is, there's very little honey in the brood box—most of it should be higher up, in the super, but the super's been removed. That means that the honey left in the nest box will suffice for three months of wintering at most.

There are many ingenious tricks for getting around that problem. In the fall, you can shuffle the nest around and add frames full of honey (which will cause the cluster to assume a strange shape, but that's no big deal—the bees can live with it!); or, you can remove the supers, force-feed the bees with sugar syrup, and let them decide themselves where to put it.

Since even these measures aren't enough, keepers will build wintering sheds for the bees (it's warmer there, so less honey is consumed), and provide supplemental feed near the end of winter.

Yet the question remains: why all the hassle? Why not simply build a brood box at least 16 inches (40 cm) deep? Dadant keepers tend to leave this question unanswered.

In fact, it's all quite simple. Most of the hives invented in tsarist Russia featured frames of precisely this depth—16 inches or 40 cm (even a bit deeper). But the Dadant hive was born in France (later, its inventor emigrated to America), where the bees remain in a cluster half the time they do in Russia. So in France 12 inches (30 cm) is enough for wintering, although even that is pushing it.

That is, Charles Dadant intended for the brood nest to be just deep enough for wintering, and no deeper—in fact, he said he'd have preferred to make it even shallower, if this weren't impossible!

And we imported this hive wholesale into Russia! Hard to believe, but it's true. It's anyone's guess as to how this happened.

I think the reason is simple. Germany, where Dadant's hive was widely adopted, was considered the leading country around the turn of the century, and was highly authoritative in technical matters; so everything German was imported and imitated elsewhere, including some things that were of absolutely no use in the local context (for example, heavy turn plows for deep tillage). On top of that, the hives and their accessories were mass-produced, making them inexpensive.

And so, in defiance of all logic, a French hive was introduced in Russia. Then came the revolution. Under the Soviets the Dadant frame, along with the hive itself, became standard, and was introduced coercively and irrevocably at every apiary in the country. The time for discussion was over...

Why am I dedicating so much attention to this topic? Because the Dadant hive remains, to this very day, the most common hive in Russia! And anyone who's even considering keeping bees will certainly encounter convinced advocates of the Dadant hive, although it must be said that their position isn't as entrenched as it once was. I've even met more than one harsh critic of this hive, even some who dubbed it a "killing machine."

The times they are a-changin'!

Just to corroborate my own thoughts and provide some additional food for yours, let me provide a few lines from a previously mentioned book by Ivan Shabarshov, which provides fascinating descriptions of the works of the renowned beekeeper Anatoly Butkevich, who at the turn of the 20th century was one of the Dadant hive's most outspoken advocates. However, his position would soon change.

I quote:

From the very outset, Anatoly Butkevich adopted the 12-frame Dadant hive. And it suited him perfectly, at least at first. He considered the hive to be practical and convenient to work with in all respects. However, difficulties associated with the hive's design soon became apparent. At the end of the flow season, for example, he would discover that the brood nests were almost empty, while the supers were chock-full of honey. To remove them would mean to leave the colony without food. So they had to be given sugar syrup or honey diluted in water for the winter.

This, in his words, "wasn't the end of the world," but it was an extremely labor-intensive chore, and even unsafe, in the sense that it promoted robbing and the spreading of disease. In addition, supplemental feeding wasn't always reliable. As a rule, it produced colonies that were easily exhausted and gradually weakened, especially by the time spring arrived. ...

In the end, Anatoly Butkevich was unable to reconcile two radically opposed beekeeping systems, or to avoid swarming, whether in Dadant hives or in the hives he made himself. "For me," he wrote, "confining the bees to their hive has proven impossible, although I've tried all kinds of methods to achieve this goal." Elsewhere, he admits: "The bees forced me to abandon my quest to overcome their swarming instinct."

Initially, Butkevich was an ardent supporter of the anti-swarming methods. He shared the ideas of his great teachers, Alexander Butlerov and L.L. Langstroth. He tried everything possible to prevent swarming, but he never managed to compel the bees to work back where they'd come from, in the Dadant hives. "Finally, as I considered the swarm bee's amazing capacity for work," he wrote, "I asked myself: does it really make any sense to try to keep bees in their hives at all costs? Wouldn't it be better to give them the freedom to obey their innate tendency to seek out new places, in order to take full advantage of the swarm bees' increased capacity for work?" Thus, he arrived at the "freedom to swarm" system, turning away from all anti-swarming techniques, which he now deemed crude, violent, and unnatural. He even gave voice to the following slogan: "Back to nature, and stop fighting your bees!" To some degree, the slogan rang true, particularly in light of the fact that in those years many "liberties" were being taken in dealing with bees, but not to the point of rejecting interference in the lives of bees that was often unnatural from the insect's point of view, but advantageous from the human's.

Objecting to Anatoly Butkevich, and pointing out his theoretical fear of "unnaturalness" in the lives of bees, Professor Grigory Kozhevnikov wrote that "we should view the bees' natural instincts as nothing more than a means—more or less amenable to our techniques—for arranging the life of bees as we see fit, and we should decide how to exploit these instincts in a way that is maximally beneficial for us."

You can continue reading this highly interesting passage in the original source; meanwhile, I propose returning to our topic at hand.

Bees in the Industrial Hive

In the literature on industrial beekeeping, you'll easily find instructions on working with Langstroth and Dadant hives (there are other designs as well, but these two are the most widespread). At first glance, they seem quite simple and understandable—just grab them and run with them. And this is enough to convince many people—including me, back in the day. So people buy up the hives, install some bees in them, and, once they've been through a couple of seasons, come to understand that things aren't quite so simple.

The bees are testy; they don't want to move into another box, they begin swarming... So you turn to the experience of other beekeepers, you look for advice, you experiment. That helps, but in the meantime things just get more and more complicated.

As a result, the enthusiasm wanes, and sooner or later the majority of people simply give up beekeeping; meanwhile, those few who managed to get by turn into industrial beekeepers, and, by their example, prove that bees are a realm for the chosen few.

It's a sad picture, but it's the reality. And how many people are there who would have been happy to take up beekeeping, but who gave up on the idea once and for all after taking a look at the literature!

Yet the root of the problem is obvious. It lies in the fact that a bee colony isn't some honey-making machine, but a living, intelligent creature! It's laughable to suppose that a colony "doesn't notice" when a human busts into its nest, shuffles the boxes around, pulls out frames filled with its young, hunts down the queen, or ransacks the honey saved up for the winter!

Let's set bees aside for a moment, and imagine the following situation. You work at your job, build a house, and buy the things you need for life. And then, once everything's set up and ready to go, someone moseys right into your house and takes everything of value in it. Or, for example, simply removes an entire furnished room and replaces it with a bare concrete box. How enthusiastic will you be about going back to work and restoring everything, when you know that the whole scenario could repeat itself at any moment? Personally, I'd abandon everything and move somewhere safer!

That's what bees do, too. They start to swarm uncontrollably!

And I've seen convincing evidence of this on more than one occasion. Luckily, it's never happened to me. Someone would take up beekeeping in the spring, add a super some time later, and then, thrilled with their fresh honey, remove the filled super and replace it with an empty one.

And the bees become unrecognizable—they stop working and begin casting one swarm after another. One person I know saw nine swarms in a row emerge in this fashion; he captured them and installed them in new hives. During the winter, only the first swarm survived. It's a typical situation.

A Word or Two About Swarming

Let's think for a moment about what swarming actually is. On the one hand, it's a natural process that seeks to ensure the survival of the species. On the other, it's a way of fleeing unfavorable circumstances.

In the first instance, swarming happens like this: a colony builds a good nest, gains strength, supplies itself with a solid "food" stockpile, and only then does it cast a large, strong swarm—usually one (sometimes two).

In the second instance, any serious sign of trouble can provoke swarming: a cramped or inconvenient dwelling, an ill-suited environment, or a lack of flow in the given area. And once the colony has decided to leave an unfriendly location, it begins to build queen cells and cast one swarm after another, until almost no bees are left in the hive.

Since any intrusion into the bee colony (reversing boxes or replacing supers) is perceived as an extremely negative situation, incessant swarming will be a fact of life for any industrial beekeeper.

Is this a good thing? Of course not! Large-scale swarming sharply decreases honey production and can cause the entire apiary to disappear!

So the beekeeper heads into battle. After all, man is stronger than nature! He will emerge victorious! And indeed he does. But where does that leave the bees?

Swarm-prevention methods are a separate and complicated topic. For anyone who'd like to delve further, I can recommend the work of Vsevolod Shimanovsky—personally, I haven't come across any more exhaustive sources. He details hundreds of beekeeping methods based around anti-swarming measures, of all things.

Shimanovsky, like the majority of beekeepers in his day, caught the virus of the scientific-industrial approach to nature, although he remained a highly scrupulous and forthright researcher. And he wasn't afraid to present alternative viewpoints in his works, including those of natural beekeepers, which is especially valuable for us.

The following quotation was taken from a modern republication of a book Shimanovsky published in 1916 (*Beekeeping Methods*. Kiev: Perun, 1996). It reads:

Methods for preventing swarming using extremely spacious hives

These techniques include anti-swarming methods that, while avoiding all violence to the bees, strive to

eliminate the conditions that encourage the bees to swarm; in so doing, the beekeeper treats swarming as a form of emigration, as the natural desire of living things to escape unfavorable conditions present in their native hive or native locale. According to beekeepers of this school, these unfavorable conditions in the bees' native setting typically only arise when the hive becomes cramped and stuffy from the overabundance of young bees, or when it becomes impossible to do any more work in the hive because it has been filled with structures and stockpiles. The beekeeper's task, then, is to eliminate these conditions.

Those who subscribe to these views certainly cannot deny that, in essence, swarming is a way to propagate the bee race, and that nature has implanted this need in all organisms of the plant and animal kingdoms; but they also claim that absent external factors—for example, a cramped hive—this need remains latent in bees and fails to manifest itself; eventually, in fact, by way of natural selection, it could disappear entirely. The weak swarming tendencies of our northern bee races are cited as an example of such natural selection. Undoubtedly, these bees migrated long ago from the south and, in the warm climate of their former homeland, swarmed just as enthusiastically as today's Caucasian bees do, casting with impunity one swarm after another, and, according to Profs. Kozhevnikov, Butlerov and other authorities, building between 60 and 100 queen cells, or even more. In the north, nature punishes this proclivity to swarm with death and hunger, and eventually the swarming instinct is weakened through genetic heredity. Today, only 20–25% of colonies in the north produce swarms, and during unproductive summers there are no swarms at all.

That which nature did in the north has been done in other areas by man, by way of persistent selective breeding. Dadant, Miller, de Layens, Dokuchaev and others claim that by pursuing such selective breeding at their apiaries and by using large hives, they've reached a point where the emergence of a natural swarm is a rarity.

There's the quotation. Now to add just one more finishing stroke.

So the industrial beekeeper somehow managed, more or less, to control swarming. But that gives rise to a question: how, without swarming, does he obtain new colonies in order to expand (or restore) his apiaries?

The answer is simple—artificially! Let's split one colony into two or more parts, and in those parts that are left without a queen, we'll plant one! Where will we get them? From a swarm colony or from a queen-breeding apiary, where queens are now produced, as a rule, using artificial insemination.

This is certainly convenient from the human's point of view (you don't have to be on the watch for swarms, and you can generate as many colonies as you need), but from nature's point of view, it's ridiculous.

In colonies obtained in this fashion, severe imbalances arise between the number of bees (young and foraging), the number of brood, and the nest size. After all, the colonies are split artificially, and by no means when they're ready for it. As a result, the highly delicate mechanisms that support their strength and health are disrupted.

Eventually, of course, the bees will work their way out of this mess, but at what cost? You don't need to look far for an answer.

A few years ago, one of my friends scoured an entire rural district searching for someone who could sell him a swarm (to install in a log hive). And it was only with great difficulty that he succeeded! Everyone seemed interested in selling him a colony, or a nuc, but no one wanted to sell swarms. Why?

One beekeeper gave him an honest answer: "Who'd sell you a swarm? Everyone keeps the swarms for themselves! They all know that you get a much better colony from a swarm than from a nuc."

And this is confirmed by a majority of practicing beekeepers. After all, a swarm is joined primarily by young, strong bees with big building potential, and, in the case of a second or third swarm, a good swarm queen to boot.

The swarming of a bee colony is an incredibly amazing, highly complex, and highly developed process. Anyone who has seen how tens of thousands of bees, as if on cue, begin to pour out of a hive entrance in waves, circle above the hives with an ebullient buzzing, and land in a thick cluster on the branch of a nearby tree (Photographs 11–12, p. 332)—anyone who's seen this cannot have failed to sense the great solemnity that surrounds the birth of a new bee colony.

There's a lot more that could be said about the creation of queen cells, about the emergence of a swarm, about the queen's mating flight, and other highly interesting details of this great sacrament, but that's another topic for another day.

The interested reader will eventually encounter all of these phenomena himself; but we, meanwhile, had better move along.

"Little to Smile About"

Today's most widespread beekeeping systems rely on manipulating brood boxes and supers to create extreme conditions that compel the bees to intensify their comb-building and nectar-gathering. The bees respond with greater aggression toward humans and with a greater tendency to swarm—which the beekeeper, in turn, attempts to suppress with various "scientific" methods.

As a rule, it is bees of local races that tend to show the greatest resistance. In particular, the European dark bee (which we spoke of earlier) simply will not stand for any rough treatment and has therefore gained a reputation as being particularly vicious and prone to swarming, although this reputation has little to do with the truth.

At the same time, one can understand the position of the industrial beekeeper—how is he supposed to deal with this bee? He can't get into the brood nest, he can't cut out the queen cells, and if the bees take it into their head to swarm, there's no way to stop them! Therefore, ever since modern beekeeping arose, there have been ongoing experiments to import other (usually, southern) races. It's worth noting that the famous Petro Prokopovych, the inventor of the first movable-frame hive, was the first to undertake this work. In time it grew into a widespread obsession, but problems soon appeared.

The diseases we spoke of earlier can be dealt with using medicines—for a time. But how, pray tell, can one maintain the purity of an imported race of bees?

Let's say you've bought a set of mountain grey Caucasian queens for your apiary. Within a few years, some of them have died, and the rest are advancing in age. What are you to do? Their offspring, after all, will already be "hybrid" (due to mating with drones from nearby apiaries) and, for the most part, unviable.

There's only one way out: buying some new purebred queens (which are much cheaper than package bees) from a queen-rearing apiary. But even that apiary can only maintain the purity of its race if there are no bees of other races for an 18-mile (30-km) radius—and this is rarely the case. This is why people came up with the idea of artificially inseminating queens.

I won't describe this procedure—it's highly unpleasant; instead, I'll present the view of Rudolf Steiner, the German philosopher, natural scientist, and founder of anthroposophy and its various offshoots, including biodynamic agriculture and Waldorf education.

This citation is taken from his lectures on bees, presented between 26 November and 22 December 1923 in Dornach, Germany.

The fact of the matter—and I'll speak more on this subject next time—is that the honey production, activity levels, and even efficiency of worker bees may rise significantly if artificial methods are employed in the breeding of bees. However, as Mr. Müller already noted, one must not approach these matters too rationally, from the exclusive standpoint of economic effectiveness. Next time, we'll take a somewhat closer look at bee breeding; we'll see how measures that, in the short run, seem extremely beneficial, and, having enshrined themselves as fundamental principles, today seem even more positive, may well completely ruin beekeeping over the course of a hundred years—if, of course, only artificially bred bees are used. If one only wishes, one can easily see how that which seems beneficial at the outset could eventually turn into something that slowly ruins the entire enterprise. We'll see that beekeeping is of great interest precisely because of the insight it offers into all of nature's secrets. And those secrets include the fact that what is extraordinarily productive in one regard may, in another, prove exceptionally destructive. In short, beekeepers may be thrilled by the advances beekeeping has achieved in a very short timeframe—but once a century has passed, there'll be very little to smile about.

This citation speaks for itself—no need for further comment. So let's move on.

Is There a Way Ou

So humanity invented the foundation frame, which gave the beekeeper new and as yet unheard-of capabilities and led to the invention of various hive designs. At this point the development of beekeeping came to a fork in the road.

Some beekeepers strove to build a bee dwelling and to devise a system that would correspond as closely as possible to the biology of a bee colony, with the intention of interfering as little as possible in the colony's life.

Others took the course of industrial beekeeping, which aimed at coaxing the maximum amount of honey from the bees using various methods, without regard to how unnatural they were, or to their possible consequences.

And to this very day, most of the world's beekeepers are continuing down the second path.

However, due to the application of the methods used by the industrial approach, a number of problems have arisen—and in their attempts to overcome those problems (without, of course, abandoning industrial methods), people have cooked up an entire science, which includes anti-swarming measures, artificial breeding, and treatment of bees for various diseases.

But did this solve all the problems? No! And this failure can be easily demonstrated.

- Production (and consumption) of honey in developed countries has today dropped to the lamentable level of 12 ounces (350 g) per person per year. For the sake of comparison, one person consumes approximately 150 pounds (70 kg) of sugar per year. Meanwhile, honey has become the world's most imitated product, which certainly hasn't helped its popularity.

• Apiculture has gone from being a pleasant and entertaining hobby for many people to a difficult, labor-intensive undertaking accessible only to professionals.

• Keeping apiaries has come to depend on constantly purchasing medicines and purebred queens.

But here's the question: is the first route still possible? Is there anyone left who's traveling it? Is it possible to design a hive that would allow us to avoid swarming caused by the bees' desire to abandon an unsuitable home?

Of course it's possible! And the attentive reader will certainly have guessed, over the course of this text, how this might be done.

The History of the Horizontal Hive With Extra-Deep Frames

Our goal (to summarize the aforesaid):

• To abandon all manipulations of boxes and supers, whether it's setting them on top or in between, since this is completely unnatural from the bees' standpoint.

• To increase the depth of the frame on which the bees winter.

• To allow the bees to arrange their winter nest themselves during the summer.

• To allow the hive's keeper to interfere as little as possible with his bees.

But how can we solve the fundamental problem of hive design—of finding a way to expand the nest during the honeyflow? To expand from below is difficult, since that would mean lifting the entire hive (which can weigh 200 pounds—100 kg—or more) and adding the new box beneath it. Such ideas have been in circulation, but they have not won widespread support. Meanwhile, expanding from the top is unnatural.

What options remain?

Expanding laterally. Some keepers had the idea (which was implemented in the Slavic hive) of attaching additional boxes to the hive from the side, but due to technical difficulties this idea failed to develop fully.

It was much simpler to make the hive **single-boxed**— that is, aimed at allowing the colony to develop maximally within a single box while expanding the nest laterally. And this method proved to have the most promise.

Such hives have been in existence for a long time, since those beekeepers who were striving to stay in tune with nature thought much along the same lines as we are now. These hives are called single-box horizontal hives with extra-deep frames (Figure 7, p. 114).

I'll run down the list of the hives I know of (in some cases, I do not know the number of frames or the exact year of the hive's invention). They all appeared either in the 19th century, or very early in the 20th. See also Figures 3–7.

Table 1. Historical horizontal hives

Name	Number of frames	Frame length and depth	
		inches	mm
Layens hive, 1864	20–25	13 x 16 $^1/_8$	330 x 410
Slavic hive,[1] 1865	10 per box[2]	8 $^7/_8$ x 18 $^7/_8$	227 x 480
Lewicki (Warsaw) hive	20–22	9 $^1/_2$ x 17	240 x 432
Vaschenko hive		10 $^1/_4$ x 18 $^3/_4$	260 x 475
Ukrainian hive	20	11 $^1/_4$ x 18 $^1/_8$	285 x 460
Dokuchaev hive	24	10 $^5/_8$ x 21 $^1/_4$	270 x 540
Dolinowski hive	15–20	11 $^3/_8$ x 15	290 x 380
Mochalkin hive		9 $^5/_8$ x 29 $^1/_2$	245 x 750

Notes: 1. Also called the Ciesielski or Galician hive. 2. With boxes added laterally.

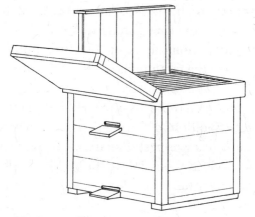

Figure 3. The Layens hive

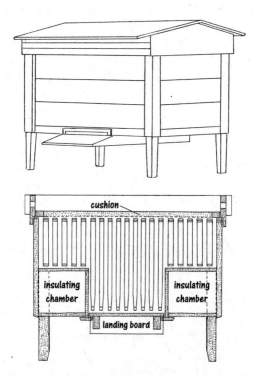

Figure 4. The Layens hive modified by French apiarist Jean Hurpin
(adapted from Jean Hurpin's 1941 book *La Ruche de Layens Modernisée*)

Note the names of the hives. Of all the hives listed above, the Layens hive is the only foreign one. However, it was created for mountainous areas, and it goes without saying that conditions in the mountains are much harsher than in the flatlands.

The information on these hives merits special attention!

The specific conditions of the Russia of their day led these inventors to create a warm, stationary, single-box hive with a deep frame, as close as possible to the log hive—which was the bee's customary home in Russia. What are its primary features?

- Good insulation. The hive ensures a good microclimate in winter and summer.

Figure 5. The Lewicki hive

- An extra-deep frame. Allows the bees to make it through a long winter, and the keeper not to worry about them throughout the winter, right up until the first flow.

- A large box size. Gives bees the ability to develop throughout the season, and allows the keeper to attend to other matters, only checking on the bees once at the end of the summer.

- This hive is poorly suited for moving, but is good for modestly sized, stationary apiaries on a diversified peasant farm.

And this was ideally suited to the conditions of tsarist Russia, where peasants made up 90% of the population, land plots were modest in size, and there were no extensive monoculture fields. At that time, the average apiary size was less than 20 bee colonies (based on 1910 data), and their owners didn't have the time to check on their beehouses every two weeks.

Here are a few words from a description of a Slavic hive in a book by Ippolit Korablyov, *A Do-It-Yourself Guide to Selecting and Building a Successful Hive* (Moscow: Novaya Derevnya, 1927):

But if this hive is simplified slightly, as was done at an experimental research apiary at the former Umansk School of Horticulture, then it can become very convenient, both for the bees and their keeper. Here, all the walls are identical; there's a single top; the bottom is on supports and can be removed, so it's very easy to clean without lifting the entire hive; its combs are perpendicular to the entrance; the hive contains 20 frames. Adding some food, cleaning the bottom, or inserting some frames takes no more than a minute. Anyone who is unable to dedicate much time to bees will love these hives.

That is, such hives existed in the early 20th century, and not all beekeepers were stubbornly trying, like Butkevich, to force their bees to adapt to vertical hives with multiple boxes and supers.

But soon the situation changed drastically. During the revolution and Russian Civil War, apiculture fell into serious decline, and when it finally began, with great difficulty, to recover, collective farms had already appeared, with gigantic fields, tractors and combines—along with industrial apiaries with specially trained collective-farm beekeepers and honey statisticians in white jackets.

At that time, by government fiat, the Dadant frame was adopted as the standard for the entire nation, and mass production of the corresponding foundation, honey extractors, and other beekeeping equipment began in earnest. Alternative systems were simply out of the question.

Why did this happen? Because in those days people believed they were capable of anything—of yoking nature to the service of humans, of recklessly mowing down forests, of making rivers flow backward, of draining swamps. And—almost as an afterthought—of forcing bees to work "on the assembly line," filling one super after another with honey, with no negative consequences.

Against this backdrop, "natural" single-box hives—just like log hives—already seemed like some anachronism left behind by one's grandparents.

We already know where all this was headed.

But perhaps I'm overstating my case? Painting too dark a picture? In that case, let's stray a bit from our topic and look at other examples.

Let's take the heavy turn plow, used for soil cultivation, that we've already mentioned before. Specialists claim that the turn plow has done more damage to Mother Earth than any other human invention. Just seventy years of thoughtless use of this tool has led to the loss of a majority of our most fertile lands.

All of Russia's once-fertile Black Earth Belt has been horribly scarred by the gully-ravine network. Huge swaths of southern black earth soil has been overplowed, eroded by wind, and salinized; our so-called Virgin Soil has been plowed to exhaustion and abandoned as useless.

Non-black earth soil has long been barren absent additional doses of fertilizer, since all that's left on the surface of arable land is almost pure clay with a slight admixture of humus, and the plants, weakened by overfertilization, are unable to fight pests without the help of pesticides. I could go on and on.

Do we need more examples of the thoughtless deployment of scientific and technical power? No need to look far!

Let's take the widespread "scientifically based" cutting of forests. And the resulting drying of thousands of rivers, the turning of gigantic stretches of territory into deserts, and climate change on a global scale.

We could continue, but I think you're as capable of that as I am—after all, anyone who accepts uncritically all of the achievements of modern civilization is unlikely to have read this far.

However, to humanity's credit, it must be said that it has already begun (particularly in technocratically developed countries) to have second thoughts and, slowly but surely, to change course. This is particularly evident in the fields of agriculture and ecology. You've undoubtedly heard of organic food (grown without artificial fertilizers and pesticides), the system of shallow (no-till) land cultivation, organic and biodynamic agriculture, and permaculture.

All of these methods of sustainable agriculture are only possible on smaller plots surrounded by windbreak belts and hedges, and with effective crop rotation and maximal biodiversity of the surrounding environment.

More and more farms are being arranged in this manner, and there is a constantly growing demand for their products.

But we've digressed a bit—we should get back to our bees.

The Modern Horizontal Hive

Can the hives that were invented and popularized before the Russian Revolution really have vanished without a trace? Is such a thing possible? Of course not! They're still around, and still enjoy great popularity in Russia, Belarus and Ukraine. But since non-Dadant or non-multi-box foundation wasn't available during the Soviet era, horizontal hives too had to adapt to accommodate standards.

Modern horizontal hives have between 16 and 25 standard Dadant brood frames and come in both stationary (insulated) and movable formats. But alas: the frame depth remained 11 $^{13}/_{16}$ inches (30 cm), so a super had to be added to a horizontal hive as well—with all of the expected consequences.

However, the horizontal hive retains one advantage: during the extended—and most critical—spring period, the colony is only able to expand laterally, which for it is entirely natural; and, in addition, there's no need to add boxes on top—just a super, since there's plenty of room as it is.

Therefore, bees are much less prone to swarm, are more docile, and grow more effectively in horizontal hives, according to the beekeepers who use them. Certainly, when it comes to wintering, the hive presents the same challenges as the Dadant (a shallow frame!). And moving the hives is difficult. For the latter reason, horizontal hives tend to be seen on modestly sized, stationary apiaries, and are especially favored by amateur beekeepers who have another job

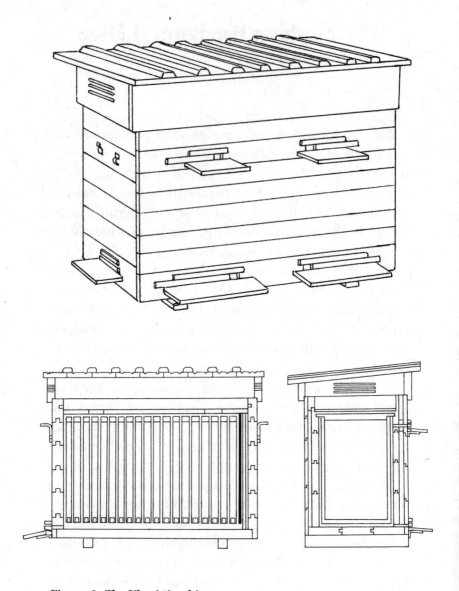

Figure 6. The Ukrainian hive

on their hands and can't spend too much time worrying about their bees.

There's also the so-called Ukrainian horizontal hive (Figure 6), the direct descendant of the Slavic hive and the others mentioned above. As a rule, it features 24 Dadant frames, but they're turned 90° to the side. That is, they have a length of 11 $^{13}/_{16}$ inches (300 mm) and a depth of 17 $^{1}/_{8}$ inches (435 mm), using a standard foundation.

This hive has its fair share of dedicated users, also among "amateurs"—that is, those for whom beekeeping isn't their main line of work. The hive's advantages include: good wintering (an extra-deep frame!) and effective springtime build-up; there's also no need to prepare the bees for winter (they take care of that themselves). The Ukrainian hive's drawbacks include its somewhat cramped quarters and, therefore, the possibility of overheating during the summer—not to mention its limited volume. Why is that?

Some strong colonies (the heart and soul of an apiary!) can occupy three Dadant brood boxes—that is, 36 Dadant brood frames—while the Ukrainian hive has only 24. And removing a frame of honey during the summer is no simple matter—some brood might be found there, and the bees won't like that.

Can the flaws of the Ukrainian horizontal hive be overcome while still preserving its advantages? If so, how? Well, it's not hard at all! All it takes is lengthening the frames.

The Horizontal Hive With Extra-Deep Frames

Here's what I did: I took the same old standard-length Dadant frame (17 $^1/_8$ inches or 435 mm long) and increased its depth to 18 $^1/_2$ inches (470 mm). Technically, this was easily done: using special connectors, I attached a standard super frame (17 $^1/_8$ x 5 $^3/_4$ inches; 435 x 145 mm), without shoulders, to the bottom of a standard Dadant brood frame (17 $^1/_8$ x 11 $^{13}/_{16}$ inches; 435 x 300 mm)—see Photographs 23–24, p. 338.

The total depth comes to 17 $^1/_2$ inches (445 mm), but since the cut of a standard sheet of plywood* for lining the inside of a hive makes it possible to extend its depth to 20 $^1/_2$ inches (520 mm), I used my workshop—where I make my own hives and frames—to increase the depth of the lower "attachment" to 6 $^3/_4$ inches (170 mm). That leaves 2 inches (50 mm) of extra space beneath the frame.

If you only have standard products at your disposal, you can leave the frame depth at 17 $^1/_2$ inches (445 mm).**

---

* In Russia, the standard size for a sheet of plywood is 60 x 60 inches (152 x 152 cm). *Ed.*

** In the US, an extra-deep frame of essentially the same size can be made by connecting (one under the other) two deep Langstroth frames (17 $^5/_8$ x 9 $^1/_8$ inches). This will produce an extra-deep frame 17 $^5/_8$ inches long by 18 $^1/_4$ inches deep. *Ed.*

How many frames should be made? Well, in keeping with maximum growth of the bee colony that we spoke of earlier—that is, based on a count of 36 Dadant brood frames. With a little math, that comes to 24 extra-deep frames that are one-and-a-half times the depth of a Dadant brood frame (just to be sure, I make 25). Experience has shown that colonies in our region won't outgrow this number.

Now, I'd like to pause for a moment and return to the Ukrainian frame, 11 $^{13}/_{16}$ inches (300 mm) long. What's the essential difference between a hive based on the Ukrainian frame and ours (with a 17-$^1/_8$-inch or 435-mm-long frame)? Let's recall our discussion of the tree hollow from the beginning of the book.

For an average-sized swarm, a narrow hollow is ideal, since it's easier to fill out with comb and winter in. But a colony can't gain much strength in a narrow hollow and will soon begin swarming. Bees may have a harder time initially in a wider hollow, but, on the other hand, it will allow them to grow into a strong colony down the road.

This makes the Ukrainian horizontal hive good for wintering and for the successful buildup of a small or average-size colony—but it won't accommodate a colony of any real strength. And strong colonies are the backbone of any apiary and guarantee a good harvest of honey.

As I've said, the traditional use of excessively short frames has its origins in an erroneous estimate of the average dimensions of a tree hollow, and for that reason it hasn't lived up to its promise.

What about extremely long frames? Such proposals have been advanced, and in the very recent past.

On this topic, I can recommend tracking down and reading through a book by Mikhail Lupanov, *Advice From an Old Beekeeper*. It's an interesting book that's full of common

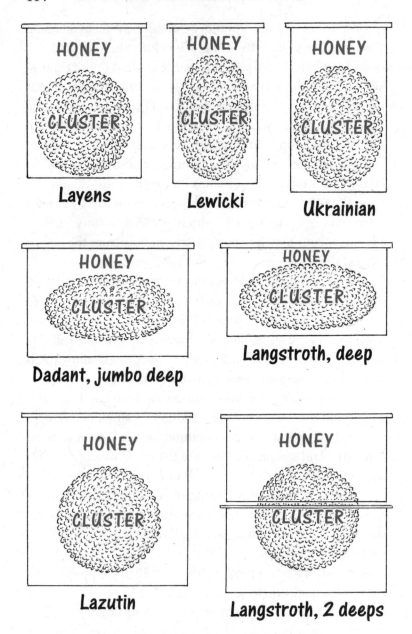

Figure 7. The extra-deep frames and "regular" deeps compared

sense. The author's rationale behind building large, warm hives is very similar to ours; yet, for all of my respect for the author's depth of experience, I can't help doubting the prospects of switching to a 20-by-20-inch (50-by-50-cm) frame. After all, such a step would require a full break with all existing standards, and a complete retooling of manufacturing processes. That's especially true for the production of foundation and the rollers used to make them, as well as for honey extractors and frames. On top of all that, moving bees from a standard frame to this one would be highly problematic.

Moreover, a 17-^{1}/$_8$-inch-long (435-mm) frame still strikes me as more natural; there's a reason it became such an entrenched feature of both the Dadant and the Langstroth hives.*

However, if all of this is true—I can hear the clever and exacting reader observing—then surely there must be people out there keeping bees on frames that are one-and-a-half or even twice the depth of Dadant brood frames (i.e., that are some 18 inches deep or more).

This supposition is entirely logical! And I've got the proof to back it up: indeed, there are such people out there, and in significant numbers!

---

* Again, the American standard for these frames is slightly more: 17 ^{5}/$_8$ inches long. Please also note that standard American frames have a spacing of 1 ^{3}/$_8$ inch on-center, but the author's frames are spaced 1 ^{1}/$_2$ inch on-center (the Russian Dadant standard). *Ed.*

Using the Extra-Deep Frame

Finding information on the practical use of extra-deep frames is no simple matter. Why? Well, because the kind of people who pursue the natural approach tend not to be too keen on reaching a wide audience with their "unscientific" ideas and becoming the objects of all manner of discussions and criticism. After all, the periodicals and books found on the shelves of bookstores are dominated by the "serious" industrial approach and create an illusion of authority and successful implementation.

Still, information on using extra-deep frames can indeed be found. It's spread by word of mouth, between friends and acquaintances, through Internet forums and through mentions in books and magazines.

I'll give a few examples.

A friend of a friend of mine has been keeping her own apiary for many years now, and with a head-turning profit. Here's how she does it: she sets two 16-frame stationary horizontal hive boxes atop one another and fills them with frames consisting of two Dadant brood frames fastened together (resulting in dimensions of $17 \frac{1}{8}$ x $23 \frac{5}{8}$ inches; 435 x 600 mm). The bees winter on 6–10 frames. In the spring, she inspects the hives, adding fresh foundation in the nest area; during the flow, she adds frames, in several stages, until the hives are full, and in the fall she removes the extras without disturbing the nest area.

The double frames, filled with honey, weigh no more than 18 pounds (8 kg); she has no trouble handling them. She doesn't use any medicines.

Some beekeepers try using the extra-deep frame without straying too far from the industrial beekeeping system. They fasten the brood box of a Dadant hive to a super, forming a brood chamber with extra-deep frames where the bees spend the winter (outdoors, of course). To gather honey, they set a super or two on top. Once they remove the supers containing the bulk of winter reserves, they feed the bees with honey or sugar syrup.

And so on and so forth. Experience with using the extra-deep frame continues to accumulate, and authors of books on beekeeping can no longer ignore it. Not long ago, under the auspices of the Moscow city government, a large, handsomely bound book was published, entitled *The Honeybee Encyclopedia* (Moskovskie uchebniki i kartrolitografiia, 2005). One section of the book, "Practical Experience and Observations," contains quotes from various beekeepers. Below is the opinion of one of them, A. Livensky:

The so-called nest system of keeping bees in double-deep horizontal hive boxes with 16–24 frames is a good one. They contain Dadant brood frames that have been fastened together in pairs using staples. The result is an extra-deep frame measuring $17\,^{1}/_{8} \times 23\,^{5}/_{8}$ inches (435 x 600 mm). These double frames are lined with full sheets of artificial foundation and added to the bee nests in the spring, first alongside the brood frames, and later in the center of the hive, gradually displacing older, darker comb farther and farther to the sides. These frames can be easily inspected, especially when checking for the presence of swarm cells. Preparing the nests for winter is simple: the side frames containing the honey are removed, but the nest is left undisturbed. Seven to eight double frames are more than enough for the winter if they're half-filled with honey during the main honeyflow. Old comb is removed from the far edges, and fresh, bright-brown comb is left for the winter and spring for the queen to use during her next egg-laying cycle. Practice has shown that this nest system is especially convenient both for elderly beekeepers and for beginners. The bee colonies aren't inspected too frequently; the bees aren't excessively irritated; and the nest microclimate is maintained. Inspections are faster than with vertical hives, especially when you're looking for queen cells after a long period of bad weather. Bees in these horizontal hives usually winter outdoors, often with two colonies in a single hive, which makes wintering more successful. Even a 16-frame double-box horizontal hive is more than enough for a bee colony in the conditions of Central Russia. The bees in them are very unlikely to swarm, and if a colony does begin swarming, it's the fault of the beekeeper for not expanding the nest in time. This "new" old hive is also a step to a 21st-century hive, if we add an open space of between 150–200 mm beneath the frames, with a removable wire mesh tray underneath for cleaning the bottom and for checking how successfully the bees are wintering. On top of that, this systems makes use of standard horizontal hive bodies and standard frames.

Another contemporary author—an ardent supporter of modern scientific beekeeping, Nikolay Mikulsky—also mentioned the extra-deep frame in his book, *Amateur Beekeeping* (Rybinsk, 2004):

Adherents of the "large frame" are pressing for the abandonment of all means and methods for handling bees, regardless of how progressive they may be. They also propose a return to the past [*this follows a discussion of log hives—Author's note*], in the attempt to demonstrate that beekeeping is a trade that demands no knowledge of any sort from the beekeeper. Everything should be simple, like the log hive. In the meantime, they're forgetting that even keeping bees in a log requires a considerable level of mastery.

If we overlook the excesses of that final phrase, there's much here of interest: the author, whose book presents the pluses and minuses of all modern hives and beekeeping systems in great detail and in a very straightforward manner, finds just one drawback in our system: its renunciation of modern scientific methods. But surely this is a question of one's worldview, and therefore a matter of personal choice.

While we're at it, the author's take on the Dadant hive is also of interest:

But keep in mind that the standard industrial hives do have significant drawbacks. Some of them are completely unable to accommodate certain promising beekeeping methods. For example, the 12-frame Dadant hive, the most common hive among Russian beekeepers, has proven highly unsuccessful. Its long-term use in our country has done great damage.

There are more mentions of the extra-deep frame to be found, but I see no reason to cite all of them. The point is that natural methods of keeping bees in single-box hives with extra-deep frames have been used for a long time and with great success, despite the total lack of information on them in official beekeeping literature.

Moreover, all natural beekeepers arrive at the very same beekeeping methods we have, by way of the very same (or very similar) trains of thought. And that's not surprising—after all, there's only one Truth, and he who seeks shall surely find.

How? Through observation, reflection and practical experience—the same path that led me to the natural beekeeping method, which I have tried to describe in as much detail as possible. In so doing, my primary goal was not simply to provide ready-made conclusions and recommendations on what you should do and how you should do it, but to try to inspire you to travel down this path yourself (although I'm happy to accompany you), with the ability to confirm the truth of every step for yourself.

I'll leave it to you to decide how successful I've been.

But for now, let's move from theory to practice.

Part II

The Practice of Natural Apiculture

A Description of the Horizontal Hive With 25 Extra-Deep Frames

Our goal is to make a convenient, high-quality, warm, stationary hive that will last for decades. It should also be attractive—it should delight the eye instead of defacing the landscape.

To that end, I personally make my hives the way they should be made, without regard to the time and labor that go into them. And, truth be told, making them can be labor-intensive and not exactly cheap. But by the same token they're solid and can stand the test of time.

This approach runs counter to the spirit of modern industrial production, which has long been oriented toward technically simple, cheap and short-lived products.

At first, I'd assemble the hive boxes from dry boards 2 inches (50 mm) thick. This is easy enough even with a minimum amount of carpentry skill; but first of all, this thickness of wood is clearly insufficient for our climate; and secondly, the resulting hive isn't too durable due to the fact that the wooden panels, no matter how well they're glued together, unavoidably warp and crack in the harsh conditions of the surrounding environment (sun, cold weather, moisture). And bees react highly negatively to any cracks in the walls of their homes.

Later, I began to line the outside of my hives with two layers of jute ($^3/_8$ inch or 1 cm for warmth), adding weatherboard atop the jute. This external siding not only provides additional insulation, but also bears the brunt of the environmental impact, ensuring stable conditions in the inner box and extending its useful life many times over.

However, a hive like this turns out to be too heavy and too labor-intensive to produce.

Therefore, I reached the point when I switched to the frame method for making the main box. Using this method, 2-by-2-inch (50-by-50-mm) stock is assembled into a hollow frame that is then lined on the inside with plywood ($5/32$ inch or 4 mm is sufficient) and filled with insulation (I use Styrofoam). The exterior is wrapped with Tyvek (roofing paper also works) and covered with weatherboard.

Almost all authors consider this technique to be ideal, since the resulting hive is extremely warm (2 inches or 5 cm of Styrofoam is equivalent to approximately 6 inches or 15 cm of wood) and durable (the weatherboard siding!), light, and resistant to any kind of cracks in the walls. As an additional advantage, the hive can, in time, be renovated or repaired by replacing the siding or the plywood as needed, and even the insulation.

The bottom of the hive is made using either the same frame technique, or fashioned using wooden boards. The bottom fits into $3/8$-to-$5/8$-inch-deep (10–15-mm) rabbets (grooves) cut in the bottom edges of the lateral and rear walls. The bottom extends beyond the front wall of the hive to form a landing board. A $3/8$-inch (10-mm) gap is left between the protruding bottom and the front wall, providing a lower hive entrance that can be left fully open during the main honey-flow, or narrowed to the desired width. It's very convenient.

The bottom is attached to the back wall with hinges, and since the hive rests on a stand with its lateral weight-bearing walls, the bottom can be swung open (downward) for spring inspection.

The interior lining of the box (not counting the bottom) takes three quarters of a 60-by-60-inch or 1520-by-1520-mm sheet of plywood, whose cut allows for an internal box depth of 20 $^1/_2$ inches or 520 mm and a width of 37 inches or 940 mm (25 frames with 1-$^1/_2$-inch or 37-mm-wide top bars). The standard length of the internal space is 17 $^3/_4$ inches (450 mm).* See Figure 8 for the length, width, and depth designations.

Rabbets (grooves) measuring $^7/_{16}$ x $^7/_{16}$ inch (11x11 mm, with a 1-mm margin) are cut in the tops of the long walls for hanging frames; I usually make the top bars of the frames touching (after all, there's no need to set boxes on top!), and, once added to the hive, they form a ceiling for the nest and their top surface is flush with the box.

A 3-$^1/_8$-inch-deep (80-mm) top is set atop the box, lined on the bottom with hardboard and insulated with some 3 inches (70–80 mm) of some kind of insulation (I prefer Styrofoam here as well).

---

* In the US, the standard interior length of the box to accommodate standard-length frames would be 18 $^3/_8$ inches. *Ed.*

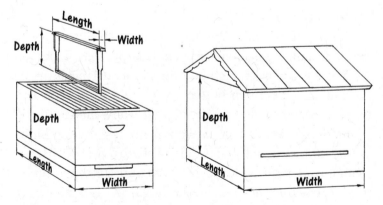

Figure 8. The conventional names of hive and frame dimensions

Small rafters are attached to the lengthwise bars of the top, to which roof boards are attached and then covered with any roofing material. The resulting gable roof (like a two-sloped roof of a cottage) has all kinds of advantages over the flat top. It's ventilated from below, thus avoiding any overheating of the nest from the sun; it forms large over-hangs on all sides that protect the box from rain and sun; and, on top of all this, it looks nicer.

Once the hive is installed at its permanent location, the roof (or, more precisely, the top it's set on) is attached to the hive using hinges screwed onto the front wall. Then, to ac-cess the nest, all you have to do is walk up behind the hive and swing open the top (Photograph 22, p. 337).

In addition to the bottom slit-shaped entrance, two round 1-inch (25-mm) entrances are made in the front wall. They are located around 9 inches (23–24 cm) from the top (near the middle of the nest's depth), and 6 $^3/_4$ and 25 $^1/_2$ inches (170 and 650 mm), respectively (the fifth and seventeenth frames), from the left inside wall of the hive (viewed from the front). During framework construction, vertical braces are attached at the points where these entrances will later be drilled, to which the lining and siding will be fastened for additional strength.

So there's the full schematic description of the hive; a detailed plan is provided in Appendix 5 (pp. 363–371).

The hive can be installed on stakes driven into the ground, but it's much better to create a stand approxi-mately 16 inches (40 cm) in height. Ideally, the stand will be made of metal. I make legs from 1-$^1/_2$-by-1-$^1/_2$-inch (40-by-40-mm) steel angles that I weld together with brac-es made of 1-inch-wide (25-mm) flat bars (Photograph 29, p. 341). These stands last a very long time, and mice have a harder time climbing up them. Pieces of board or stone slabs can be set beneath the legs, while also insuring that the hive is level.

Building a hive typically requires basic woodworking equipment, but it can also be cobbled together using very simple tools. This is exactly what my friend Konstantin did—he built two such hives this summer in Chernigov in Ukraine and successfully installed bees in both of them.

The main thing here is the basic principle. The materials and the technology are largely a matter of imagination and whatever is available to work with.

Now, let's address practical beekeeping techniques.

How to Keep Bees in a Horizontal Hive With Extra-Deep Frames

Here, it must be made very clear that pursuing natural beekeeping methods requires strict observance of a number of principles. In this sense, you're either an industrial bee-keeper (in terms of your principles, not the number of your hives!) or a natural beekeeper—one or the other! And this is very important to remember!

That is, it's not possible to adopt some principles of natural beekeeping while rejecting others. If you tamper with even a single detail of the bee's natural mechanism, you shouldn't expect it to work dependably. How can we then go on to complain about the imperfections of nature that supposedly make human intervention a necessity?

Keep in mind that bees, over the course of millions of years, have learned to solve any and all problems they might encounter in their natural environment. But a bee colony is simply incapable of overcoming the trials dreamed up for it by man, since nothing like them is to be found even in the deepest recesses of its genetic memory. For example, when a beekeeper splits a colony in half. Or when, in the fall, he takes all the honey and feeds the bees sugar. Or when he ships off southern bees to live in the north.

Let me repeat: there is no sense whatsoever in some half-way or partial adoption of the natural approach. Please forgive me for speaking so categorically! But this is my most deeply held conviction, based on practical experience not only in the sphere of beekeeping, but also in other areas of life.

By the way, a word or two regarding terminology (which I've been meaning to mention, but have kept postponing).

The term "beekeeper"—that is, one who "keeps" bees—inevitably implies an industrial approach, when man assumes control for all aspects of a bee colony's life. Perhaps the term "apiarist"—one who keeps an apiary—would be more appropriate for the natural approach, according to which man strives to interfere as little as possible in the life of his bees. Moreover, an apiarist can be an amateur or a professional who lives off the money he earns from his bees.

The Central Commandments of Natural Beekeeping

• Only keep bees of the local race (in our case, the European dark bee). If you stop buying and importing bees of foreign races, gradually acquiring colonies (queens) of the local race instead, then your bees will become increasingly "local."

• Keep your bees in natural horizontal hives with extra-deep frames, or in log hives. The hives should be warm and spacious and should be left at a single location year-round.

• Never feed your bees sugar (swarm colonies that haven't managed to gather enough reserves may be fed with supplemental honey). Don't pull honey for the duration of the summer honeyflow. Surplus honey may be pulled during the fall or spring, leaving at least 50 pounds (25 kg) of honey for an average-size colony for the winter.

• Don't bother the bees unless it is extremely necessary, with the exception of the two major annual inspections, one in the spring and one in the fall.

• Only propagate your bees naturally, through swarming.

• Allow bees to arrange their winter nest themselves— that is, don't rearrange it yourself during the fall.

• Don't subject your bees to any sort of medical treatment; let them cope with diseases themselves. It's no catastrophe if a weak colony perishes. Any surviving colonies will produce strong and healthy offspring.

• In addition, a natural beekeeper is simply obligated, in working with his bees and eating their honey, to gradually improve his own health, and with his overall appearance inspire those around him to set up a bee colony or two.

A Beekeeper's Tasks in Spring and Summer

Once warm weather sets in and a steady spring flow is underway, it's time for the spring inspection. Where I live, near the city of Kaluga (Zone 4), this comes sometime from early to mid-May. By this time, you should have between 3–4 frames with foundation on hand for each bee colony.

Here's what I do. I swing open the top, remove the division board, and move all the frames, one by one, toward the wall opposite the wall where the bees wintered (*Figure 9.A–B, p. 138*; Photograph 7, p. 330). As I move the frames, I lift each one a bit and inspect it. Since the frames' top bars touch, the bees can't climb up and remain calm.

Upon inspection, you'll notice that some of the frames contain the brood, both open and sealed (just seeing it once is enough to learn how to recognize it)—Photographs 8–10, pp. 330–331. This is the nest portion of the hive, which should be put back in place, in the same order, once the inspection is finished. The remaining frames will either be completely empty or will contain a certain amount of beebread and honey.

If the bees started the winter with large honey reserves, then any surplus honey should be pulled, leaving no more than approximately 20 pounds (10 kg) in the hive.

Next, it's time to create a space for the coming wintering period; the bees will be at work all summer setting up this space. First, add one or two of the good honey and beebread frames you set aside during the inspection; then, 3–4 frames with foundation, and then, in the same order you found them, return all of the remaining frames to their places and press them into place with the division board (*Figure 9.C*).

Why are the frames arranged in this order? Well, the queen generally prefers not to lay eggs on the farthest frame (the one closest to the edge), so that's where we put the frames with the reserves, which also encourages the bees to develop the new frames with the foundation as they make their way to the reserves. And since these new frames are very close to the entrance, the queen will be inclined to go work on them.

As we return the brood frames to their original locations, it's very important to preserve the integrity of the brood section of the nest, allowing the bees to maintain the microclimate necessary for raising their young.

Beekeeping literature often recommends placing some of the foundation frames in between the brood frames to encourage the bees to draw comb on them more quickly, but this strikes me as unnatural, especially since the bees do a fine job of drawing comb on them anyway when they're placed from the side.

So, the spring inspection is complete; there's no need to get near the bees for a good two weeks or so (until warm weather sets in for good).

The whole procedure doesn't take long, and at that time of year the bees aren't too active yet, so they regard this low-impact intervention very calmly. To keep the inspection time to a minimum, I usually do it together with my wife. Inspecting all twenty of our hives takes around 4–5 hours total.

What if, for some reason, the bees find themselves without a queen (you can easily tell by the lack of brood)? The simplest and easiest option is to unite this colony with a successful one. To do so, just move the frames into any hive that you've already inspected.

But, to avoid any conflicts, the two colonies shouldn't be completely merged right away; they must be given at least a day or so to simply live alongside one another. To this end, you can keep the colonies separated using a sheet of newspaper, which the bees will gradually chew through; or, they can be temporarily separated with netting.

You can try to save the queenless colony by adding a frame with day-old brood from another colony, or by waiting until you're able to find a young queen or queen cells. But by removing brood from another colony, we're already disrupting its vital rhythm, which contradicts our principles, and finding a young queen any earlier than the end of May isn't realistic in our climate.

On top of that, the life cycle of a colony that has survived the winter without a queen has already been seriously disrupted due to the lack of young bees, to whom so much of the work is entrusted within the colony. Therefore, it's not worth trying to save a queenless hive—better to spend your time trying to create a new one.

This opinion was shared by Georges de Layens. Here's a citation taken from Edouard Bertrand's book, *Managing the Apiary and the Beekeeper's Calendar* (translated from the French, published by A.F. Devrien in Petrograd in 1914):

> The Layens method is very simple. The first inspection is carried out no sooner than the 9th day after the first spring flight—that is, when you should certainly be able to find sealed brood in a successful hive, using it to judge the quality of the queen—and certain measures are taken to help failing colonies, preferably by uniting them with others.
>
> A successful beehouse [*an archaic expression for a hive or log hive—Author's note*] is arranged as follows: one of the entrances is left sealed until the start of summer, and

the colony is moved next to the other entrance. Its frames are arranged in the following order, starting from the side wall where the entrance is located: 2 frames with empty comb, [then the brood frames,] then frames with [foundation and] partially-drawn comb to the end of the hive. Ideally, the empty comb frames would have some honey near the top, and in greater amounts the farther the frame is located from the nest and the entrance.

Once the frames have been arranged in this order, the hive is closed, and quite often the beekeeper won't return to the apiary until the fall, to pull honey and prepare the hives for winter. As they make their way to the honey at the far end of the hive over the course of the summer, the bees will happily fill their empty frames with comb and maintain cleanliness in the hive, defending the foundation from wax moths.

The brood, as we know, will be concentrated near the entrance, where there's more fresh air; the queen will stay there as well, so building drone cells in the far end of the hive won't be a problem. This comb won't be filled with eggs, but exclusively with honey. The portion of the hive farther from the entrance, which is free from brood, is well suited for centrifugation, but de Layens himself prefers pulling all surplus honey at one time, in fall.

De Layens believes that his method for keeping bees is most in keeping with their nature, in addition to being highly profitable and less labor-intensive.

Once upon a time, this passage, along with a description of the Layens hive (see also Figure 3, p. 103), was a true revelation for me! By the time I came across it, my bees were already living in horizontal hives with extra-deep frames, and my system for keeping them was practically identical—as I now learned—to the one used by Georges de Layens almost a century and a half earlier.

·Indeed, there's nothing new under the sun! Moreover, the book that described this system back in its day (the one Bertrand cited in 1882) had a highly amusing title: *The Latest Beekeeping Techniques*. There you have it!

But let's return to our topic at hand, having found support from a natural beekeeper who was renowned in his day. Again I must reiterate why a spring inspection is necessary.

One of a beekeeper's main tasks is to ensure the constant renewal of comb in the nest portion of the hive. We handle this task by adding fresh frames with foundation to the nest area every year. By performing this procedure each spring, we gradually remove old comb from the nest portion (and eventually remove it from the nest altogether) and replace it with fresh comb.

The mildness of our springtime intervention is ensured by the fact that, after the foundation, the nest (brood) frames are put back in the same order they were found in. That is, we do not violate the integrity of the nest the bees built to care for their brood; we simply move it, in its entirety, toward the empty area of the hive.

Now, a question: is it possible, once you've filled the whole hive with empty comb and foundation frames right after inspection, to leave the hive completely unattended until fall?

For strong colonies, the answer is—absolutely. I've done so myself, and had no apparent problems.

But what about weak colonies? For them, things will be much better if we leave an insulated division board separating the nest from the remainder of the hive, at least until warm weather sets in for good.

And now that we're on this topic, let me say a word or two about the division board. It's most easily made from

2-inch-thick (40–50-mm) Styrofoam, by cutting out a rectangle approximately $3/16$ inch (5 mm) wider than the internal dimensions of the hive and carefully wrapping it in polyethylene. A division board made in this way will fit snugly in the hive and won't be chewed through by the bees.

A division board can be made using any other method, as long as it fits snugly against the walls and can be easily moved.

One special feature of this division board is that it comes $3/8$–$3/4$ inch (10–20 mm) shy of the bottom of the hive. This is very important! But why?

First, this lets the bees "know" that they have a larger dwelling at their disposal and have room to grow, and they'll develop based on this knowledge. Therefore, moving the division board to add new frames won't change their sense of the hive's volume, and won't lead to any surprises for them. By the way, once upon a time there were log hives consisting of several chambers linked by narrow passages. And those hives worked better than single-volume hives.

Second, during hot weather you can find a large number of bees sitting on the walls in the empty portion of the hive. This is likely a great place to relax for forager bees not involved in work inside the hive.

Third, if for some reason you missed the time for expansion and the bees have begun to feel cramped, they can easily cross the division board into the empty space and continue their work. But if there are no frames there, the bees will begin drawing comb from the ceiling, as they would in a tree hollow (I've encountered this situation myself). Therefore, if you're planning to be away from the apiary for an extended period, you should add frames to the empty part of the hive, all the way to the division board. If you have both empty comb and foundation, it's best to alternate them; if you only have foundation, then add it.

A. Open the hive; remove the division board

B. Move all frames to the opposite side; inspect contents

H = honey
P = pollen
C = dry (empty) comb
B = brood

C. Move the frames back; add foundation; replace the division board

H = honey   F = foundation
P = pollen
C = dry (empty) comb
B = brood

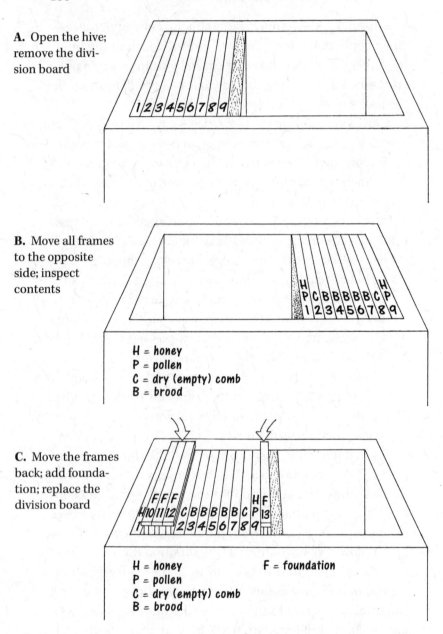

Figure 9. The sequence of operations. A–C. The spring inspection

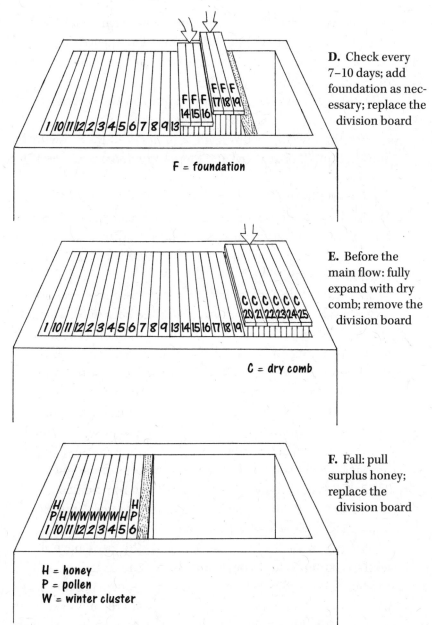

D. Check every 7–10 days; add foundation as necessary; replace the division board

F = foundation

E. Before the main flow: fully expand with dry comb; remove the division board

C = dry comb

F. Fall: pull surplus honey; replace the division board

H = honey
P = pollen
W = winter cluster

D–E. Spring–summer: expand the nest. F. Fall: pull honey

Those who are never far from their apiary can do as I do. Once every seven to ten days, I walk around the entire bee-yard and peek into the hives, opening the top and slightly moving the division board to the side.

If the bees have begun to build comb on the second-to-last frame and are already crawling around on the last one, I move the division board aside and add 2–3 frames with empty comb (if I have any) and foundation (*Figure 9.D–E*). If there aren't any bees yet on the second-to-last frame, then I leave everything as is.

Checking up on my apiary takes no longer than half an hour. For identification purposes, I mark any hives that have a strong colony and are full of frames, and leave them un-touched until fall.

This procedure for adding frames takes, quite literally, just a few seconds and doesn't disturb the bees in the least. One should simply avoid waiting until the colony is already actively working on the last frame. In that case, the bees re-gard the movement of the division board as an attempt to break into their nest, and they react accordingly.

But if this is avoided, then there are no problems what-soever. Our bees, for example, are among the most irascible you'll find anywhere (believe me!), but their presence on our land, as I've said before, doesn't bother us or our guests. There are just a couple of hives that I recommend keeping one's distance from (those bees have an attitude!), but the rest can be approached with no worries.

Starting in mid-July (in our region), the bees have ef-fectively stopped drawing comb on the foundation, and the heavy honeyflow is over, unless you've made a point of planting late-blooming nectar plants. So there's no need to approach the hives until September, unless you simply feel like it.

Fall Procedures

The next stage is the "harvest," which is combined with the fall inspection and preparing the bees for winter. When should this stage be completed?

Don't do it too early—there are still a lot of bees in the hive, and they behave very aggressively during the warm dearth period. In addition, at this point the danger of robbing by other bees, which can be initiated by opening a hive, is too high. By the same token, pulling the honey too late also isn't good. You'll have to pick the time yourself, based on the local weather and your own situation.

I prefer the second half of September, when there's no longer any brood in the colonies, the honey is ripe and capped, the bees are calm, and there aren't that many of them.

By the way, not too long ago information appeared claiming that in the old days honey was pulled not on Russia's Savior of the Honey Feast Day (August 14th), as is traditionally believed, but rather on the Orthodox St. John's Day, September 11th. This is entirely plausible. And some keepers of log hives (according to information from the literature) observed the tradition of pulling honey in the spring. I think this is easily justifiable for log hives, since it's much easier for bees to repair any damage done by man during early summer than during the fall.

Readying bees for winter is based on two principles I've already mentioned above, but which are worth repeating here.

First: a total of approximately 50 pounds (25 kg) of honey should be left in the hive for the winter for a colony of average strength.

Second: the certainty that bees are perfectly capable of ideally arranging their winter nest themselves, without human help. Our job, then, is simply to stay out of their way.

But is this even possible in a standard industrial hive? Let's read in the aforementioned book, *500 Questions and Answers About Beekeeping*—question No. 278:

> *Is it necessary to rearrange a brood nest for the winter? Last year the bees wintered just fine without my rearranging the frames.*
>
> Bees arrange their honey reserves so as to use them successfully during the winter. However, when supers and additional boxes are removed, the place the bees had prepared for storing honey and arranging their nest is disturbed. Therefore, during the fall, one must check the amount of honey in the nest, and make sure that there aren't any frames left in the center of the nest that have little honey or are full of beebread.

But even in a Dadant hive, bees somehow manage to do things their way. *Beekeeping* magazine (No. 3, 1951) describes an interesting study. In mid-September, researchers assembled nests in ten Dadant hives according to the traditional arrangement, while weighing each frame. A month later, they inspected the hives and again weighed the frames. And it turned out that during that time, in all ten hives, the bees had been hard at work, redistributing the honey within the hive as they saw fit. And things were done a bit differently in every individual hive.

As for our hives, they don't have supers, and there's no need to disrupt the nests that the bees build for the winter. This means that our task is restricted to simply pulling the surplus honey.

In essence, this procedure is extremely simple. We remove the frames, starting with the end of the hive farthest from the entrance. There's no longer any brood in the frames, since, with the advent of cooler weather, the bees slowly begin to form a cluster, to the edge of which we gradually draw nearer.

At this point, we have two options. First, having removed the majority of the frames from the hive, we can first move the remaining frames (with the bees), as we did in the spring, into the empty portion of the hive, and put them back following the inspection. Once we've made sure there's at least 50 pounds (25 kg) of honey in the hive, we can leave it for the winter. I prefer this method, since one may find frames full of honey next to the walls of the hive that can be removed (in accordance with the total amount of reserves), or frames that have not been filled with comb, which it makes little sense to leave for the winter.

Or, having removed the frames filled with honey, we can simply replace the division board without disrupting the nest (*Figure 9.F*). Then we can lift the hive up on one side to estimate, by weight, the amount of honey it contains (comparing the weight of a full hive with that of an empty hive). I tend to use this method with new colonies that started from swarms during the given season.

Extracting honey in the fall is much easier than in the spring, since the honey thickens during the winter, and in places may even completely crystallize. But failing to leave enough honey for the winter is still much worse than leaving too much and pulling the surplus in the spring.

After all, the bees certainly won't eat more than they need, so any excess honey we may lose in the fall will be recovered come spring.

Likewise, the 20 pounds (10 kg) we have to leave for the bees following the spring inspection will be recovered in the fall, and with a surplus. And so on and so forth.

And since the beekeeper's biggest enemy is greed, which always goes hand in hand with dishonesty, making the transition to the natural beekeeping method is impossible unless you part ways with this wonderful duo. But this goes without saying.

Let's move along to installing the division board. Once, as I was preparing a hive for winter, I accidentally forgot to install the division board after removing the frames. I only discovered this fact in the spring—but the bees had wintered splendidly, and there wasn't a trace of moisture in the hive. Meanwhile, in some of the other hives, the far frame, closest to the division board, had grown damp.

What did I conclude from this incident? The bees prepare the nest area for the winter when there's no division board in the hive and the air can circulate throughout its entire volume. By adding the division board and cutting off more than half of the hive, we alter the ventilation conditions.

What can be done to compensate for this change? Perhaps we could leave a gap between the division board and the nest area. But this won't do, since the bees might begin to draw comb in the empty space come spring.

Therefore, I add a frame with foundation in between the nest portion, where the bees will winter, and the division board. The thin sheet of foundation doesn't prevent the air from circulating, and in the spring, if we happen to be a bit late with our inspection, the bees will have room to build. It's a nice little trick.

Atop the "ceiling" formed by the touching top bars of the frames, before closing the top, we can lay down a thick piece of fabric (perhaps in several layers) reaching the hive's edges and covering all of the gaps. Now the hive is ready for the winter.

Should the gap beneath the division board be sealed up? Personally, I don't, although I haven't drawn any final conclusions as to which option is better.

And that just about does it. Your fall work is done; you've come full circle. You can happily go about your business without worrying about your bees, until the warm spring weather arrives, and with it the first good honeyflow.

Indeed, it's high time I completed this section and went to work on my grounds; outside, fall is here, and with it, there's plenty to keep us country folk busy. On top of that, my wife is lurking behind me with increasing frequency, peering disapprovingly at my back as I sit hunched over my computer keyboard.

Yet, if I'm to give a full picture of the natural approach, a few more brushstrokes must be added to our canvas. And then it will indeed be time to part ways, only to meet again in Part III over a cup of aromatic tea with some fresh, fragrant honey from your own hives.

How to Make
Extra-Deep Frames

Unfortunately, the extra-deep frame, 17 to 20 inches (445–500 mm) deep, has yet to be adopted as an industrial standard, leaving its adherents to deal with certain technical difficulties.

Keep in mind that the ideal situation for the bees is a single wax field within the frame without any internal beams. To achieve this, the frame should be made with bars that are thicker than usual (1 x $^3/_4$ inch; 25 x 20 mm), strung with 6–8 rows of wire and filled out with one and a half sheets of Dadant deep foundation—or two sheets of standard Langstroth deep foundation. This option—I repeat—is the best (see Figure 14, p. 370, and Photographs 25–26, p. 339). But honey extractors aren't made to fit such frames. A good craftsman can, of course, fashion suitable extractors without much trouble, but a simple user like me rarely has the time for that.

Therefore, one may have to join a Dadant deep frame with a super frame (or join two Langstroth deep frames). But this results in a thick horizontal beam running across an extra-deep frame Photographs 23–24, p. 338). To what extent does this bother the bees—if it bothers them at all? I can't say with any certainty, but in my experience it doesn't bother them to any considerable degree.

In a Dadant hive, for example, the bees draw comb in the super despite its bars and the $^3/_8$-inch-high (1-cm) vertical gap between the frames, and will winter wonderfully there if the super is left undisturbed.

Personally, my bees build comb in both the upper and lower portions of my extra-deep frames, and fill both portions with honey (not always, of course), so I haven't seen any problems with this arrangement.

Some time is needed to disconnect the upper and lower halves, but it's not much. On the other hand, the connecting staple also serves to properly spread adjacent frames. And that's a big plus.

Despite all this, in time I plan to build or order an extractor made for intact extra-deep frames and try my luck with it.

Brushstrokes

So, the annual cycle is complete. With sufficient honey reserves in a nest the bees have arranged themselves, there's nothing to worry about until spring. Even during the winter, though, I sometimes walk up to my hives and listen to the bees buzzing inside, meditating a bit on how strangely and wondrously nature works, with its harmonious alternations between summer heat and winter cold, each with its own peculiar joy and beauty.

One winter nuisance for bees are mice. One obstacle for them are steel supports, or wooden ones wrapped mid-way with strips of tin (I use empty soda cans). In addition, one can cover the lower entrance with netting or some entrance barrier.

By the way, even without these precautions, mice have only gotten into my hives on just a few occasions—once into a weak colony which perished as a result (or maybe for some other reason?), and once into a strong colony, which survived.

During the winter, some bee colonies may die off—and that's inevitable, a normal, natural phenomenon. Weak colonies die, and strong ones leave behind healthy descendants. The main thing is for the beekeeper to avoid contributing somehow to their ruin.

And unless we do something unnatural (no need to repeat myself on this count), then we can have a clean conscience before Nature, and the bees' death will be an effective means of purifying the local bees' gene pool from foreign admixtures introduced by human activity.

But one question remains. If bees practically never swarm in our hives, then how are we to generate new colonies? The answer is simple.

We have a simple, natural method for encouraging the bees to swarm. When there's a need to produce swarms (I'm repeating myself a bit), we must choose those colonies most desirable for propagation and cause them to swarm. How?

Following the spring inspection (and having added 3–4 frames with foundation to the nest), or even without any inspection or addition of frames, the nest is not expanded and the gap beneath the division board is sealed, leaving the bees unable to enter the empty portion of the hive.

In these conditions, a strong colony (and only strong, healthy colonies should be selected) will assimilate the available space fairly quickly, and then begin swarming. Once the swarm has left the hive, we can remove the division board and add frames.

The earlier the swarm is cast, the better. It's common knowledge that a weak swarm at the very beginning of June is better than a strong one at the end of June. The procedure for capturing a swarm is described in Part III—it's also good to see someone do it, in person or on video. There's nothing too complicated about it, but situations may arise that involve a bit of hassle.

Once the swarm has been caught, I leave it until evening in a cellar or other cool area. If the queen is in the swarm box, the bees will sit calmly and will easily enter their new home that evening.

Strong and early swarms may be easily installed onto pure foundation, although if you have any empty comb, it's not a bad idea to add 1–2 frames of it. I add a total of 6 to 12 frames for a swarm, depending on its size. The frames are pressed to the side with a division board and the lower entrance is sealed for the entire width of the empty portion of the hive.

Then a sheet of plywood is placed right under the bottom entrance, with a small incline so that the bees will have to move upwards a bit, and the bees are gradually (not all at once) dumped onto this sheet from the swarm box (Photograph 14, p. 333). With rare exceptions, they will head into the new hive on their own accord. This procedure should be done in the evening, but not too late.

Capturing and installing a new swarm is always a great joy. It's so nice to see new life on your grounds that it becomes hard to resist the urge, for several days thereafter, to walk up to the hive and take a peek at your new bees.

Should the swarm be fed? Most likely a strong early swarm can be left alone until spring; sometimes honey can even be pulled from it in the fall. A late swarm with a lackluster honeyflow will likely need to be fed. One option is to add, during the fall inspection, a couple of frames full of honey to a weak colony, but it's better to hang an uncapped honey frame in the empty portion of the hive, or to add a container with honey so that the bees can move it wherever they see fit. Moreover, the lower entrance should be covered—even fully, to avoid robbing by other bees. This shouldn't be done too late, by the end of August.

Speaking of which—during the second half of August, when the colonies are still strong and there isn't much flow, the lower entrances—ideally for all colonies—can be narrowed to a couple inches (a few centimeters), particularly if there's another apiary nearby whose beekeeper has extracted all the honey and left his bees on a starvation diet.

And now, a few more tips for those who are ready to get down to business.

How to Capture a Swarm
In a Swarm Trap

One of the simplest ways to start an apiary "from scratch" is to catch "no-man's" swarms, of which there are usually plenty regardless of your location. Where do they come from? From apiaries large and small whose keepers have missed a swarm, or have simply abandoned their bees; or they're from some "wild" forest colony.

Swarms can appear from neighboring apiaries just a few miles away, or they can fly from great distances. Having flown tens of miles, such swarms will land on a tree, settle down for a day, and replenish their honey reserves before flying farther. These swarms are the most highly valued.

In modern conditions, when there are practically no old-growth trees with hollows left, finding an appropriate home is often no easy matter. And this is a real problem for a bee swarm hunting for a home. When they fail to find a suitable location, swarms will settle anywhere and everywhere: in abandoned buildings, beneath the eaves of houses, in mailboxes, and even in metal buckets! Understandably, they have little chance of surviving in such homes.

And there, all of a sudden, your swarm trap appears, hung by the caring hands of a natural beekeeper—filled with extra-deep frames, and offering the opportunity to move into a swanky new housing development with lots of living space and growth potential! The temptation is irresistible (Photographs 15–18, pp. 334–335).

Seriously, though—a swarm trap is a light-duty small hive with frames that is hung from a tree; it can be made of any material that happens to be at hand. I make swarm traps from $^1/_4$–$^3/_8$-inch-thick (6–10-mm) plywood, with 8 extra-deep frames, to make it easier to move the bees into stationary horizontal hives. Halfway down the box, I make a slit-shaped or a round entrance, covering it with a screen during transportation.

I outfit my swarm traps with foundation frames and make sure to add (if I have one) at least one frame with empty comb, ideally with somewhat darker comb (for some reason this appeals to swarms). And I hang them on trees at a height of around 10–12 feet (3–4 m).

From this point on, you have two options. The first (and best) is to check the traps every day and, in the evening of the very same day you discover a swarm (before the bees have time to get used to their new location), to move the trap, with the swarm, to a stationary spot at the apiary. A

few days later, when the bees have settled in, you can transfer them to a stationary home *located at the very same spot*.

Another option is to check the swarm traps less frequently. But here, problems arise with transferring the swarm traps with the bees to the apiary. If you're not moving them very far—no farther than 3–4 miles (5–6 km)—then the worker bees who fly from their new location in search of nectar are highly likely to return to the location where the swarm trap was hanging. What can be done about this?

One can hang any empty box at the spot where the swarm trap was located, and transfer any bees that gather there to their new hive late in the evening. And you'll have to do this from several days to a week, until all the bees have grown accustomed to their new location.

To accelerate this process I use a little trick I read about in an article by a certain amateur beekeeper. When he brings a swarm trap to his apiary, he stacks a few branches over the

hive's entrance, making it a bit tougher for the bees to exit the hive. When they realize that something outside the hive has changed, the bees carry out an orientation flight before heading "into the field" and form a mental map of their new location.

There's another option for moving a swarm trap to an apiary: first, move the bees around 6 miles (10 km) away, keep them there for a few days, and then take them to your apiary.

Or, if possible, you can temporarily leave the hive beneath the tree where the swarm trap was hanging. You can then move it to the apiary during late fall or early spring.

All in all, catching swarms is a truly effective and very humane method for acquiring bees. Sure, it involves a bit of work—climbing up trees, checking the traps every day. But on the other hand it's cheap!

That leaves just one last detail that you've probably guessed at yourself. Namely, there's no telling what race these newly arrived bees belong to! This past summer, two colonies arrived at my apiary (straight into empty hives with frames), and both of them were clearly not European dark bees. One, judging by its habitus—to use some scientific jargon—was closer to the Carpathian bee, and the other to the Caucasian.

Of course, one could install European dark bee queens in these new swarms. But where can the queens be found? How should they be installed? Of course, certain methods are well known, but I'd do anything to avoid using them...

And this is one occasion when I don't have a ready-made solution—which means that we'll have to search for a solution together. One possibility is to add a weak late swarm to the already-installed swarm—see Part III.

The main thing here is to observe the principle of the natural approach and not to forget the responsibility we assume when we get involved with natural living things.

But that's another topic, worthy of its own chapter.

Responsibility

The issue of responsibility is so subtle that it's hard to find the right words to approach it with. Most likely, this issue belongs to the realm of feelings that must first be comprehended, and, once comprehended, correctly formulated into words.

The idea I'd like to get across is that you shouldn't begin keeping bees unless you're prepared to assume responsibility for their lives. You can't simply hang a swarm trap if you have no idea of how to proceed further, or without having set up a nice well-insulated hive for the bees to move into, or without a good place to put it.

How many people have tried their hand at beekeeping! And how many of them have been scarred for life by the sight of empty, dead hives, their bottoms littered with corpses.

Of course, it's always very sad when bees die, but it's much sadder when you are to blame for their death.

After all, some subtle connection develops between any living thing and the human beings who care for it—a connection we all feel, but about which we know almost nothing. Even beekeepers who live in the city and only rarely visit their bees always think of them and wonder how they're doing. And when they do arrive at their country house, before unloading their things or even stepping inside the house, they run immediately to their hives and breathe a sigh of relief when they see that their bees are still there, alive and well.

If you go down the path of industrial beekeeping, you should realize that from the moment you begin keeping bees in a Dadant or Langstroth hive you'll have to follow a strict schedule of required tasks throughout the year. And any slipup or untimely procedure could threaten to ruin the entire undertaking.

And this is a very serious matter! If you aren't prepared for this responsibility, then you shouldn't even begin. In order to form a realistic picture of the yearly work required by modern beekeeping, I can recommend reading a book by Vladimir Tsebro, *Day by Day at the Apiary* (Lenizdat, 1991). It shares the experiences of a real practicing beekeeper who accurately and dutifully describes all of the techniques he uses.

Only having carefully assessed your own abilities should you begin to take action.

What about natural beekeeping? Of course, this responsibility remains! Although I have a much easier time of it than an industrial beekeeper, and not only because my bees give me much fewer hassles. I know that I'm not doing them any

harm and try to make sure that their life is, at the very least, no worse than it would be if they were "free." And even better, if possible!

But if I were to simply stop tending to my bees, then within two or three years, as you've already seen, they'd simply continue swarming until there were no bees left, and in their place would appear various creatures on the prowl for honey—wasps, mice, wax moths, and many others.

Is that what I wanted when I spent all that time building my hives and frames, and bothered with installing my colonies in them? Of course not! That means that I should carry out the tasks I described above, and I should carry them out on time. And you should be prepared to do that.

On the other hand, working with bees provides me with tremendous pleasure, and rewards me with the most healthful product in the world.

I'm also comforted by the fact that if, for whatever reason, I fail to carry out a certain task, or to carry it out on time, then the bees won't die. For example, let's say I miss a spring inspection. It's not a catastrophe! I'll be able to simply add some frames on the sides in June—or, if they're still left behind the division board from the previous fall, then there's nothing left for me to do all summer.

Or let's say I filled the entire hive with frames in early summer, but wasn't able to make it back to the apiary and pull the honey during the fall. Fine, no big deal! The bees will winter splendidly, and I'll pull the honey in the spring!

The sceptical reader may suspect that all of this sounds a bit too simple. Indeed it is. But then, this search for simplicity and sense is what brings meaning to my life. What about you?

What do you think—why were human beings endowed with intelligence? To complicate our lives, or to simplify them? To create new problems by violating nature's laws, or, by going with the natural flow of things, to achieve our goals simply and easily?

What do you like more: the joy of creating or the tribulations of life? Backbreaking daily drudgery, or joyous and meaningful work?

From the most ancient, prehistoric times, humans have observed bees and been amazed at how intelligently and rationally their life is arranged—a life that contributes so much to its environment, and to man, without doing the least bit of harm.

Can the same be said of modern man?

Questions and Answers - 1

Where can I get bees?

There are special apiaries out there that specialize in breeding and selling European dark bee queens and colonies. (I am not directly acquainted with them and can't provide any addresses). Bees can be bought from them. Or you can look for a beekeeper in your area who keeps European dark bees. It seems to me that people like this can be found anywhere. Or you can simply hunt for a beekeeper who never buys bees and only keeps his own. People like this are easy to find through any beekeeping store or local beekeeping association, or at a market where honey is sold. Ask about beekeepers who don't buy Carpathian bees, but only keep their own local bees.

When we inquired at the local beekeeping store about such a beekeeper, they spoke up right away. A strange guy, they said. What's so strange about him? we asked. Well, they said, he never buys medicine for his bees. Aha! Sounds like our kind of guy! Let's pay him a visit!

Look at the bees themselves. They would be black, without any bright yellow or light blue stripes. The yellower the bee, the more southern blood it has. And may specialists please forgive me this rather crude description.

How can I transfer bees from a regular hive to a horizontal hive with extra-deep frames?

Of course, bees are bought in the spring, as soon as the first honeyflow begins. It's best to move the existing hives to your apiary and let them sit for a few days at their future permanent location before transferring the bees into their new hives.

Here's how we did it. We set the new hive behind the existing one, then prepared extension frames with connectors. Then, one person removes a frame from the old hive, while the other quickly attaches the lower extension frame from below and fastens it with small self-drilling screws. Next, the finished extra-deep frame is added to the new hive, where we've already added 3–4 foundation frames, just as we would during a spring inspection.

Then the old hive is moved aside and the new one is installed in its place. The old hive with the bees remaining on its walls is set on its side and moved as close to the new one as possible. There's no need to shake the bees out of it—they could become angry. Once all the bees have left the old box, we remove it from the apiary. Mission accomplished.

How many bees should I start with?

Ideally, start with three colonies. You don't need many until you feel confident enough in your abilities. But just one colony isn't good, since the bees could always die, and that would be a blow to your confidence. But if one out of three colonies dies, it's not so bad, and you can easily replace the dead colony using the remaining ones.

How should I extract my honey?

Honey should be extracted in a heated space, 80–85°F (25–30°C), since honey is very thick in its raw form and simply won't come out of its cells if it's too cold (believe me, I've tried!). To remove the comb capping, I use two knives; while I'm cutting with one, the other is kept in hot water, warming up. There are other methods out there (e.g., a special uncapping fork), but choosing one is up to you—whatever you're used to. Fresh comb capping is a favorite treat for kids, who always seem to be running around while the honey is being extracted and "helping." Even my wife and I prefer capping to honey, and continue enjoying it long after the extraction is done.

How should I store empty comb?

Once the honey is extracted, we leave our frames out to dry (allowing the bees to remove any remnants from the walls of the cells). To this end, we put them either in the empty sections of hives (having taken precautionary measures against robbing), or simply near the apiary, at least 100 feet (30 m) away. *One should never, ever place frames recently emptied of honey alongside hives!*

We use the same technique to dry out the honey extractor and all related equipment.

Empty comb shouldn't be stored in a heated environment—it could attract wax moths. It's better to store it in a cold shed or in empty hives; you can also store it in empty sections of hives with wintering bees.

Of course, we cull black comb and melt it during the winter for wax.

How should I add foundation to my frames?

I stretch four rows of wire across the larger upper frame, and two in the lower frame. The first row of wire should be close (no more than $3/4$ inch or 2 cm) to the top bar. I add the foundation by passing a current through the wires (using an ordinary car battery), but only through two wires at once, instead of through all four. I stretch the wire two rows at a time as well. Be sure, when adding the sheet of foundation, that it draws flush with the top bar.

How can I prevent robbing?

During the dearth period (in our region, it begins in the second half of August), the lower entrance should be made as small as possible. And if a colony is robbed, you shouldn't worry about it excessively. This too is a matter of natural selection. The honey won't be wasted, but rather simply redistributed among the remaining hives.

What can I do to protect the bees from disease?

In addition to general principles of natural beekeeping, you can:

- Not remove brood or transfer it to other colonies (this should be obvious, of course).
- If a colony has died, then before installing a new one, scorch the hive with a blowtorch, or, having cleaned it thoroughly, treat it with a heated lye solution (an ash infusion).
- Cull any suspicious empty comb, especially comb from any colonies that have perished.
- Set your hives as far from one another as possible, and paint them in different colors to ensure that the bees don't accidentally fly to the wrong hive.

How can I choose the right time to work with bees?

Ideally, any handling of the hive should take place during nice, calm, sunny weather. Never peek into your hives before a storm, when a storm front is moving in, when the wind is beginning to pick up, or when the weather is taking a turn for the worse.

My preferred time of day is after lunch, closer to evening, but not too late. At that time, some of the bees are still in the field, and the ones in the hive, tired out after their day's work, behave calmly.

Epilogue to Parts I and II

The time has flown by almost unnoticeably, but it's been more than three years now since I wrote Parts I and II. To my surprise, their publication met with a considerable reaction—during the years since, I've received several hundred warm and encouraging letters full of thanks, interesting ideas, stories from readers' experiences with natural beekeeping, and references to serious new sources of information. Some of the letters included photographs of handmade horizontal hives with extra-deep frames, and described those initial forays into beekeeping. What could be more delightful for an author! Many thanks to everyone who wrote these letters!

While preparing this new edition and carefully rereading Parts I and II, I understood that there's nothing I wish to change about them. My mission, as I saw it, was simply to share with you the minimum amount of information that is absolutely necessary to begin keeping bees. Although certain insignificant details might be presented a bit differently, the basic propositions and ideas haven't changed—in fact, in the interim, they've only found further evidence to support them. However, both now and when I first wrote the book, I would never presume to say that I've exhausted the topic of natural beekeeping once and for all. Progress has certainly been made: thanks to my practical experience in working with bees, and to my readers' letters, the system is constantly being refined and perfected. Below are the main

ideas and additions that have been suggested and implemented in practice since Parts I and II were first written:

• The hives now have just one entrance, slit-shaped,
$^1/_2$ inch (12–13 mm) tall and running the entire length of
the front wall. Only the 6–10 inches (15–25 cm) facing the
nest frames are left permanently open; the rest of the slit
can be closed. For the updated hive plans, see Appendix 6,
pp. 373–383.

• The slit entrance has "broken loose" from the bottom
and risen upward; it is now located 16 inches (40 cm)
from the ceiling of the hive.

• There are now four 1-inch (25-mm) openings at the
very bottom of the back wall, covered with a fine screen
and opened only during the main honeyflow to improve
ventilation.

• There is now a large open space beneath the frames
(5–6 inches; 13–15 cm) that, for the winter, is filled with
dry bog moss (*Sphagnum*) or any other suitable water-absorbing material to soak up any moisture that develops
during the winter.

• There is now a new, more promising technique for
spring inspection and for maintaining the bee colony
throughout the year, which involves moving the nest portion of the hive.

• More attention is paid to swarms: I now unite weak
swarms, or I install them with weak colonies, and I feed
them honey during periods with a weak honeyflow.

- I've begun paying a lot of attention to the age of the queen bee: I encourage older colonies to swarm, or I install with them weak swarms, along with their young queens.

These and a few other ideas involving the continued development and elaboration of the system for naturally keeping bees in horizontal hives with extra-deep frames are presented in Parts III and IV of *Keeping Bees with a Smile*.

PART III

The Finer Points of Natural Beekeeping

The real secret to beekeeping is knowing your bees' custom and following it. Anyone who wants to keep bees successfully should mirror wild bees' way of life to the greatest extent possible.

Nikolay Vitvitsky (1764–1853)

Three Years Later

More than three years have passed since I wrote Parts I and II of *Keeping Bees with a Smile*. It might seem that little has changed since then; I'm sitting at the same table, in front of the same computer screen—and when I look up, I see my apiary, just as I did three years ago. The tops of the hives are sporting high "hats" of snow (Photograph 32, p.342); the honey has long since been pulled and stored safely away in the cellar, and there's absolutely nothing to do in the bee-yard until spring. So now is the perfect time to take stock of things and reflect a bit on this fascinating venture—bee-keeping—and on the bees themselves, who bring us so much benefit, joy, and mystery.

So, what's changed during the past three years? A lot, when I really think about it. The apiary has grown considerably, and turned from a pleasant hobby into something that is almost my primary pursuit. I've met a lot of interesting people, enjoyed many captivating conversations, and learned a ton of new and interesting information. I've seen how many people are taking up beekeeping seriously, and have become real "fans" of our native European dark bee and are engaged in preserving and propagating it (Photograph 30, p. 341). And during these years I've become more convinced than ever of the truth of natural beekeeping principles.

My guests often ask me: "Seriously now, does this really work? Do you really inspect your hives just twice a year, with minimal interference in the life of your colonies?" And here's my response: "No, it's not working! Two times a year is two times too often; recently I've been doing just one inspection per year and am considering the possibility of avoiding even that." "What about queen cells?" the professional beekeepers ask. "You do cut them out, to keep the colony from swarming?" "Actually, no," I answer. "Quite the opposite. My bees aren't really into swarming; in fact, I have to specially induce swarming to have any new swarms."

The longer I work with bees, the more I am convinced that the most important aspect of the natural approach is knowing the laws that govern the life of a bee colony, as well as a thorough understanding of what the beekeeper does, and the effect his actions have on the bees. And the more understanding we gain, the less need there is for the actions themselves. That is, one might say that the number of actions is inversely proportional to the depth of our understanding. That's not to say that the number approaches zero, of course. An apiary requires a certain amount of work that can never be avoided entirely. But that work must be precise and timely. This is essential—otherwise, the bees might begin swarming, or even die off. And is that what we got into beekeeping for?

One of my friends, Dima, who just acquired his first bee colony last spring, asked me in the fall to help prepare the hive for wintering. We swung the top open, stuck a moss cushion underneath the frames, added a warm division board on the side and sealed off the gap underneath it. The whole procedure took less than five minutes. "And that's it?" Dima asked, surprised—he'd expected some long and grandiose operation. "Of course," I answered. "What's the point of bothering the bees—instead, let's go have some tea with honey and discuss our plans for next summer." By that point, we'd also pulled the honey frames from Dima's hive—and this also took no more than five minutes.

Still, the question remains: are things really that simple when it comes to natural beekeeping, and with apiculture in general? Is it really possible to keep bees without expending much energy or time? There's no clear-cut answer to this question. The answer is both yes and no. Many people have successfully kept bees in horizontal hives with extra-deep frames, but others have been less successful. What's the reason behind this? Well, we can name several. The most common include failure to carefully follow the technique, and neglect of the bees—for example, when a keeper skips the spring inspection, when he fails to expand the nest on time, or when he disturbs the bees excessively, or at the wrong moment. Or perhaps he bought his bees from a nearby beekeeper who'd spent his whole life experimenting with various races of bees. But these reasons are obvious. There are others that have less to do with us, the keepers, that remain quite mysterious. After all, bees are living creatures, with their own peculiar character and motivations, which don't always have a rational explanation.

Therefore, if you've had problems, there's no reason to despair. Pause to reflect; take stock of your own experience, and that of others; try to understand where the problem lies. Keep trying, and the results won't be long in coming. Nature richly rewards those who act out of love and in keeping with its laws.

Principles of Natural Beekeeping Revisited

For many practicing beekeepers the natural approach inspires serious and perfectly expectable doubts, due to its radical nature. But the simple fact is that this system works! One can find any number of examples of successful apiculturists who have kept and continue to keep bees in the old-fashioned way: they prefer to keep the local bee race, leave their hives outdoors for the winter, and effectively avoid the use of any medicines. I sometimes hear tell of some "bizarre" extra-deep frame hives, made back before World War II, that beginning beekeepers threw out when they inherited an apiary from a grandfather.

And it was precisely World War II that marked a milestone in beekeeping: Russia's entire economy, not to mention beekeeping, was largely destroyed and had to be restored from the ground up, starting with mass production of Dadant hives. And what had been before was quickly forgotten.

But here we go (if these are still fresh on your mind, you can confidently skip to the next section):

Keep interference in the life of a bee colony to a minimum
Any experienced beekeeper will confirm that the less the bees are bothered, the better. Excessive interference distracts the colony from gathering nectar, drastically increases the likelihood of swarming, and triggers aggression, particularly in the European dark bee. Keeping bees in

170

horizontal hives with extra-deep frames reduces the number of interventions in the life of a bee colony to just one per year—namely, the spring inspection, carried out as early as possible, when the bees are less perturbed by an inspection of their nest area.

Use an extra-deep frame, which allows the bees to prepare fully and independently for the winter

For the ideal placement of the winter cluster and of honey reserves, a bee colony at our latitude (Zone 4) needs comb that is at least 16 inches (400 mm) deep. The Dadant brood frame was invented in southern France, where, according to the careful calculations of the hive's inventor, a depth of $11 \, {}^{13}/_{16}$ inches (300 mm) is more than sufficient. With an extra-deep frame (standard length, $18\text{-}{}^{1}/_{2}$-inch or 470-mm depth), a bee colony is able to independently—without interference by the beekeeper—prepare for the winter, and to winter successfully. Ideally, the frame will be free from internal barriers—that is, it will ensure unobstructed movement across a single comb surface. The actual depth of the frame depends on the climate.

Don't use additional boxes and supers

Any changes to a hive during the active season—including pulling honey, adding and removing boxes and supers, and inspecting nest frames—engenders profound discomfort for the bee colony, and one of the results may be swarming. In most cases, anti-swarming methods require yet another intervention in the colony—and a vicious circle ensues. One sensible way to avoid all this is to keep the bee colony in a single box that is designed for maximum colony growth throughout the season and for effective storage of all the honey gathered during the season.

Pull surplus honey just once per year, in the fall, after all of the brood has emerged and the colony has finished preparing for winter

This principle flows logically from the two previous ones.

Don't give the bees supplemental food, including sugar-syrup-based foods

As is well known, worker bees feed on nectar or honey by drawing on previous stockpiles. In addition to carbohydrates, nectar contains vitamins and micronutrients, while honey also contains traces of pollen. Unlike these natural products, sugar-based supplements contain nothing but carbohydrates. Therefore, sugar-based food is one of the main reasons for bee diseases, including the widespread Varroa mite. One principle common to all living things is that an organism weakened by a shortage of necessary substances is most likely to be targeted by pathogenic microorganisms and parasites. And it is simply impossible to avoid such problems unless bees live on their wholesome natural diet.

Don't medicate your bees in any way

This principle is directly tied to the previous one. You can only stop using medicines if you do not feed your bees any artificial food and work with the local race of bees only.

Propagate your bees by swarming only

Artificial propagation of bee colonies is a fully controlled process and is certainly convenient for the beekeeper—but from our point of view, it is a completely unnatural procedure. And at the same time, many beekeepers regard swarming as a serious problem that should be fought against. However, under natural conditions, absent various kinds of emergencies, only strong colonies with old queens are prone to swarming—and when they do, they cast no more than two or three swarms. In this case, even colonies that have swarmed still survive, and in most cases the swarms result in full-fledged colonies. Unlike an artificial splitting of a colony into several parts, natural swarming does not result in drastic disruptions of colonies' makeup and all of the resulting problems. Queens that are produced by a colony naturally are far superior to those that are raised and inseminated artificially. Therefore, successful long-term work with bees can only be based on swarming as the natural mechanism for producing new bee colonies.

Bees only winter outdoors

Much as in the previous item, having bees winter indoors is beneficial and convenient for the beekeeper, since it allows him to preserve the maximum number of bee colonies and save on winter consumption of honey. However, many researchers have noted that wintering indoors weakens bee colonies' immunity and promotes negative selection. Therefore, if one takes a long view of beekeeping, extending several decades into the future, then allowing bees to winter in natural conditions is the correct and only possible choice.

Only keep bees of the local race—in our case, the European dark bee

All of the aforementioned principles, such as outdoor wintering, no medication, etc., are only possible if one keeps bees of the local race—in our case, the European dark bee—which is ideally adapted to the local climate and honeyflow. However, as a result of an entire century of large-scale imports of southern bee colonies and queens, the local race has been lost almost everywhere, and what remains of it has degenerated greatly due to negative selection. Therefore, our challenge now is not only to restore local bee races, but also to aid selection by allowing the strongest and most successful colonies to swarm. By transitioning to natural beekeeping, we will be assisted in this by the forces of nature itself: weak mixed-race colonies will be filtered out, and strong ones will reproduce.

Where did these principles come from, and are they absolutely mandatory? The answer to the first question can be found in Part I, where I've tried to present, as systematically as possible, the thoughts that led me (and many other beekeepers, both past and present) to adopt each of these principles. The answer to the second question is obvious: it's up to you whether or not to follow them. As a rule, beekeepers are highly independent and freedom-loving people—there's no telling them what to do! Personally, I've made my choice, and I'm happy with it! And now I don't even regard it as a choice of principles, but rather as a choice of one's path in beekeeping and in life in general. And when problems do arise, I try to analyze them, draw conclusions, and move ahead, delving deeper and deeper into the fascinating world of natural beekeeping—the natural interactions between human beings and nature, and, in the broadest sense, a natural way of life on this Earth.

The Recipe for Success In Beekeeping

- Nectar resources.
- The race of the bees and their strength.
- The hive design and beekeeping system.

Nectar resources

The order in which the above ingredients are listed is no accident. The hive design and beekeeping principles—the subject of such dispute in the professional literature—take third place. First place goes to the nectar resources—that is, the plants surrounding the apiary, the landscape, and the microclimate. The honeybee's effective flight radius is 1–2 miles (2–3 km), which means that a bee colony has approximately 6,000 acres (2,500 hectares) of terrain at its disposal. What does that terrain look like? Pristine meadows with a tremendous variety of plant life, or wheat fields that are of no use to the bees? A broad-leaved forest with an abundance of lindens and maples, or nothing but spruce trees? This is the single most important factor in the success and productivity of a bee colony. A given bee may be able to fly farther than 2 miles (3 km) in search of nectar, but this takes a lot more time, and a significant portion of the harvested nectar will be consumed by the flight itself. This is an extremely inefficient way to work.

It's hard to overestimate the importance of nectar resources. Even a weak colony, regardless of its hive design, will quickly fill all available room with honey if it lives in an area rich in nectar; on the other hand, even the best hive, full of wonderful bees, won't deliver anything if it is located in a nectar-poor region. This topic brings to mind any number of anecdotes, some of them quite amusing, some less so. For example, a certain keeper installed a Dadant hive in his garden. No one else in the area kept bees, so all of the honeyflow belonged to this single colony. With a setup like this, you can expect to "bathe" in honey, as they say—and the next winter, an article appears on an online beekeeping forum extolling the remarkable qualities of the Dadant hive and concluding that it's senseless to wish for anything better.

Or, take another situation. Someone asks me whether it's possible to keep bees in his native village using the natural approach. The problem is that for many miles around him, in every direction, the fields are planted with rape, and there's almost nothing else. That means that there'll be an explosive, abundant flow for a few weeks out of the year, but the rest of the time there'll be no nectar whatsoever. On top of that, bees are typically unable to winter on honey made from rape (which belongs to the Cruciferae family). What can I tell a person in this situation? Unfortunately, nothing too encouraging...

The way things stand now, bees can't be kept just anywhere in this modern world of ours—not to mention kept using natural methods. There are several reasons for this: huge swaths of land planted with monocultures, catastrophically impoverished and polluted natural environments, the large-scale use of pesticides and GMOs (genetically modified organisms). At the same time, a tremendous number of valuable crops (including fruit) depend on bee pollination.

Therefore, so-called developed countries have recently been sounding the alarm concerning a sharp drop in the number of bee colonies, but there's nothing they can do about it. After all, improving the situation would require moving in a completely different direction and beginning to search for an alternative path for all of humanity. Are we prepared to do that?

In Russia and a number of other countries from the former Soviet Union, the situation remains much more favorable for natural beekeeping than in a majority of developed countries. We still have numerous islands of relatively wild nature, abandoned fields surrounded by forests, and clean creeks flowing through floodplains covered with willows. Russia's temperate forest region, Altai, the Far East, and many other regions could become a mecca for natural beekeeping, and, as it did of old, supply the rest of the world with genuine, delicious, and organic honey. And, as we

know, nature itself will only benefit—since bees are a necessary part of it: when they disappear, the plant world suffers, and when they reappear, it flourishes anew.

What might such a massive beekeeping movement look like in practice? The answer is simple—19th-century beekeeping literature paints a vivid picture. In an orchard or in a forest glade, there's an apiary; three miles (5 km) farther, there's another; and another, and so on and so forth, throughout the entirety of our sprawling country. Each apiary could contain fifty or more hives, depending on the abundance of nectar-bearing plants and the unique characteristics of the area. Methods for evaluating a region's honey-producing capacity can be easily found in traditional beekeeping literature (for example, in Alexey Rybalchenko's *The Mystery of the Bee Swarm*, published 1983, on page 65).

If the area surrounding your apiary isn't as favorable, it doesn't mean you can't improve it. With a little effort, there's not much we're not capable of! How? Very simple: plant trees (Photograph 6, p. 329). Lindens, locusts, various types of maple (except for the box elder, which is highly invasive), various kinds of willow, oak, ash, etc. Planting a tree is easy, but the effects of this simple action are simply astounding. A linden, for example, can grow for centuries, providing, throughout its life, us (and our descendants) with outstanding first-class honey. And although in our climate (Russia's temperate forest zone) it doesn't produce nectar every year, when it does produce, the entire tree will simply be abuzz with bees. Specialists have estimated that each adult tree yields up to 110 pounds (50 kg) of honey each season; a little math gives you some sense of the economic effect over several centuries of one simple act: planting a tree. Of course, a tree's benefits extend far beyond honey alone. They include fresh air, fertile soil, and much, much more.

I've heard stories of an elderly beekeeper who in his youth planted lindens and other trees in the areas surrounding his village; now, when he pulls his honey every fall, he couldn't be happier that, once upon a time, he found the time and energy to plant a few trees; or that it even entered his mind then to undertake such a simple project. All of this goes without saying—after all, many of us have strolled through the grounds of prerevolutionary estates. The estates themselves, not to mention their former masters, have long since disappeared, but the magnificent linden trees stand to this very day as a living reminder of the good people who planted them so long ago. What else could serve as such a beautiful memory of a human being?

Sure, trees are something we can leave behind to ensure a better future. But what about the present? How can an area's honey productivity be enhanced if it's sorely lacking in nectar-bearing plants? Well, quite simply, those plants have to be planted. And this isn't as hard as it might sound at first. Sowing nectar-bearing plants doesn't take much: just a tractor with a few pieces of agricultural equipment, which can be found at a nearby farm or from a neighbor. It's best to use a sowing machine (which can usually be arranged too), but you can also sow by hand, simply by scattering the seed. For plantings of up to ten hectares, this is completely doable, as long as you observe the recommended sowing density and learn to scatter the seed more or less uniformly. Personally, I sow mustard and phacelia (annuals), as well as sweet clover (*Melilotus*) and viper's bugloss or *Echium vulgare* (biannuals) for my bees every spring. And I'm also experimenting with perennial nectar-bearing plants such as sainfoin (*Onobrychis viciifolia*), goat's rue (*Galega officinalis*), great globe thistle (*Echinops sphaerocephalus*), and many others (Photographs 3–5, pp. 328–329). But the first four are a solid and practically can't-miss option for our climate.

Sowing nectar-bearing plants is a large separate topic, one for another book. How to prepare the soil, how to sow the seed, sowing timeframes and densities, and many other issues are involved. But it's definitely worth it: the effects are immense. Watching bees working happily in a blossoming field is a pleasure in and of itself! Don't spare the time and resources spent on sowing; your investments will pay for themselves many times over—all the more so, since you have the option of sowing mixtures (the classic variant combines phacelia and viper's bugloss)—that is, once every two years—or, sowing a mixture of perennials will take care of things for many years. You can combine sowing nectar-bearing plants with other agricultural pursuits—after all, many nectar-bearing plants can also serve as fodder grasses and very good green manure crops (that is, they improve the soil). But then, agriculture is also another topic. Back in the early 19th century Petro Prokopovych (1775–1850) developed a so-called "bee-field" system of agriculture—a set of agricultural practices that also benefited bees and improved soil fertility. We only need to find and carefully read the old texts. However, for now, I see my task as lying elsewhere: in gradually restoring natural meadows, which are the richest "bee pastures," not to mention necessary components of an unadulterated natural landscape.

When we moved to a rural area many years ago, we were surrounded by long-abandoned fields, planted at some point with perennial pasture grasses, which are extremely rugged and resistant to other plants. The result was a homogenous green carpet in early summer, and a dried-out one, yellow like straw, in late summer—and not a single flower for a bee to visit. And where could seeds from a wider variety of plants come from, when this same picture extended for tens of miles in every direction? Of course, if we don't touch anything, then over the course of several centuries (or millennia) the soil's fertility will be restored, along with plant diversity. But can we wait that long? After all, we human beings, with the powerful technical capabilities at our disposal, are capable of damaging the earth, but also of helping it restore itself. In my view, one wonderful opportunity for doing the latter is by planting nectar-bearing plants. Over the course of a few years of non-intrusive (shallow) tillage, we can boost soil fertility, knock out stubborn rhizomatous grasses, and restore the rich natural variety of meadow plants. And all of this will be immensely beneficial for bees, not to mention economically. But, I repeat, this is a separate issue, one we'll certainly return to at some point. For now, let's continue with our main topic: the recipe for success in beekeeping.

Bee Race and Colony Strength

The topic of nectar-bearing plants is so important and so wide-reaching that it's hard to leave it behind. One need only imagine the natural world bees inhabited for tens of millions of years. If we ignore periods of catastrophe (climate changes, earthquakes and ice ages), the unspoiled natural world has always been fertile and abundant. From early spring to late fall, bees could find the nectar needed for springtime growth, fall buildup, and the creation of good, high-quality reserves for the winter—a variety of tree species, rich meadows, an abundance of clean water and many poisonous plants that are "useless" for humans, but which provide bees with the natural medicines they need. Having all but completely destroyed this magnificent world, we then have the audacity to be surprised that bees sometimes get sick and die. On the contrary: we should be surprised that they're still alive at all! Not to mention giving thanks for this fact to a generous and all-forgiving Nature.

The situation with bee races is much the same. As early as the 19th century, many well-known beekeepers were sounding the alarm over the degeneration of our local bee. Back then, the massive imports of southern races of bees hadn't yet begun, but the problem itself had already appeared in connection with the practice of killing the entire colony in the fall in order to collect its honey, when bees were kept in small, thin-walled "log gum" hives similar to skeps. This was the term for sections of tree trunk that had been hollowed out and stood up vertically on a piece of board, or directly on the ground. Nikolay Vitvitsky, a prominent apiculturist of the time, roughly divided bees into several classes, taking into account their honey productivity, their ability to winter, and their resistance to disease. The first class included "completely wild" bees living in tree hollows; the lowest class included "extremely exhausted bees that have spent the winter in cellars and other damp and stuffy spaces and have been exposed to starvation and disease" (cited from Ivan Shabarshov's book *A History of Russian Beekeeping*, Moscow, 1996, p. 156).

Over the past century, the situation has become many times worse due to the massive influx of southern bee races; eventually, it reached the point where even finding a local bee in Russia's temperate forest zone became practically impossible. Apiaries are dominated by bees that are either obvious crosses of imported and local bee races, or European dark bees "in name only" that show a substantial number of traits inherited from their southern cousins. Of course, this problem is not unique to Russia; it is present in almost every corner of the industrialized world.

As a small illustration, we can cite a story told by professor Grigory Kozhevnikov (1866–1933) concerning a 1928 expedition to Bashkiria to study the forest-dwelling European dark bee that was local to the area. In the wake of this expedition, he became more convinced than ever of this bee's superior qualities—specifically, of its ability to provide itself with reserves and generate surplus honey even in lean years. At a certain apiary in Bashkiria, Kozhevnikov found that the yellow coloring inherited from a single imported Italian queen remained apparent in dark-colored local bees for 14 years! He proposed prohibiting all imports of bees and queens of other races to Bashkiria, to the Far East, to Siberia or to the Caucasus (ibid., p. 344). But, as we know, his proposal went unheeded.

As far as I know, the real European dark bee can only be found in a few geographically isolated regions (including some located in Tatarstan and Bashkiria) and in certain apiaries that have made it their job to preserve and propagate the European dark bee since Soviet times. Today, we should be grateful to those apiculturists and dedicated amateurs who have left us the opportunity to restore and multiply the local race of bees, not to mention pursuing natural beekeeping, which would be impossible without local bees.

However, experience has shown that buying bees from a breeder also doesn't come with any guarantees. Apiaries usually sell bee colonies in the form of nucs—standard boxes containing four Dadant brood frames with bees on them. According to the accepted standard, three of the frames should contain brood, and the fourth should contain reserves of honey and beebread. Of course, a fertile queen should also be in there somewhere. So, given equal starting conditions (at least those that can be judged based on appearances), colonies derived from purchased nucs can develop very differently. Some grow actively, producing plenty of honey and wintering splendidly; some are mediocre; and some eventually peter out completely. Why? Because of the inherent qualities of the individual colony—or, more precisely, the queen herself. And these qualities are ultimately a question of genetics. That's why all serious apiculturists, both in the past and the present, have been involved in selective breeding to one degree or another. That is, they've tried to propagate strong and successful bee colonies.

On this topic, there are many questions that are difficult to answer. Do all beekeepers selling bee colonies engage in such work today—namely, selecting and breeding only strong colonies? Is such work being done in commercial queen-rearing apiaries, particularly since the collapse of the Soviet Union? What traits serve as the basis for selection? Honey production and docility alone? What about resistance to disease, the ability to winter outdoors, or to prepare independently for wintering? I'm not so sure about that! After all, an overwhelming majority of large apiaries and queen breeders tend to feed their bees sugar and rearrange their nests in preparation for winter, and to carry out preventative treatments against a number of diseases. Yet the methods used by the people we buy our colonies from have a great deal to do with the bees' fate when we move them to our apiaries and subject them to the demanding conditions of natural beekeeping.

Why do I say "demanding"? Well, that's what they are, from the standpoint of today's mainstream practices. After all, I don't "winterize" the bees; I don't even peek into the nest portion of the hive in the fall. I only inspect the nests in spring; how the bees prepare their nest for winter is up to them. The approach is simple: I do my part—namely, I give the colony a warm, solid hive and extra-deep frames, and I don't pull honey throughout the summer. But how the bees arrange their honey and beebread reserves, where they position their passageways through the comb, how they form their winter cluster—none of this is any of my business. If they do everything right and winter successfully, that's great; if they mess up and don't survive the winter, then it's certainly a pity, but nothing can be done about it. On the other hand, those colonies that do survive can produce strong, healthy offspring that will be very likely to survive the next winter just as successfully. By the same principle, I don't check for the quality of winter reserves. "Smart" bees will leave honey from the main honeyflow in their nest area;

the honey that's not fit for wintering (for example, honey-dew honey) is stored to the sides, as an emergency stockpile, and is then pulled in the fall. Of course, I don't treat my bees against diseases in any way.

A certain number of bee colonies will die off during the winter. Many a "traditional" beekeeper will shake his head reproachfully when he hears this. From their point of view, a real beekeeper should do what it takes to prevent even a single colony from dying. But when they learn of my demanding approach, they're even more surprised, since, in their view, the entire apiary should die out under such conditions. But it doesn't! The number of colonies gradually increases, even though I don't make any special effort to encourage it. That is, I don't engage in artificial propagation (I don't make splits), and I induce swarming only on a small scale, for experimental purposes. The only thing I do in a serious fashion when it comes to developing my "bee operation" is to "collect" European dark bees in my apiary, gathered from all over the place. I have nominally European dark bee colonies from the Ryazan region; I have purebred European dark bees from a queen-rearing apiary in Oryol; I have so-called "Kazan" bees, which are European dark bees from Tatarstan. I'm also planning to spend some time in Bashkiria and bring a few colonies from there. Why? Well, speaking scientifically, to establish good starting genetic material for creating my own local bees. After all, the population that once lived here in the Oka river basin can no longer be found in its pure form, so it must be created from scratch. Therefore, the larger my apiary and the more European dark bees of various kinds it contains, the better. Using natural methods of selection, I can gradually create a good, winter-hardy, productive, and docile local bee. This is one of my goals. I invite you to join me in pursuing it!

The issue of bee races and bee colony strength is crucial for beekeeping—especially for those who are just beginning to keep bees. As an example, I'll cite the experiences of another friend of mine and "brother-in-bees," also named Dima, who several years ago started three bee colonies in horizontal hives with extra-deep frames. He got two nucs from a beekeeper he knew south of Kaluga, but they didn't really "take" well; they didn't produce much honey, and the next year they completely went to pot. Dima picked up another complete bee colony, in response to a classified ad, just six miles (10 km) away from me. Their former owner was moving and selling everything he couldn't take with him. And this colony turned out to be extraordinary! In the course of three years, it single-handedly produced 70–90 pounds (30–40 kg) of honey per year, and wintered wonderfully. This year, by all appearances, this colony has begun swarming (Dima works in the city and is unable to track the swarms), but next year, I believe it will regain its strength and produce honey again.

And I've heard many such stories. Many have told me how their colonies, especially those bought from breeders or derived from purchased nucs, seem to barely get by; they show weak growth and don't deliver much honey. And this can go on for several years; or, in the worst case, such colonies simply die. But some purchased colonies suddenly begin to grow phenomenally, and by fall, to their keeper's delight, they produce an outstanding harvest of honey. So, where's the root of the problem, and how can the situation be improved? Of course, it all goes back to the queen—as any serious book on beekeeping will tell you. All that's left for us to do is emphasize the most important points. But before we talk about the queen, I'd like to say a few words about the "mean bees."

On the Mean Bees

Just recently, a highly experienced beekeeper from Arkhangelsk told me a story from his own practice about how he'd acquired several colonies from an elderly beekeeper who'd decided to hang it up. He dedicated very little time to his bees: he'd "toss on a new super and run away as fast as he could." He'd been keeping the bees for many years, his frames were old, and the bottoms of the hives were littered with several years' worth of accumulated debris.

The new keeper was completely incapable of working with these bees: when he tried to do an inspection, they attacked him with such ferocity that, despite being well clothed, he was unable to get anything done. Of course, the people who happened to be nearby at the time didn't get off scot-free either. What was he to do? That evening, he packed up the hives and took them to a faraway outyard, to another beekeeper he knew. But a few days later, the new keeper was forced to get rid of the bees—they'd stung the only neighbors living near his apiary when he attempted an inspection. Their former owner had to take the hives back and look for somewhere else to unload them.

Any experienced beekeeper can tell many such stories, but they all come down to the same thing: as soon as you begin inspecting a European dark bee colony, the bees just "go bonkers," attacking the beekeeper, any animals that happen to be nearby, and, of course, the neighbors. Aside from that, the bees are fantastic: they winter extremely well,

188

they produce plenty of honey, and they aren't too prone to swarming. Hence, the very logical question arises: what if you just left them alone? The answer is simple: *don't bother them, and they won't bother you.*

As I mentioned, our apiary houses European dark bees from various locales. And it's a good idea not to spend too much time near the entrances of certain (not all) hives without a mask: the guard bees will notice you and might attack. But 70 feet (20 m) away from the apiary, the bees' presence is completely unnoticeable, aside from the audible buzzing of the busy bees, happily working. During the past summer, for example, the bees never stung my wife or my son, who are constantly present on the grounds. Still, I know for certain that if any of my colonies is bothered, they'll react accordingly. Therefore, during the first half of the summer, I simply add some frames, and from early July on I don't even peek into the hives. I may, out of sheer curiosity, wander into the apiary and watch by the entrances to see what the bees are up to.

I have to emphasize once again that such an approach is only possible in the context of natural beekeeping. All modern industrial methods call for "working" with the bees throughout the season, including inspections, adding and removing additional boxes and supers, anti-swarming methods, repeated pulling of honey during the summer, artificial propagation, and much more. The temperament of the European dark bee makes all of these operations highly problematic. Only one way out remains: working with more "docile" races, such as the Carpathian or the Caucasian bee. But these races winter much worse in our climate, are more prone to swarming, and are less resistant to diseases. Hence the need for medicines and anti-swarming measures, and thus the vicious circle begins. On top of all that, maintaining a completely pure race is all but impossible, since the "southern" bees, when they mix with local bees, lose their special qualities and, within a couple of generations, become mongrel bees that are often much more aggressive than the purebred local bees.

This is an entirely standard situation, confronted by any modern beekeeper. Some keepers adapt by periodically buying "purebred" Carpathians from specialized queen-rearing apiaries located somewhere to the south, while others completely abandon beekeeping, exhausted by trying to cope with these problems.

There's only one logical solution: to do whatever we can to restore the local race of bees, wherever we may live. Then we'll be able to catch and install swarms, knowing that they'll result in strong, healthy colonies; meanwhile, the enterprise itself—beekeeping—won't depend on queen-rearing apiaries or the chemical industry, which is always cooking up new medicines to combat the ever-rising number of bee diseases.

The Queen

The queen is the heart of a bee colony. All of the bees in a hive—and at the height of the season they may number up to a hundred thousand—are her children. The average lifespan of a worker bee during the summer is forty days; a drone can live for several months; but a queen can live and work for up to eight years (according to documented cases). Her "egg-laying capacity" (the ability to lay a certain number of eggs during a given 24-hour period) determines the colony's strength and rate of growth; her genetic make-up determines the traits of the bees themselves. Of course, her genetics are only half of the picture. The other half is left to the drones the queen encounters during her mating flights.

A great deal has been written about queens. The first descriptions to come down to us were written by ancient Egyptians, who considered the queen a kind of royal figure who governed all activity in the hive and dispatched her subjects into the field to search for nectar. The ancient Greeks were convinced that the queen would not allow her bees to remain idle, and made certain that all the hive's combs were made solidly and beautifully, and that the brood was being dutifully raised (Naum Ioirish, *Bees and People*, published by Nauka, 1974, p. 18). Throughout the ages, the bee colony has been held up as an ideal society and the queen as its center. In Russia, since time immemorial, she was consistently referred to as the "tsarina."

Supersedure queens and swarm queens—that is, those produced in special "queen" cells from eggs laid especially for that purpose—are considered to be the highest-quality queens. Emergency queens, which are produced (in the event of the sudden loss of the previous queen) from eggs initially laid for worker bees are of slightly lower quality. However, no clear consensus has been reached in this matter, since not all authoritative researchers support this view (namely, that emergency queens are weaker).

There's another kind of queen bees: those bred artificially. And these are the bees you'll typically be getting when you buy nucs from specialized apiaries. Such bees have one big advantage—they're purebred. That is, if the apiary's workers carefully follow the appropriate rules and guidelines. But there's a big minus, recognized by the majority of specialists: artificially bred queens are weaker than real, naturally produced ones. After all, such queens are essentially "emergency" queens; the only difference is that they've been produced with human involvement. Here, we get into certain technical subtleties and nuances that can be easily explored by reading special bee-breeding manuals. In a lecture, Vladimir Kashkovsky, a research apiculturist from Novosibirsk with a tremendous amount of experience, tells that occasionally he would get a good, full-fledged queen from a breeder, but this is typically the exception, not the rule.

Experienced beekeepers will tell you that the quality of a queen's colony of origin says nothing about the quality of the queen herself. Some are very good, some are average, and others are below average. More work has to be done. There are a great number of selection methods, ranging from the very simple to the highly complex. And each beekeeper has to decide for himself which of them to follow, and whether to follow any at all.

How many years can a queen remain productive? As we've said, up to eight, and possibly even more. But in any case the most "productive" years are the first three. What happens to a queen when those three years are over, and why is a young queen considered better than an "elderly" one? Here, there are two major issues at play:

First: the rate of egg-laying. During periods of rapid build-up, particularly in spring, the queen must lay her eggs at maximum rate in terms of the number of eggs laid in a given 24-hour period. The maximum rate—and the literature includes examples of up to 3,500 eggs per day—depends on the race, and on the quality and age of the queen. The older she is, the harder it is for her to attain high rates.

Second: the probability of death. As the queen's age increases, especially after three years, there is an increased likelihood that she'll go "out of commission"—that is, that she'll lose her egg-laying ability, or simply die. How and when does this happen? The problems typically arise either in the winter—especially if the wintering isn't going well—or during those periods when the highest demands are placed on the "tsarina," that is, during the colony's buildup period, during spring and late summer. Consequently, there are three fundamental "scenarios" for how the events play out:

- If a queen dies during winter, then the likelihood that the entire colony will perish also sharply rises, since the bees become agitated and therefore consume more honey, with all of the expected consequences. But even if such a colony does survive until spring, then, under natural conditions, it is doomed to ruin, since it cannot produce a new queen. In an apiary, an experienced beekeeper can "fix" the colony by adding a new queen, or comb with freshly-laid eggs from another hive. By expanding a standard comb cell, the worker bees can raise a new (emergency) queen from eggs up to three days old.

• If a queen dies in the spring, having laid at least some eggs, then things are not as critical: the bees will produce an emergency queen themselves, and the colony will survive, although its growth will be significantly reduced.

• If the queen dies in late summer, the colony still has practically no chance of survival. Why? Because about a month is required for the new queen to mature, to complete her mating flights, and to begin laying eggs—and the period of fall buildup will be missed. The summer bees that worked during the main honeyflow will gradually die off, but new ones won't be there to replace them. Such colonies will weaken by fall, and be unable to survive the winter, even with good honey reserves. There's another problem associated with losing a queen in late summer: robbing. In late summer, a colony without a fertile queen will be much more likely to be subject to invasions by other bees.

Are other scenarios possible when queens begin to age? Of course! They are, namely, supersedure and swarming.

Bees carry out supersedure themselves when the colony senses that their queen is aging and is failing to fulfill her duty—laying eggs. Information regarding the queen's condition is conveyed throughout the hive by the scent of a special liquid secreted by a fertile queen, which is continually distributed by all the bees. This liquid contains information concerning the state of the queen and gives each colony its own peculiar scent. Having "taken the decision" to go ahead with supersedure, the colony creates several queen cells for raising a new queen (Photograph 20, p. 336). The young queen eventually matures, completes her mating flight, and gets to work, and the colony recovers.

A second scenario is swarming. Here, the older the queen, the more likely the colony is to begin swarming. The old queen will leave with the first swarm, leaving behind sealed queen cells, and the colony remaining in the hive will be renewed. We'll speak more about swarming further below, but for now, let's draw some conclusions: what are we to make of all this information?

Well, that the queen is the "key figure" in a bee colony, and that under natural conditions a queen is regularly replaced. Swarming is the primary replacement mechanism; the second is supersedure. And, interestingly enough, these mechanisms may be combined. According to some authors, a supersedure occurs quite often in first swarms once they've set up in a new location and the primary honeyflow has begun.

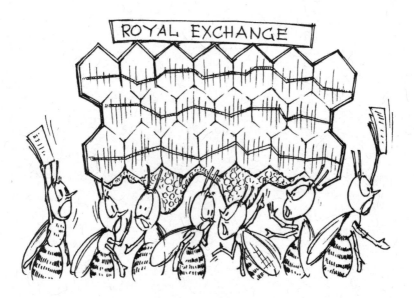

And what happens at industrial apiaries, where beekeepers do everything possible to prevent swarming? It's all very simple! The keepers replace the queens themselves. Herein lies one of the main commandments for successful honey production: change all queens each year, or every two years at the most. Therefore, requeening is the industrial beekeeper's foremost concern, and each one has his own methods and special tricks. However, we won't dwell on generally accepted techniques for producing new queens and replacing old ones with them, since plenty of specialized literature has been devoted to this topic. Our task is to try to understand where all of this leaves us "natural" beekeepers. But before addressing that question, let's talk a bit about the vital rhythms of a bee colony, in which the age of the queen plays such an essential role.

The Vital Rhythms of a Bee Colony

Let's imagine a queen, making her way day and night around the comb, accompanied by her court and constantly laying eggs. Twenty-one days later (the maturation period of a worker bee), each cell produces a new young worker ready to dedicate her entire life to working for the sake of the colony. During the summer, she'll live for 40 days, after which a new bee will come to take her place, taking up the baton of selfless service. During the summer, 5–6 generations of bees will come and go—that is, the hive's worker population will be entirely replaced 5–6 times. Let's assume that the queen maintains her egg-laying rate at 2,500 eggs per day. That means that every day, 2,500 young bees will be born, and just as many will die of old age. In reality, bees don't die from old age; instead, they eventually work themselves to death. Therefore, during rainy weather, when the flight window contracts sharply, they may live significantly longer; by the same token, their lifespan may be somewhat shorter during the main honeyflow. Meanwhile, bees of the fall generation (born before the start of winter), who don't have to fly for nectar or feed the brood, will live for half a year or more.

Multiplying the queen's productivity (2,500 eggs per day) by the average life span of an individual worker bee (40 days), we arrive at a very rough figure for the hive's "population"— 100,000 bees. If the queen's egg-laying slows, then the number of bees in the colony will begin to drop in time. If she stops laying altogether, then in approximately two months (21 days—the maturation period of already-laid eggs, plus 40 days—the lifespan of the worker bee), the hive's population will dwindle to almost nothing. Here, a professional may bicker with me a bit, and he'll be well within his rights: worker bees tend to live longer in queenless colonies. But this doesn't alter the big picture. The entire "arithmetic" of a colony's life flows from the figures provided above. A strong queen will have a strong, teeming colony, while a week queen who is unable to lay many eggs will have a weak and unproductive one. On top of that, there's heredity: a queen with high-quality genes will produce workers who are healthier and more active.

How does a new bee colony form under natural conditions? As a result of swarming. In practice, prime swarms (the first swarms, which include the old queen) are the strongest. They have every advantage: they're the earliest swarm (they have the whole summer ahead of them!), and they're the most numerous in terms of bees. On top of that, the old queen who leaves the hive with the first swarm doesn't need to go on a mating flight, and "gets down to work" immediately. Therefore, first swarms tend to settle in successfully at their new location, and, as a rule, produce some quantity of surplus honey. At the same time, the aging queen is a first swarm's major disadvantage. Hopefully, she's a two-year-old (that is, she was "born" in the previous season). But what if she's three years old or more? Then, the situation becomes more complicated, since she is more likely not to endure the fall buildup, or to die during the winter. This is why it often happens that an excellent first swarm that has had a very productive summer and gathered sufficient honey may not live until fall, or will not survive the winter.

The situation with an afterswarm (a second, third, or any subsequent swarm) is completely different. All afterswarms emerge with young queens—and this is both an advantage and a disadvantage. It's a disadvantage because the young queen will have to "make the rounds"—that is fly out of the hive multiple times in order to encounter male bees, called drones—before she can begin laying eggs. During this time, she could die, or fail to return to her hive for some other reason. Additionally, the young queen could prove to be "defective"—that is, sterile—or have some kind of inherited disability. All of this means that a certain number (according to various sources, around 10%) of "installed" afterswarms will not make it until fall, unless, of course, the beekeeper checks on them and fixes things in time. "Wild" nature, by the way, has its own solution for a problem like this. If swarms are left to their own devices (with no one catching them), a "problem" colony may be joined by another swarm that has detected, by smell, that the first colony has no queen. I've had one such incident myself.

What is the advantage of a swarm with a young queen? Well, if it can build its nest and winter successfully, then there's an almost one-hundred-percent guarantee that it will remain a strong and "honey-rich" colony for the next two years. And it's swarms like these—with queens who were "born" the previous summer, or the summer before that—that make up the backbone of an apiary. And this group includes not only swarm colonies, but also colonies that have cast several swarms—that is, those that remain behind in the original hives. By the way, these colonies have a number of advantages over the swarms themselves. After all, a colony that has cast its swarms is left not only with a young queen, but with solid honey reserves, existing comb, and the existing brood left behind by the old queen.

What happens next? The whole situation is repeated, and everything comes full circle. The queens age, and each young colony may, in the fullness of time, begin swarming, or perform supersedure, or die.

The Death of Bee Colonies

The one thing about the natural approach that causes the biggest doubts among experienced beekeepers is not using medicine. To my mind, however, this has more to do with personal convictions than scientific theory. For my part, I am deeply convinced that bees are perfectly capable of coping with their diseases, if—and this is the main thing—we don't feed them sugar and try to keep bees belonging to the local race. Personally, over the last ten years, I haven't used a single gram of medicine—not even natural treatments. And my apiary hasn't been wiped out by disease—as everyone predicted it would be. In fact, it continues to grow, although not quite at the rate I'd prefer.

Of course, some colonies die off. During a given winter, up to 30% of colonies would perish; but in the summer the apiary would inevitably restore itself and grow in size. And it's perfectly obvious that the offspring of successful colonies will likely be equally strong and successful themselves.

The death of bee colonies is a very sad topic, but it's one that no beekeeper is likely to avoid. Speaking purely theoretically, it would seem possible to save colonies from dying, if we were to replace their queens each year, dutifully treat them against all diseases, and set up storage sheds to shelter the hives in winter. And there are some beekeepers out there who do all these things, but even they meet with certain surprises from time to time, such as a very rough year, some new epidemic, or something else of that nature. And once again they're forced to restore their apiary.

If bee colonies didn't die away, their number would gradually rise around the world. After all, a majority of beekeepers do propagate their bees in one way or another—they catch and install swarms, split colonies, and create nucs. And add to that the output of specialized breeding operations. However, the global number of bee colonies is falling, which means that each year more colonies die on average than are created. And success stories in which beekeepers maintain their own number of colonies and even sell the extra ones represent the happy exception, not the rule. And this is a great pity. It's important to get to the bottom of this problem.

How did things stand in pristine nature, still untouched by man? Strange as it may sound, things were more or less the same. The only difference was that the number of colonies would continue rising until they filled their entire environmental niche. But, large as it may be, the number of bees cannot rise indefinitely. That means that once a balance is reached in a given area, the "extra" colonies will indeed begin to die off, since new ones are created every year. There's no stopping the swarming instinct. What's the sense behind these harsh laws?

Let's think a bit. The worst case for the bees is when their ruin comes during winter. But, as we've said already, this just means that the colony failed to prepare adequately for winter, or failed to cope with disease, which is most threatening around this time of year. Why, then, should such a colony be "allowed" to have descendants? As a rule, death in the summer comes less cruelly. In essence, only a queen will die during warm weather, leaving the remaining "population" to successfully move in with another colony in a majority of cases. This usually proceeds as follows: when bees from other hives sense that all is not well in a certain colony, they'll "break the defenses" and begin robbing the reserves. Once the bees from the failing colony "see" that there's nothing they can do to stop it, they join the robbers and, having moved the reserves to the new hive, they stay there. In this case, the reason behind the colony's downfall is simple: natural selection. The colony with a strong, productive queen survives. The same thing happens in situations when nectar is scarce (or, similarly, when there is an excess of colonies), when the stronger and more active colonies stand a better chance of providing themselves with winter honey reserves and remaining alive.

One other "purpose" behind the death of bee colonies in nature is to periodically disinfect and free up the bees' homes—tree hollows. When a colony perishes, the old, blackened comb left behind in the hollow, along with the pathogenic agents that have built up in it, is destroyed by wax moths and all sorts of other creatures of the forest. Once this has happened, the cleaned hollow is again ready to welcome new and hardworking residents.

So, the two basic "purposes" for the death of colonies in nature are natural selection and renewing nests while simultaneously disinfecting them. Nature pursues its own interests, which are far broader than the preservation of any single bee colony. These interests include pollination of plants, maintaining balance, and preserving the bee species for thousands and millions of years to come.

What is our job then, as beekeepers? It's a good question, one whose answer will demand an entire lifetime, not this short section. For now, though, let's return to the topic of colony death—more precisely, let's ask what we should be doing about it. I see several options.

Various Approaches to Natural Beekeeping

A hands-off approach

One approach might be called "natural" natural beekeeping. That means installing all swarms separately, not replacing queens, and giving no assistance to weak colonies. That is, we leave everything as is. At the same time, we still perform all of the necessary tasks throughout the year. This is roughly the approach taken by Vladimir Dmitrievich, a senior, highly experienced beekeeper from the region of Ryazan, a fascinating man and an ardent advocate for the European dark bee. He openly admits that a certain number of the colonies in his apiary (which includes more than 120 hives) die or get robbed every season. The number fluctuates year to year—ten colonies and upwards. But to him, this isn't a catastrophe. Each spring, he induces swarming in his strongest and most successful colonies, and generates a sufficient number of good early swarms. Vladimir Dmitrievich doesn't use artificial propagation as a matter of principle, following instead the natural mechanism. The apiary was passed down to him by his father, who in turn had inherited it from his father. The only drawback is that he didn't manage to maintain the genetic purity of his grandfather's bee stock—all kinds of bees came and went at the neighboring farms, from Italians to Carpathians and everything in between. Vladimir's apiary not only produces honey, but bee colonies as well: every spring a certain number of his colonies goes on sale, and has for many years and even decades now. But, as I've said before, such examples are rare.

Many beekeepers have noticed that if the situation is allowed to run its course—that is, if queens aren't replaced and weak colonies aren't "fixed"—then some of an apiary's colonies will be strong, some average, and some weak. And it's also been noted that the chances of a weak colony regaining strength all on its own are very low. We aren't talking here about weak swarm colonies from the previous year, which, having survived the winter, may develop into very powerful colonies during the spring. We're talking about colonies from the previous year who, upon spring inspection, are found to have little brood and show weak growth throughout the spring, just barely managing to draw fresh comb. If such colonies fail to reach normal strength by early to mid-June, then they are very likely not to collect sufficient honey, and to perish in the fall or winter. This has been confirmed repeatedly in practice. Hence the phrase coined by Gennady Kondratiev (1834–1905): "A beeyard lives by its strong hives alone."

Fixing weak colonies by uniting them with swarms

We will search for an answer as to why the bees in such colonies do not bring about a supersedure a bit later, at the end of this section. But the fact remains that a weak colony very rarely recovers on its own. Therefore, professional beekeepers tend not to leave such colonies untouched, but rather requeen them or unite them with other colonies. Lately, I've begun doing something similar on occasion. Taking advantage of the horizontal hive's design, I install a weak swarm with a young queen in the empty section of the hive, and a couple of weeks later, once she has completed her mating flight and come into her own, I unite the two colonies. This generates a single strong colony with a young queen from two colonies that, alone, have a bleak future (presented with two fertile queens, the bees will always choose the younger and stronger one). This united colony will generate surplus honey and will thrive over the next couple of years as well.

How are two colonies united? I remove the division board and, without touching the nest frames, fill the space between the two colonies with foundation frames and empty comb. Between two of these frames, I insert a sheet of galvanized steel cut to fit the interior dimensions of the hive. Multiple holes with diameters of no more than $^1/_8$ inch (3 mm) have been drilled into the sheet ahead of time. After a couple of days, the two colonies will have established an identical scent, and will not come into conflict when united. I remove the sheet late in the evening, pulling it carefully upward. Uniting the two colonies goes most smoothly at this time of day, especially once the sun has set.

Here, a very reasonable question arises: is this procedure in the spirit of natural beekeeping? I think the answer is clearly yes. After all, such things also happen in nature, when a late and weak swarm like the one in question drops in on an "orphaned" colony, or when bees from a failed colony re-settle with a young, strong one. Of course, this procedure is a bit more complicated than the strictly hands-off natural approach described above. Let's dub it the "advanced" natural approach. Its advantage is that it allows us to avoid the disappointments connected with the death of a colony, and to manage our apiary more effectively.

What other methods might be a part of this "advanced" approach? Perhaps uniting swarms. Practically all beginning beekeepers, striving to generate as many new colonies as possible, install each swarm separately. Meanwhile, all bee-keepers with a bit of experience tend to unite their swarms. Why? There are several reasons for this. The first is the low viability of late swarms. It is believed that a 2-pound (1-kg) swarm in early June is fine, but by late June it's good for nothing. The reason is that a month and a half will be required for the young queen to complete her mating flights and get up to speed with laying eggs, the first brood to emerge, and the young worker bees to begin to forage for nectar. For a late swarm, this moment will come in mid- to late-August—and by that time there's little flow to be had. Therefore, during that first month and a half, the bees that arrived with the swarm—and there weren't many of them to begin with—will be entirely responsible for maintaining the colony. And their tasks include building the nest, feeding the young, and gathering winter reserves. Late, weak swarms are highly unlikely to cope with such challenges. Therefore, before in-stallation in a new hive, such swarms are combined in pairs or in threes. Or, they're added to swarms that have already been installed. This is done late in the evening, and in this case there are rarely any conflicts among the bees, since late swarms always emerge with a young queen who has yet to develop her own scent, and the swarm bees feel no need to defend her.

As we've mentioned already, afterswarms can be used to "fix" older colonies, or can be united with first swarms. First ("prime") swarms are always installed separately, since they tend to develop well and, as a rule, produce surplus honey. But if the first swarm emerged from a hive that did not swarm in the previous year, then that means that the swarm's queen is three years old or more. And that means a good chance of difficulties down the road. Therefore, a first swarm like this can be treated just as we treated the weak colony above: by installing a late swarm in the free section of the hive and uniting them two weeks later. Both colonies will benefit from this procedure. As for extremely late swarms (late July, for example), there's no sense whatsoever in installing them separately or combining them with another such late swarm. They're always added to already-installed weak swarms. Truth be told, nature does make exceptions even in cases like this; I've heard tell of extremely late swarms that have in fact survived, but this remains the exception, not the rule.

And, now that we're on the subject of swarms, it's worth pausing on certain technical aspects. But first, let's bring our discussion of supersedure, as fascinating as it is important, to a close.

More on Supersedure

One might assume that nature simply has no need for supersedure in old colonies. After all, under natural conditions, a swarm with a young queen that has settled in a small, empty tree hollow will completely fill it with comb in just a couple of seasons. A larger hollow will require three or four seasons, but this is commensurate with the lifespan of a queen (up to eight years). And once the hollow has been completely filled, natural mechanisms will lead the colony to begin swarming. The old queen still has the strength to fly away with a strong first swarm, and at the new location, once she's begun laying eggs, the colony will replace her with a younger one (it's all very logical!). And this is where supersedure comes in handy, to allow the colony to winter successfully in its new location and to continue to grow in the spring.

But in our hive, we remove old comb each year, and add foundation frames, thus maintaining the bees' sense that their "hollow" still has room for new construction. Natural swarming mechanisms don't kick in, and only a small number of colonies (in my experience, no more than 20%) will spontaneously begin swarming. And this would seem to be just what the doctor ordered—it's less trouble for us. But the queens get old, and a certain number of the colonies gradually lose their productivity and begin to fade away. This explains the "natural" natural approach described above. What can be done about this?

Industrial beekeepers, as we've seen, proceed very simply: they requeen every year or two. But what should we do? The answer is obvious: we should compensate for those natural mechanisms that we ourselves have eliminated. I think that it's a good practice to induce swarming in all colonies whose queens are three years of age or older (i.e., in any colony that hasn't swarmed in the past two seasons). That is, if we've installed a swarm with a young queen this summer, then in all likelihood it will get on splendidly and produce honey for us (and for itself, of course!) for the next two seasons. And the following spring, during the spring inspection, once we've removed any empty or damaged comb from the colony, we'll limit the colony's growth with a solid division board, sealing the gap underneath it. In late May, the first swarm will emerge, and soon, in early June, a second. At that point, we'll remove the division board and expand the colony with foundation frames. We'll install the first and second swarms separately, and add any subsequent swarms (if any) to weak colonies, or unite the swarms themselves. Swarms require a bit of "jogging," but it's not that big of a deal, and only happens for one month out of the year. On top of that, the surplus of colonies that will almost inevitably result can even be sold. And good colonies can bring good money nowadays!

Swarming

I await the swarming season with great anticipation—almost like a holiday. I've built a special gazebo, protected from the bees by glass and screens on all sides, on the edge of my apiary, among the hives, to make it easier to work and watch the bees. There I assemble frames and add foundation, and watch for swarms. Here my friends and I often simply sit with a cup of tea, listening to the friendly buzzing of the bees and watching entire streams of bees flying into the fields and returning home with their healthful and delectable cargo.

I don't have many swarms; sometimes, after a period of bad weather, I may have three or four in a single day, but that's a great rarity. Usually, there are no more than one or two. Colonies that are "set" on swarming will rarely cast just one swarm. The norm, as far as I can tell from my many years of experience, is two to three swarms—that is, the strong first swarm with an old queen, and one or two smaller swarms with young queens. Very rarely will you see four swarms cast by a single hive.

Which colonies begin swarming spontaneously? All else being equal (that is, with a timely spring inspection and addition of foundation frames), colonies with older queens (three years and older) are much more prone to swarm. Another possible factor is some failure within the colony or overheating in the sunlight, but these causes can typically be ruled out if the beekeeper is good. A third factor is when the nest expansion is delayed. Secondary factors affecting swarming include, in my opinion, the direction the hive entrance is facing. If a hive is located in full shade, then the direction has no palpable effect. But if the hive is in direct sunlight, then an entrance facing south can certainly provoke swarming. Therefore, lately I've been positioning all my hives with the entrances facing east, such that the sun hits them during the first half of the day, while, during midday, when it's hottest, they're in the shade. Some serious researchers actually recommend that all entrances should face north. But it seems to me that this advice is more appropriate for more southerly regions.

Natural swarming is more than sufficient for keeping an apiary in good working condition, and even for expanding it. And this is precisely how I've run my operation for many years now. But now, reflecting back on my experience to date, I tend to favor the system described above. This method, under which the older colonies are artificially encouraged to swarm, has another advantage. The swarms are cast earlier than in the case of natural swarming, and they have more time to develop and gather reserves for the winter. Colonies that have finished casting their swarms also have time to recover successfully and even, like first swarms, to gather a certain amount of surplus honey. If we want to rapidly expand our apiary or produce colonies for sale, then we can compel colonies with three-year-old queens to swarm. But with younger queens—say, two years old (that is, swarms from the previous year)—I would not do this, since such colonies are reluctant to swarm, even when there's little free space in their hive.

Beekeepers know that if a colony has begun swarming, then it can't be expected to produce much honey. All its energy is spent on reproduction, and on occasion the keeper even has to "fork out" some honey to help the young colony survive. Therefore, in the old days, there were two kinds of apiaries, geared towards either swarm or honey production. The details of these two kinds of apiaries, and how they differed from one another, are carefully described in Illarion Kullanda's book *Popular Beekeeping* (1882, p. 32). It seems to me that in the coming decades a well-run "swarm" operation, especially if it involves high-quality local bees, could prove highly successful. In any event, during the swarming period—that is, from late May through late June—I always keep two or three swarm boxes ready, as well as a smoker, a soft brush for sweeping off bees, a big wooden scoop, in case bees have to be gathered in a truly inconvenient spot, and a beekeeper's outfit: a jacket, mask and gloves. There's no need to be constantly present at the apiary, keeping a lookout for swarms. Even from a distance of 200 feet (50 m) or farther, it's practically impossible to miss a swarm, since once it leaves the hive it will fly around, in a large, buzzing cloud, for 5–10 minutes above the apiary before it begins to gather on a tree branch, a neighboring hive, or any other suitable spot. People with good hearing can unmistakably identify an emerging swarm by its sound, since the bees' buzzing has a peculiar, inimitable tone on such occasions.

How to Collect a Swarm

A swarm is collected in two stages. First, having positioned the box just under the swarm, we "shake" the swarm into it, so that the bulk of the swarm winds up inside, along with the queen, which is always somewhere in the thick of the swarm. Then, we close the box and set it up (hang it) as close as we can to where we found the swarm (Photograph 13, p. 333). The next stage consists of slightly opening the box and collecting those bees who have remained outside. If the queen is inside the box, then all we have to do is encourage the bees a bit to get moving—from the ground, tree branches, or the exterior of the box itself—with a smoker and a bee brush. Once they're in the air, the bees will eventually fly into the box to be closer to their swarm and to their queen. Here, the wooden scoop can come in handy for carefully "scooping" up the bees and tossing them right into the box. My bees are European dark bees, so I do all of this work wearing a mask and gloves (just in case), but there's little cause to fear the bees at that moment; caught up in the swarming fever, and with maximum amounts of honey stored in their honey stomachs, bees are very unlikely to attack during this period. Children or guests often watch me collect swarms from a distance of some 20 feet (5–6 m), usually without even wearing special clothing or masks.

There's an art to collecting swarms, since conditions are always slightly different. Sometimes a swarm will land so conveniently that all it takes is shaking it down into the box and

closing the lid; at other times, they'll cluster around the trunk
of a thick tree, or even plop down directly on the ground, pre-
senting the keeper with a difficult challenge. But such challenges can always be met! I don't know anyone who, with
sufficient desire, has failed to learn this art, and who wasn't
elated the first time they collected a swarm themselves! In
time, this sense of elation wanes, but it never vanishes completely, since interacting with nature, and working together
with this newly born, intelligent, and amazing organism not
only affects one's mind, but reaches much deeper.

So now the swarm has been collected and shut up in the
box. In some cases (early first swarms) beekeepers recommend installing the swarm in a new hive right away. But I
always postpone this procedure until evening, and until that
time I keep the swarm in a dark, cool location. By evening, I
mean between approximately six and eight o'clock. Before
installing, I get the hive ready. For a weak swarm, I add six extra-deep frames, eight for a moderate swarm (up to 5 pounds;
2.5 kg), and all twelve for a strong one. I close off the frames
with a division board, and temporarily, for a period of several
days, seal the gap under the division board—the gap joining
the space prepared for the swarm with the empty portion
of the hive. I've had a couple of cases in which the swarm,
for reasons known only to it, entered the empty section and
began building comb there just as it would in a tree hollow—
that is, drawing comb directly from the ceiling.

It is widely held that very early and very late swarms
should be given a little extra empty comb, while swarms
that are cast during the height of the swarming season can
be "installed" onto fresh foundation. In the latter instance,
however, I personally include at least one frame with some
good empty comb. I do this to ensure that bees have somewhere to store their nectar right away, and that the queen,

especially if she's fertile, has somewhere to lay her eggs. In addition, a swarm will take to its new home more enthusiastically if it contains some existing comb. And the most caring beekeepers will give each installed swarm at least 4 pounds (2 kg) of honey, more or less. "No honey pays for itself like the honey we use to feed new swarms." This phrase belongs to the German beekeeper Baron von Ehrenfels. Why do we give swarms honey? To get the young colony off to a good start. After all, it's much better to dole out a couple pounds of honey early in the summer, to help a colony build up its strength, than in the fall, when you discover that the colony doesn't have enough reserves to last the winter.

Generally speaking, "installed" swarms shouldn't be abandoned to the whims of fate. If the summer is a good one, then there won't be any problems—the bees will take care of everything themselves. But if, after a swarm is installed, the weather is extremely hot and dry, or, on the opposite, if there's continued rain, then where will the bees get their nectar? During times like these, an older colony can live off the reserves it stored in the spring, but a young one doesn't have any reserves, except for what it brought with it from its previous hive. And those will only last for a few days, no more.

The swarm installation itself is a simple process. Place a sheet of plywood near the entrance, at a slight incline (so the bees will have to climb upward), then carefully shake the bees out of the swarm box and onto the plywood (Photograph 14, p. 333). If you need to unite two swarms, then dump one first, and, once the bees from the first swarm are happily on their way into the hive, shake out the second one in their wake. 95% of the time, all the bees will peacefully enter the hive and settle there. The other 5% are the "pesky" swarms, usually late ones with young queens. By the next morning, they may form a "beard" beneath the landing board or even gather on a nearby tree in order to try to continue whatever journey they have in mind. I collect them yet again and, again keeping them waiting until evening, install them in a different hive, sometimes using harsher alternative methods. For example, I'll shake the swarm directly into the hive, quickly add the frames from the top, and close the lid. This usually helps. As you can see, working with swarms even involves a certain element of artistry and flying by the seat of your pants. But this makes working with bees all the more lively and interesting.

The majority of professional industrial beekeepers frown on swarming and do everything in their power to prevent it. And indeed, instead of being on the lookout for swarms for an entire month, collecting them and installing them in hives, isn't it easier to make a few splits in the course of a single day, and then be done with propagation? Of course it's easier! But let's recall what Rudolf Steiner said in his lecture on bees in 1923 in Dornach, Germany: *"If one only wishes, one can easily see how that which seems beneficial at the outset could eventually turn into something that slowly ruins the entire enterprise."* The lecture concerned artificial methods for inseminating queens, but the citation holds true for our current topic as well.

So, what are the drawbacks of artificial methods for creating new colonies? It's hard to formulate a well-supported answer to this question, since I've yet to come across serious studies on this topic, and any arguments I make may seem strained and subjective. Nevertheless, I'll list a few here:

- The number of eggs a queen lays in a day depends not only on her fertility, but also on the colony's ability to warm and feed the brood. Therefore, there's constantly a delicate balance in a bee colony between the quantity of brood, the quantity of forager bees and nurse bees, the honey and beebread reserves in the hive, and the nectar available outside. With artificial propagation (splitting one colony into two or more), this balance is inevitably disrupted, and the bees are forced to expend a great deal of time and energy on restoring it. This likely explains the frequency with which "nucs" only begin functioning normally the year after they are created.

• The microclimate within the nest is inevitably changed when it is split into two or more parts, among which the bees are unevenly distributed. The most frequent result of this is an outbreak of diseases such as chalk brood (*Ascosphaera apis*).

• The colony, as an integral, intelligent entity, becomes disoriented.

• The ability to reproduce normally is gradually degraded.

These problems can only be completely avoided through propagation by swarming. With swarming, the colony itself chooses the right moment, it "decides" how many bees and which bees to send from the hive with the swarm, how to arrange its new hive, and how to handle its brood.

Of course, the quality of a nuc depends to a great extent on the skill of the beekeeper who creates it. Still, in my personal experience, a weak swarm colony that has successfully wintered develops at a much faster rate than an equally sized nuc bought in the spring. And if we consider the long-term prosperity of beekeeping—that is, for many hundreds and even thousands of years into the future—then artificial propagation is hardly likely to play a positive role. On the other hand, creating new colonies by swarming helps preserve a normal, viable "bee tribe" for our distant descendants.

At this point, many readers may have some fully justified questions. The procedure described above—keeping
watch at the apiary for swarms—is applicable to a large apiary, whose keeper is well advised to devote at least one full
month out of the year to his bees. But what if you have just
a few hives, and have no choice but to leave the bees during the swarming season, for work or for some other obliga-
tions? In that case, how can one renew and maintain the apiary? The answer is simple: have more swarm traps. Building
and handling these traps is described in detail in Part II, so
there's no reason to repeat everything here. But based on
what I've seen, this is a good, effective way to maintain an
apiary that you're only able to check in on occasionally. Each
spring, I too make certain to hang out several swarm traps
in the small forest next to my apiary, and I also "rig out" all
my empty hives to attract stray swarms. That is, I intersperse
foundation frames with any empty comb I have around—
usually old frames that are not too high in quality. I've had
cases where such hives were occupied by swarms from my
own apiary, who moved directly from their old hive into the
empty one, in violation of classical theories on swarming...

While I'm at it: when you buy bees from a breeder, I personally would advise you not to expect good "profit" from
them during the very first year. Even during the second year,
the situation may be doubtful at best, since everything depends on the age and quality of the queen that came in your
nuc. Genuine, strong, profit-generating colonies only arise
further down the road, when the purchased colony casts
swarms with young queens, and those swarms successfully
spend their first winter. They're the ones who will form the
foundation of your future apiary. By the way, even the former nuc will tend to grow into a strong, honey-producing
colony once it has cast a swarm and wintered successfully.

The same principles can be applied to selling bee colonies, if you've decided to pursue this very important enterprise. A majority of beekeepers tend to view selling swarms as not entirely kosher. The reason is that the swarm queen could turn out to be deficient, or, once the swarm is installed in a new hive, she might not return from her mating flight, or the young colony could perish during the winter for one reason or another. In any case, the person who buys such a swarm from you will regret his wasted time and money. Therefore, the way to do things is to install a swarm with a young queen in your own apiary and only sell it in the spring, as a complete, full-fledged colony. In this case, our conscience will be clear, as sellers—and our customers can be confident that they'll have no problems. Of course, a full-fledged colony should come with a higher price tag. The price should include the foundation frames and empty comb, the beekeeper's labor, and a guarantee that the colony isn't missing anything. In addition, the volume of even a modestly sized colony during the spring (seven to eight extra-deep frames) should be two to three times the volume of a standard nuc (four Dadant brood frames). However, a full-fledged colony like this will more than pay for itself with the honey it collects during the very first summer, and it's almost certain to winter successfully and, next year, either produce at least the same amount of honey, or, if you so desire, produce several good swarms. The apiary will begin to grow—which means it's time for us to move on to our next big topic: procedures to be performed with a horizontal hive with extra-deep frames over the course of the year. But before describing the first such procedure—the spring inspection—we need to go on a small but absolutely necessary digression. It concerns a very important element of a hive's design: the entrance.

The Hive Entrance

In the initial "models" of my horizontal hives I arranged the entrances precisely as was recommended in the majority of do-it-yourself manuals for building hives—that is, one slit-shaped entrance near the bottom, and a second round entrance approximately halfway up the front wall. But then came years of experiments, observations, and conversations with experienced beekeepers. And here's what I arrived at:

- Presently, I only make one entrance, a slit-shaped one, across the entire length of the front wall of the hive. I only leave a portion of it open, a 6–10-inch (15–25-cm) segment facing the area where the nest frames are located. The remaining segment I seal using a strip of jute (a roll-fed insulator used in buildings made of logs and timber) that I've rolled up into a small rope. But some other available material could be used instead. Why should the entrance extend across the entire front wall? It's necessary in light of the versatility of the horizontal hive—namely, when temporarily keeping two colonies in a single hive, when moving the nest portion, and in a number of other cases.

- The entrance should measure $1/2$ inch (12–13 mm) top to bottom—wider than it was before ($3/8$ inch; 8–10 mm); this allows the bees to walk along the top and bottom without getting in each others' way. This is especially important during the main honeyflow, when the bees usually exit the hive along the top entrance surface (upside down) when leaving to search for nectar, and use the bottom surface when returning. That is, the extra entrance space makes it much more flexible.

• In the most recent "models" of my hive, I've followed the examples of certain experienced beekeepers by raising the entrance higher from the bottom of the hive. If there's a lot of free space beneath the frames (5–6 inches; 12–15 cm), the entrance can be positioned directly below the lower frame bar (18 $^1/_2$ inches or 47 cm from the hive ceiling), or a bit higher. If there's not that much open space (say, a hive has an internal depth of 20 inches or 50 cm), I place the entrance 18 inches (40 cm) from the top bar of the frame (the ceiling of the hive).

An entrance raised above the bottom of the hive has several advantages:

• There's no longer any need for a landing board, since its purpose is now served by the front wall of the hive (there's more than 4 inches or 10 cm of space beneath the entrance);

• There's no longer any danger of the entrance being blocked by the snow or by dead bees during the winter (Photograph 32, p. 342);

• Specialists claim that an entrance raised above the bottom of the hive helps a colony to independently heal itself from mite-related diseases, since the bees are much less likely to crawl around on the bottom of the hive and come in contact with mites that have fallen to the bottom.

When carrying out various procedures with bee colonies (most of which fall under the category of "advanced" natural beekeeping), the entrance has to be "shifted" at certain points during the course of the year—that is, one segment has to be opened while the other has to be sealed. Aside from these instances, I do not regulate the width of the entrance during the year as I did initially (I used to widen it in the summer and narrow it in time for winter, and, during an intense robbing period, I would only leave room for one or two bees to pass through at a time). Now, I've done away will all this fuss; I keep the entrance open to approximately 6–10 inches (15–25 cm) all year long. During the dog days of summer, at the height of the honeyflow, I open vents located on the back wall of the hive, toward the bottom (see hive plans and description in Appendix 6), providing the bees with ventilation near the base of the hive. Before winter, I don't worry about the entrance; a strong colony will leave it fully open, while a weaker one will partially seal it with propolis. As for robbing, bees can guard a single entrance more effectively than they could two or more. Furthermore, as I've gathered from the existing literature and confirmed through experience, when a good fertile queen is present, the chances of robbing are very low even for a weak colony, but if the queen is hardly functioning or has died, then the colony is practically doomed, no matter its strength. Scouts from other hives will easily detect the queen's status, and even her own bees will be reluctant to defend their hive.

So when our hive is built with a single entrance extending across the front wall, we have at our disposal an ability to steer the life of our colony. The method is very simple: shifting the open portion of the entrance. Here, we draw on one of the laws of the life of a colony—namely, that during the summer the queen prefers to lay eggs on comb located near the entrance, while, at the same time, worker bees prefer to store nectar farther away from the entrance. During the winter, the bee cluster tends to gather near the entrance, and a bit above it. Therefore, by shifting the open portion of the entrance, we can, within certain limits, exert some degree of control over the life of the colony—for its benefit, and for ours!

Spring Inspection of Bee Colonies

At our latitude (Kaluga Region, 100 miles or 140 km southeast of Moscow, Zone 4), the end of winter comes around mid- to late March, when snow is still on the ground, but the sun is already warming it up, forming small thaw holes and clean, happily babbling little streams. On a warm, sunny and windless day like this, the bees begin to slowly venture forth from the hive. This isn't the cleansing flight, just a bit of "reconnaissance," when a few solitary bees walk out onto the front wall of the hive and take off into the air, in what is the first brief exploratory flight of the season. The real cleansing flight will come a bit later and may take place *en masse* on the same day, or may last more than a week.

The purpose of the cleansing flight is to cleanse the bees' intestines. Over the course of the long winter months, the bees consume honey, but are unable to leave the hive, so waste builds up in their intestines. When you consider the fact that by spring this waste may constitute half of the bee's total mass, it becomes clear why the bees would jump at the first opportunity for an outdoor flight, even a quick one.

For a beekeeper, this collective spring flight is always a celebration! It marks the start of the season, and signals that all is well with the colonies. However, I've noticed on many occasions that one shouldn't expect a direct correlation between the numbers of flying bees and colony strength. It sometimes happens that successful colonies are in no hurry with their cleansing flight, and may even postpone it for as long as possible. This is easily explained: in a strong colony, each individual bee consumes significantly less honey than in a weak one, and if the honey reserves are of high quality, and the hive isn't damp, then there's no urgent need for the cleansing flight. On the other hand, if following an early cleansing flight there are a large number of dark spots on the walls of a hive, that points to overflowing intestines, or to intestinal matter that has been affected by some pathogenic microorganism, including those causing nosema. One should keep a close eye on such colonies, since they could encounter problems down the road.

On more than one occasion, I've even encountered the extreme situation in which a colony makes no cleansing flight at all. That is, the entire apiary has completed its flight, but a few hives behave as if there are no bees in them at all. But if you put your ear up near the entrance and knock on the outside of the hive a bit, you'll hear a friendly, quickly subsiding buzzing. That means the colony is fine. More than likely (as I believe) this means that the winter was passed almost "ideally." That is, by the end of winter, the bees' intestines haven't reached critical capacity, and they'll cleanse them as they begin to work during the initial honeyflow.

In our region, the first palpable honeyflow begins approximately in mid-April. During that period, the major nectar-bearing plant is the willow, which has already begun blossoming when, here and there in the thick forest or on north-facing slopes, one can still see traces of snow on the ground. Willows bloom abundantly and for an extended period, especially since individual trees will bloom at different times depending on their location, whether in open, sunny glades or in a shady river basin. Almost simultaneously with the willow, there appear a number of early bloomers, such as coltsfoot (*Tussilago farfara*) and, a bit later, hazel and maple. The first spring flow is of special importance for a colony, since it helps it recover after the wintering period and embark on the first period of the coming season: spring buildup.

Spring is the time to inspect bee colonies; it's the only time during the year that I take apart and inspect the nest. Here, there are two ways of doing things that are fundamentally different. The first is a "late" spring inspection with the simultaneous addition of three or four foundation frames; this process is described in detail in Part II (pp. 132–133). I complete this procedure during the period from early to mid-May, but no later. Prior to that time, I limit myself to an external once-over; if the colony is active, the bees are carrying pollen pellets, and there are sufficient honey reserves in the hive, then I don't even peek inside it until the inspection. How do I know if there's honey inside? I try to judge the weight of the hive. To do so, I grab the end of the hive where the colony is located and lift it slightly. I even invite any guests who happen to be around at the time to participate

in this procedure. And anyone who has "weighed" a hive without bees first, and then one with bees, can immediately determine whether or not a hive contains honey reserves, and even their approximate amount. Since I always try to leave a bit of extra honey for the winter—that is, no less than 50 pounds (25 kg)—there should be around 20 pounds (10 kg) left in each colony for the spring, in which case there's no cause for concern. But if a hive seems too light, that points to a critical situation (this usually happens with weak swarm colonies from the previous season), so I give them some honey in a feeder or add a good honey frame.

I've begun employing the second option for the spring inspection over the last couple of years, and it strikes me as being quite practical: I call it the "early spring inspection." How does it differ from the late inspection? First, the timeframe. An early inspection can be carried out during the first warm sunny days, which in our region come in early April each year. That is, almost immediately following the mass cleansing flight. A second difference involves moving the nest portion of the hive (*Figure 10.A–B, p. 236*). If a colony wintered in the middle of the hive (more on that later), then I shift it to one side or the other; if it wintered against the side wall, then I move it to the opposite end of the hive. To do this, I release a couple of puffs of smoke into the hive entrance and, opening the top of the hive, I remove the division board and begin inspecting the frames, one by one (Photograph 7, p. 330). I remove the empty frames (without brood or honey reserves) altogether; after a quick inspection, I shift the others, in the same order, toward the side wall. Frames with honey and beebread reserves should always be present on the nest's edges (at least one on each side); its center should contain frames with the brood, in the same order they were found in. Before reinserting the warm division board, I add one frame with foundation, for monitoring purposes and to provide the colony with room to build should it find itself "in the mood" to do so. And, to complete the operation, I "shift" the entrance. That is, I open a 6-inch (15-cm) segment of it facing the new location of the nest (but closer to the division board), while sealing the old entrance. And that's how I leave the colony until early to mid-May—that is, until warm weather sets in and the honeyflow begins in earnest.

What are the reasons behind this procedure? Here are a few:

• A very early inspection makes it possible to evaluate the colony's condition as soon as it comes out of the wintering period, including the most important criterion—the presence of brood, and by extension the queen's performance. If the colony appears normal but there's no brood present, then one can "fix" it easily enough, using the simplest and most common technique out there. We take one frame with a fresh "batch" of eggs (one to three days old) from a strong colony that's wintered successfully and, carefully shaking off all the bees, we move it to the problem colony, near the center of the nest. The eggs are located at the very bottom of each cell; one can easily make them out by looking. It's hard to confuse them with larvae, which look like little white worms, from very small to very large, occupying the entire wax cell. This procedure almost always brings results—namely, the colony gaining full strength by the start of the main honeyflow.

• During the inspection, you can easily gauge the honey reserves and, if necessary, replenish them. To do so, we begin our inspections with the strongest colonies, which may have surplus honey. Such colonies have no use for

this extra honey; therefore, we can extract it, or ɓ.
those colonies who are low on honey (each colony should
be left with around 20 pounds or 10 kg of honey).

• During the winter, moisture inevitably accumulates in
the outer frames and especially in the walls of the hive,
and with it comes mold and various pathogens that
cause bee diseases. If we leave the inspection until May,
then the bees will have to clean and dry out the nest area
themselves—which means extra work. While conducting an early inspection, we remove the unneeded comb
with traces of moisture and mold, and also shift the entire nest to the dry portion of the hive. A day or two after
the bees have calmed down, we can (and must!) quietly
open the hive and treat the section where the colony wintered, which means cleaning the bottom and scorching
the walls with a blowtorch or a heat gun. This thermal
treatment is considered the best disinfection method. If
you don't have any of these tools available, you can carefully clean the walls with lye (which is what they did in the
old days) or some solution of modern disinfectant, such
as potassium permanganate. All serious beekeepers, regardless of what type of hive they have, including Dadant
or Langstroth hives, carry out such a procedure. I've even
heard tell of one beekeeper who, to avoid the accumulation of pathogens, simply burns his old hives after several
years of use and continuously replaces them with new
ones.

• By shifting the nest to the dry portion of the hive and
removing any surplus frames that have been emptied
during the winter, we help keep the colony as warm as
possible. And during this period, when it's still quite cold

outside and the colony has yet to gain full strength, this provides it with an additional impulse for growth.

If you conduct an early spring inspection, there's no need for a late inspection. Subsequently, you'll just need to shift the division board and add frames with foundation and empty comb. But this brings us to another topic—to spring buildup.

Spring Buildup of Bee Colonies

When spring arrives in full force and stable warm weather sets in, colonies enter a new phase of growth, which is usually called the spring buildup. In our region, this comes in early May, give or take a bit from year to year. A large number of young bees accumulate in the hive (the result of the queen's activity during early spring), capable of feeding all of the rising number of offspring as well as undertaking other jobs that are no less important—in particular, expanding the nest as the work season approaches. During this time (from approximately mid-May to late June) the colony sees its highest level of building activity, which must be taken full advantage of. Therefore, mid-May is the absolute latest time for completing the spring inspection and expanding the nest by adding foundation frames.

Part I (pp. 132–133) provided all the details on performing the late spring inspection, so we won't repeat ourselves here. If an early inspection has already been performed, then we'll leave the nest portion alone this time around, and simply move the division board to the side and add three or four foundation frames and, if we have one, a single frame with good empty comb that's white as snow (*Figure 10.C, p. 236*). But the procedure doesn't end here, since we still need to "shift" the entrance again. We open it as far as the division board and seal the portion that was open in the spring when the nest was moved. As a result, near the center of the hive, about 6 inches (15 cm) of the entrance remains open. Later, as we add more foundation frames, we can open the entrance a bit wider in the direction of the newly added frames. What's the point of this crafty little trick? There are several:

• Under the "early spring inspection" option, all of the foundation added during spring and early summer ends up closer to the center of the hive—that is, at the very spot where the open portion of the entrance is shifted to. Since the queen prefers to lay on comb located near the entrance, once the fresh comb has been drawn, she'll spend all her time here, laying eggs in freshly built cells. And this is what it takes to ensure healthy offspring down the road.

• On the other hand, bees will store surplus honey farther from the entrance—that is, to both sides of the nest portion, making use, on the one side, of comb standing empty after the winter and, on the other, comb added in preparation for the main honeyflow. To store their reserves, the bees won't have to move as far from the nest portion as they would if it were located right up against one of the ends.

• In preparation for winter, the colony is likely to set up here, opposite the entrance, on good, fresh comb—and here too, in the spring, it will begin to generate its first brood. Since a colony will draw an average of seven to eight extra-deep frames per season, the nest portion will be essentially completely renewed each year.

• During the fall inspection, we remove frames with surplus honey from both sides of the nest portion, which allows us to more accurately determine the position of the winter cluster and check for reserves, which we are leaving on either side of it.

- The winter cluster is positioned in the center of the hive, surrounded on two sides by warm division boards. This provides extra insulation from both sides, along with hydroscopic, water-absorbing materials (see Part IV on wintering).

The bees themselves alerted me to the possibility of using this system with a horizontal hive. I've tested various ways of manipulating the entrance, including, in the case of some strong colonies, opening it to the full width of the hive during the summer and not narrowing it in the fall. And in a number of cases the colony itself "decided" to winter not right up against one of the side walls, but near the center of the hive instead. And in the fall, I had to remove honey frames from both sides of the wintering nest, instead of from one side as usual. There were also other "hints" that led me to the idea of moving the nest portion. For example, sometimes in the spring I would discover that the nest portion is damp (this was before I began using moisture-absorbing materials) and decided to move all the frames to the opposite side of the hive. The only problem was getting the bees used to the new location of the open portion of the entrance, but within a week of the move, everything was going fine. One final piece of evidence that this approach was acceptable came from 19th-century beekeeping literature.

It turns out that shifting the entrance and, accordingly, the nest portion of the hive, was the primary approach taken with large horizontal log hives. This served the same purpose: periodically disinfecting the nest portion and freeing it from old, blackened comb. To this end, two entrances were made: one near each end of the hive, but on opposite walls (one on the front, one on the back). Consider the description of this procedure from Julian Lubieniecki's book *A Complete Practical Guide for Beekeepers* (Moscow, 2002, p. 181; the book was first published in 1859):

> During the height of the honeyflow, turn the hive around and open the entrance on the left-hand side while closing the one on the right. The bees, who usually winter near the entrance, will now move toward the left-hand side and build a nest in fresh comb. Then, in the fall, you can remove all the old comb, filled with honey, from the right-hand side of the hive. In this way the hive will be renewed without any harm whatsoever.

To complete our discussion of the spring buildup, we should mention another possibility: combining the two methods described above. This will be the "laziest" way to do spring inspections, since it practically eliminates any intrusion into the nest. We can skip the early spring inspection and, during the late one, also leave the nest portion in its place, while adding foundation on the side and moving the entrance toward the center.

In this case, during the first expansion (early May) we can move several outer frames aside and, when we've reached the edge of the nest, make sure that there's brood and that the queen is active. Then, following the technique for moving the nest toward the center, we add a few foundation frames. Obviously, if we use this technique year in and year out, then the wintering location will gradually shift: directly against one end of the hive, to the central part of the hive, and directly against the other end of the hive. The advantage of this method is clear: we don't have to take apart the nest portion at all. The drawback is that we lose all of the advantages of the early spring inspection listed above. But, if the bees have wintered well, this may not matter too much.

The next stage of the spring buildup comes between late May and early June. Good colonies will grow rapidly during this period, and one mustn't miss the moment when the bees are drawing close to the division board. Therefore, you need to check in on the bees again no later than two weeks following the first spring expansion. Good colonies receive 3–4 more foundation frames and one frame, two at the most, of good empty comb. Good comb, because it's being added to the part of the hive where, over the course of the summer, the queen may come to lay her eggs. At this time, there's no honeyflow to speak of yet, and the colony is in no need of a large amount of "storage containers" for storing its nectar, especially since a lot of nectar is being used to feed the brood. At the same time, comb construction is at its peak, and in this respect the young worker bees should be given a "full load." This stage of expansion is the same for all methods of spring inspection; the only difference is that for the "early spring inspection" option (with the nest portion in the center), you also need to open the entrance a bit more toward the center of the hive (opposite the newly added foundation). Then, once again, you can leave the hives alone for two weeks, particularly since there are plenty of other things to do around the apiary, as we are now entering the swarming season.

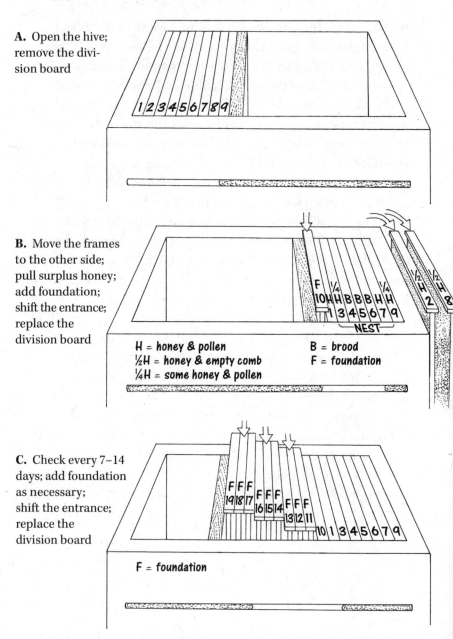

A. Open the hive; remove the division board

B. Move the frames to the other side; pull surplus honey; add foundation; shift the entrance; replace the division board

H = honey & pollen   B = brood
½H = honey & empty comb   F = foundation
¼H = some honey & pollen

C. Check every 7–14 days; add foundation as necessary; shift the entrance; replace the division board

F = foundation

Figure 10. The sequence of operations. A–B. The spring inspection

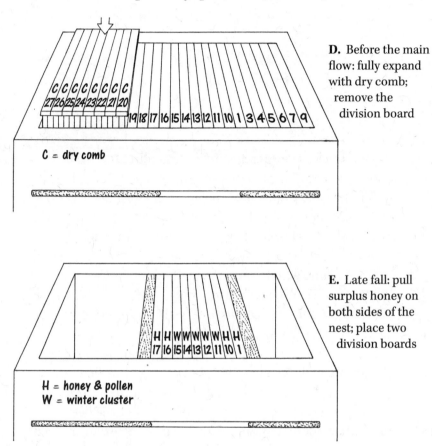

D. Before the main flow: fully expand with dry comb; remove the division board

C = dry comb

E. Late fall: pull surplus honey on both sides of the nest; place two division boards

H = honey & pollen
W = winter cluster

C–D. Spring–summer: expand the nest. E. Fall: pull honey

Preparing for the Main Honeyflow

One final stage remains: fully expanding the nest. As a rule, this period falls between mid- and late June—that is, before the main honeyflow begins. This step involves fully removing the division board and filling all empty space in the hive with frames (*Figure 10.D*). If the foundation closest to the division board is well covered with comb, we can add another frame with foundation, and fill the rest with empty comb only. Here we can use empty comb frames of less-than-ideal quality, since this area is intended exclusively for honey storage. The worse (the blacker) the comb is, the farther it should be placed from the nest portion of the hive.

One must be certain to always carry out this final procedure on time. It's better to do it a bit prematurely than to do it too late. When the main honeyflow begins, the bees limit all other work to a minimum, concentrating exclusively on gathering nectar. This changing of gears is perfectly understandable: nature gives our local bees no longer than a month or two to gather their strategic reserves for the entire year. For the rest of the year, the flow either provides subsistence at best, or is completely non-existent. The real honeyflow, bursting with blossoming plants and abundant with nectar, comes just once per year, during this period. The entire spring season involves, in essence, nothing more than preparing and gathering up strength for this crucial "push." And here, the more "storage containers" there are, the better. If you peek into the hive during a good honeyflow and remove a frame (assuming the bees let you!), you'll see that it appears slightly moist when held in the light. This is fresh nectar spread in a thin layer across the cells. Before it becomes real honey, the bees will still have to process it, fermenting it and removing excess moisture. To do so, they'll need the maximum number of empty cells—many more than the finished honey will fill. This is why beekeepers equate a shortage of empty comb during a major honeyflow with a direct loss of honey crop.

This is where the bulk of my beekeeping work ends, and for the remainder of the summer (from early July through October) I rarely even approach the hives, unless it's simply to check on the progress of swarms and problem colonies. In terms of comb area, 25 extra-deep frames correspond to almost 40 Dadant frames—more than three standard-size brood boxes. At our latitude, when bees are kept in a single location, this is essentially the biggest a colony can get—meaning that the bees will never feel cramped. But this certainly doesn't mean that the bees are obligated to fill this entire volume with honey, as much as we might like them to. The actual result will depend on the totality of factors listed above—namely, on the strength of the colony, the natural resources of the surroundings, and on the specifics of the given season. The most favorable weather conditions for nectar production are a temperature of 72–83°F (22–28°C) and a sufficient amount of moisture (rain). If things are dry all summer and the temperature is near 100°F (40°C), or if, on the other hand, the weather is cold and it rains nonstop, then abundant honey crops are not to be expected. Strong colonies that haven't cast swarms may still produce surplus honey, but younger swarm colonies should be watched carefully to make sure they're producing enough to survive on.

This means that our job is to give our bee colonies maximally favorable conditions for spring growth, and a maximum amount of "storage containers" for the main honeyflow... and then to rejoice in the results. At my apiary, a single colony that has wintered successfully will produce an average of 30–50 pounds (15–25 kg) of honey, depending on the season. That is, some colonies may generate up to 130 pounds (60 kg) or more, and others significantly less, while those that have cast 2–3 swarms will generate almost nothing. But this is in the case of "natural" natural beekeeping. When I use "advanced" methods such as fixing weak colonies, then my average harvest per colony rises considerably.

Is 30–50 pounds (15–25 kg) a little or a lot? Given the little effort I expend on my apiary, and the high quality of honey that results, I consider this figure to be entirely respectable. The honey is completely mature (it's pulled in the fall!), without a trace of sugar or medicines, and it will fetch prices significantly above the average market price. Also, this figure even exceeds the national average for honey production (30 pounds or 15 kg per colony). Extremely high production usually results from colonies that are hauled around during the season or in regions with an exceptional abundance of nectar-bearing plants; or when the bees are fed with sugar syrup. For examples of the latter practice, you don't have to look far—they are extremely common in modern beekeeping. For example, I once spoke with a neighboring beekeeper who claimed to average 90 pounds (40 kg) of honey per colony, and when he heard that I was getting just 45 pounds (20 kg), he shrugged his shoulders in astonishment. I began pressing him for details. It turned out that in the spring (or fall) he unites weaker colonies or adds them to stronger ones, and over the course of the season he gives at least 30 pounds (15 kg) of sugar per colony (which is the rough equivalent of 45 pounds or 20 kg of honey). So, a little math will reveal the end result, taking into account the cost of drugs and the extra hassle during the summer.

What remains to be said about the spring and summer period? Perhaps that the system we've described allows for individual variations. Everything depends on the beekeeper, and whether or not he lives near his apiary or can only visit occasionally. I always carry out the most important spring-time procedures—the inspection and the initial expansion with foundation frames—as described above, and never miss the deadlines. During the next phase, prior to the start of the main honeyflow, I peek into the hives more frequently than I said above—about once a week—adding frames depending on how the given colony is progressing. If I see that a colony is doing really well, then I'll add several frames; if

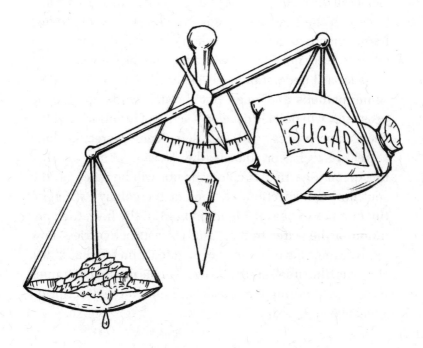

it's doing poorly, I add just one or two, or none at all, waiting until next time. Such a quick survey of the apiary takes just an hour or two, but in return it allows me to constantly keep my "finger on the pulse" and to have a definite idea of what's going on in each hive.

What does this survey look like in practice? I walk up behind each hive and swing open the top. When opened, the top doesn't block the entrance, and the keeper is on the side opposite the entrance—which allows the bees to continue working peacefully. I move the division board aside and look to see whether or not there are bees on the outer frame. If there are, and they've already begun drawing comb on it (the outer frame is always a foundation frame), that means I'm already late, and I have to add several frames immediately. If there aren't, then I move the outer frame aside and look at the next one. If there aren't any bees on it either, then we can leave the colony as is for now, or add a single frame just in case. If the bees are already busy on the second-to-last frame, then two new frames should be added. Frames can be added very quickly and without using the smoker.

As far as I understand, beekeepers do have to start with some methods and rules, but through working with the bees, they will quickly develop a sense of intuition, and the beekeeping process will, to a significant degree, become a creative endeavor. That is, the decision about whether to expand a particular colony or not will be taken on the spot during inspection. We look at the colony's strength, the number of bees flying in and out of the hive, the condition of the outer frames, and our journal entries (how many frames have already been added, and of what kind). However, the timeframes and the average number of frames to be added during the season will match the description given above.

As for keeping a journal, it can be a big help in beekeeping, especially as your number of hives increases. I try to make entries with as much detail as possible: the colony's origins, when it has cast swarms, the weight of the swarms and the hives they were installed in, how the colony wintered, how much honey it produced, and all of the stages of expansion, including the dates and the number of added frames. Over time, these entries begin to provide a great deal of interesting information that can be aggregated and analyzed. This way, keeping an apiary also turns into an interesting research endeavor whose results can be shared with friends and kindred spirits.

There remains one traditional question, often asked by the most ardent adherents of the natural approach: in the spring, during the first inspection, why not fill the entire hive with frames and leave it alone until fall? I've tried this several times, and have noted that if the hive is expanded suddenly and drastically, a bee colony's growth rate drops considerably. Of course, the stronger the colony, the more successfully it will weather this procedure. We've already discussed the reasons why. Spring is a period of rapid build-up, during which the queen tries to lay as quickly as possible, but there aren't, as of yet, many worker bees in the hive, who are responsible for warming and feeding all of the young. In the area where the brood is kept, the worker bees maintain a temperature of around 96°F (36°C), even while outside, especially at night, the temperature remains quite cool. Therefore, during the spring, and especially early spring, every last calorie of heat is important, and helping the bees conserve energy is the keeper's main task.

In early June, some colonies can already be expanded fully, but I would never recommend doing it in early May. In my view, three spring expansions (early to mid-May, late

May, and mid- to late June) seem the ideal arrangement. The timeframes may shift depending on the local climate and the weather, and they can be pinned down based on the bees' activity levels and on the blossoming of plants. And this, by the way, is a very interesting area of research that I've barely begun to touch on. In the old days, beekeepers considered the start of the primary willow blossoming, the oaks leafing out, the blooming of the gooseberry and, finally, the linden tree to be the "benchmarks." If we think carefully about it, we can very precisely pinpoint the optimal time-frames for conducting all the necessary procedures. After all, plants are much more sensitive to the subtle changes of nature than we modern humans are.

So, by the start of the main honeyflow, we must have completed all of our spring work at the apiary; we must have captured and installed all of our swarms and fully expanded all of our strong non-swarming colonies. But what goes on in the hives during the height of summer, when we leave our bees alone and turn our attention to other interesting oc-cupations?

The Main Honeyflow and the Second Half of Summer

At our latitudes, the main honeyflow comes with the full onset of summer—that is, of stable warm weather, and of the widespread blossoming of plants. Sometimes this period can be pinpointed quite accurately, and sometimes not—and in some years it never comes at all. That is, the concept of the main honeyflow is a relative one, but such a thing does indeed exist. At a certain moment, we suddenly discover that the entire apiary has abruptly "gone into high gear": in strong colonies, the bees move into the fields in a long, uninterrupted stream, and when they return, they quite literally plop down on the landing board, weighed down by their sweet burden. A large amount of nectar is sprinkled on the comb, and the bees are at work all night at the entrance, fanning their wings, blowing the excess moisture contained in the nectar out of the hive. This is another unmistakable sign of the main honeyflow: when, late at night, a quiet humming can be heard at the apiary, and the air is full of the delicate and wondrous aroma of nectar.

What does the queen do during the main honeyflow? As before, she continues laying eggs, but much less now than during the spring buildup. That is, as beekeepers say, she's "taking a break." By this point, there's little sense in laying a lot of eggs, since the offspring that would hatch from them, once they fly from the hive, wouldn't be in time for the height of the honeyflow, and if there are a lot of bees left in the hive by late summer, then they would needlessly consume the "strategic reserves." Therefore, the queen's task at this time is simply to maintain the minimal population of the hive. Additionally, feeding the brood is a big job that distracts the bees from working in the field. And during the main honey-flow, this too would be senseless. During the height of summer, young bees don't sit around in the hive for long; they begin foraging by the time they reach one week in age—that is, twice as quickly as usual.

There's also a physical reason for the drop in the queen's fertility: the bees are bringing in a lot of nectar and filling all the empty cells with it. By their nature, if the amount of comb is limited and the colony has to decide how to use the empty cells—for brood or for nectar—they always give preference to nectar. This law applies both during the main honeyflow—leading to a sharp drop in egg-laying—and during swarming. How?

It turns out that swarming depends not only on the instinct of procreation, whose effect increases with the age of the queen, but also on a series of purely physical factors that were first established by Alexander Butlerov (1828–1886). What are they? If in spring or early summer the colony feels cramped (has a shortage of available space), then at a certain point all the available cells will be taken up either by nectar or by brood. The queen now has nowhere to lay eggs, which means that the amount of young brood requiring care is reduced. "Throngs" of young nurse bees are left without work, as are builder bees, who have no room for new construction. The hive will now be prone to swarming.

The trick is that once all of this has happened, the urgent addition of foundation brings no results in most cases, and the colony begins to cast swarms. That's why one should never delay the spring inspection and expansion. And on the other hand, if we want to produce swarms, all we have to do is not add any foundation after the spring inspection, and to seal the passage beneath the division board. After generating one or two swarms, one should quickly expand the nest and allow the colony remaining in the hive with their young queen to develop normally.

But let's get back to summer. When the main honeyflow ends, and the nectar, transformed into mature honey, has been packed tightly into its waxen storerooms, the queen again has "room to maneuver" and can accelerate her egg-laying. And now this acceleration will serve a purpose, since the aging bees, having worked hard during the main honey-flow, will "retire"—that is, die— throughout August, which means that the young bees rising to take their place will be needed in greater numbers. The colony's main job in late summer is to raise an entire young generation of bees that have not been worn out harvesting nectar and feeding the young, and, consequently, are capable of wintering success-fully. This important time, called the fall buildup, ends in August and September, depending on the latitude and the particular year.

This same period (especially late summer) is a time of particularly rampant bee "invasions," when there are still many worker bees, but not much nectar in the fields, and "scouts" begin to track down access routes to other colonies' reserves. But if everything's fine in a hive, then the bees won't allow anyone to steal their honey. However, during this time I still keep an eye on my apiary, if only, in the case of disaster, to keep the honey reserves for myself. Otherwise they'll be robbed and distributed among hives at neighboring apiaries.

Pulling Honey and Preparing for Winter

For bees, September is the time for final preparations for wintering. In the nest portion of the hive, the season's last brood emerges, freeing up space for the winter cluster (which normally settles on empty comb) and for the final "packing" of winter reserves. During this time, they may also move honey and seal up any cracks in the hive, particularly in its upper portion.

During the first years of working with horizontal hives, I would begin pulling honey from my hives in mid-September. I also examined the nest to check for reserve amounts. In terms of the knowledge I acquired, this was certainly interesting, but it left me feeling awkward: the bees were hard at work, readying their nest, and sealing up all the gaps with propolis. Then I bust in and disrupt everything—and what for?

More recently, I've postponed pulling honey, first to late September, and then as late as mid-October. The right time for pulling honey depends on the weather—after all, the bees begin to form a winter cluster when the daytime outdoor temperature no longer rises above 54°F (12°C). During this time, the outer frames are already completely free of both brood and of any bees sitting on them. We can remove them with no trouble at all, moving as far as the edge of the cluster—that is, the first small group of bees sitting between two frames (*Figure 10.E*). But the two outer frames immediately adjacent to the cluster should never be removed, since they contain the reserves that will sustain the colony during early spring, when the cluster has already broken up, but there is not yet any honeyflow outside. Once we've pulled the honey (from one side or from both sides of the nest portion), we can test the weight of the hive—that is, carefully lift it from one side. One can always tell if there's honey inside. But, if we think logically about it, there's not even much sense in checking the honey reserves of strong colonies. After all, if the colony had surplus honey that we've now collected, that means that it was able to store up the necessary reserves for winter. Therefore, it only makes sense to worry about swarm colonies, especially the later ones.

The condition of swarm colonies should be gauged earlier, in mid- or even early August—that is, immediately after the end of the main honeyflow. If there's clearly not enough honey (due to a weak colony or a poor season), then I provide some in a feeder, which, in the form of a frame, is added inside the hive (Photograph 21, p. 337). It's much better to provide honey at this time than to add a honey frame to the nest prior to wintering (as some keepers do). Why? Because this allows the bees to arrange the honey as they see fit, and if reserves are in place the queen will be much more successful during the fall buildup.

The final stage—that is, the final preparation for wintering—is simple to perform. The details are laid out in Part IV, but here's the gist of the procedure:

In hives with a lot of open space beneath the frames (I'm currently leaving 5 inches or 130 mm, with a total internal hive depth of 23 $^5/_8$ inches or 600 mm), I lay a canvas sack filled with sphagnum bog moss or some other water-absorbing material. This should leave a minimum of $^3/_4$ inch (2 cm) of free space between the bottom bars of the frames and the sack. On one or on both sides (depending on the type of wintering) the nest is bordered by insulating division boards, beneath which there should be no gaps leading to the empty section of the hive.

In hives with little open space beneath the frames (1 $^1/_4$ inch or 30 mm, with a total internal hive depth of 19 $^3/_4$ inches or 500 mm), I situate the water-absorbing material to one side, or to both sides, of the nest area. This material can take the form of cushions similar to the one described above, or special partitions built in the form of a box, with one side (the one facing the nest) permeable for water vapor. This box is filled with any available water-absorbing material (I use silica gel). It's best to add a standard insulating division board between the water-absorbing cushion (or water-absorbing partition) and the empty section of the hive.

Just two final details. Before closing the top and leaving the hive until spring, I add an additional layer made of some thick fabric above the frames in order to completely eliminate the pocket of air between the frames and the top. I cover the entrance with a piece of wire mesh with $^3/_8$-inch square (10 x 10 mm) cells to prevent mice from entering the hive while allowing bees to pass through easily. And this brings our cycle of seasonal procedures to a close.

What's there to be done at the apiary during the winter? If the entrance runs along the bottom of the hive, it should be swept free of snow every once in a while; but if it's located any higher, then even this chore is no longer necessary. If you want, you can put your ear up against the entrance and listen to the bees buzzing. Beyond that, it's a matter of waiting for spring to arrive, and with it the start of a new season, bringing new (and mostly pleasant!) duties, new experiences, and new joys from interacting with bees—our fascinating and enigmatic neighbors on this Earth.

Questions and Answers - 2

Why do you use such synthetic materials as foam polystyrene when building hives—isn't it bad for the bees?

Of course, it's better to use natural materials as your insulation, such as straw, moss, jute, etc., and it would be useful to experiment with various hive construction techniques based on those materials. It's a question of priorities: for me, the most important thing was to develop techniques for keeping bees on extra-deep frames and to begin working with the European dark bee. The materials my hives are made from were of secondary importance. Foam polystyrene (Styrofoam) is excellent insulation, so many beekeepers use it. If a hive has an interior lining, then the foam is unlikely to hurt in any way. Natural insulation, such as straw board, have up to one-and-a-half times higher thermal conductivity, which would necessitate making the hive walls thicker to compensate.

Is it really so important to leave much free space in the hives beneath the frames?

I have yet to reach a final conclusion on this question—I haven't had enough time to compare. Some of the hives in my apiary are older models, with an interior depth of 19 $^3/_4$ inches (50 cm); others are new models, with an interior depth of 23 $^5/_8$ inches (60 cm) and a screen located about $^3/_4$ inch (2 cm) beneath the frames. For wintering without silica gel, the new-model hives are clearly better, but when a silica gel partition is used, there's no noticeable difference between the hives. Some free space beneath the frames certainly doesn't hurt, but it does make building hives more complicated. Whether or not it presents any serious advantages remains an open question. However, if the hive's interior depth is left at 19 $^3/_4$ inches (50 cm), then it's better to "raise" the entrance from the bottom of the hive. I'd recommend locating it 15 $^3/_4$ inches (40 cm) from the top of the frames.

Why is hardboard recommended for the top of the hive?

High-density fiberboard—or, as we've grown accustomed to calling it, hardboard—is used for purely economic reasons. It's significantly cheaper than plywood, but less resistant to moisture and "environmentally friendly," which are not major concerns for the top. Of course, plywood can always be used instead.

How do you feel about bees wintering in bottomless hives?

A friend of mine tried out this system: he made a 4-by-4-inch (10-by-10-cm) opening in the bottom of the hive and protected it from mice with a wire mesh screen. We did the spring inspection together: the hive was good and dry, but all of the honey in the nest had been consumed. This is easily explained: it was cold in the hive. I've had instances when the boards that formed a hive's bottom shrank from drying, and in the spring I found gaps in the bottom up to $^3/_8$ inch (1 cm) wide that had been present during the winter. The result was the same: there was no moisture in the hive, but significantly more honey had been consumed than in other hives. That is, where there's usually a band of still-capped honey left in nest frames when spring arrives, there wasn't any here. Therefore, I choose to limit the influx of air into the hive to a single open entrance, while using moisture-absorbing materials.

Can you give a list of work accessories needed at an apiary?

A special jacket, a veil, gloves, a smoker, a hive tool, a scraper for cleaning the bottoms and walls of hives, a special soft brush for sweeping up bees, swarm boxes, gigs for stretching wires onto frames; gigs for adding artificial foundation to frames; a side feeder; a solar wax melter; a honey extractor; an uncapping fork for opening comb; and a screen filter for honey.

When the apiary begins to expand, the need will arise for some sort of cart for transporting frames, especially frames filled with honey. This could be an ordinary garden wheelbarrow with a box for the frames, or a customized wagon.

How do I make and use a feeder?

Using $^3/_4$-by-1-inch stock (20 x 25 mm), make a regular-length frame about 12 inches (30 cm) deep. Glue all frame joints thoroughly so they won't leak. Attach a $^3/_8$-inch-thick (10-mm) top bar with self-drilling screws. Cut two pieces of hardboard so it covers the frame completely on one side and leaves a 2–3-inch (6–7-cm) gap on the other side (see Photograph 21, p. 337). Apply wood glue to the frame everywhere the hardboard will touch it, and nail the hardboard with its shiny surface facing inside. Make a small "raft": drill $^5/_{16}$-inch (8-mm) holes in a thin plank of wood that fits loosely inside the feeder.

After filling the feeder, insert this raft so it floats on the feed. Bees will walk on the raft and get the feed through the holes. Without a raft, many would drown.

To install the feeder, move the division board to the side and insert the feeder, its access window facing the frames. Then place the division board back on the other side of the feeder. Install the feeder in the evening—the bees will happily work through the night. Two or three quarts of feed (2–3 L) will be consumed in a day or two, but sometimes overnight. Wait for 3–4 days before removing the empty feeder: bees continue to guard it for some time.

The best feed is 100% honey. But if honey is scarce, add 2 pounds of sugar to a quart of boiling water (1 kg per 1 L), let it cool, then add 2 pounds (1 kg) of honey and let it sit for another 24 hours before giving it to the bees.

I only feed my bees to provide one-time "food aid" to newly installed weak swarms or nucs.

Do you use pollen collectors?

I don't use pollen collectors. Theoretically, you can use them, if you do so carefully and not indefinitely. There is evidence that pollen collectors, especially low-quality ones, can injure bees, so they should be used with caution.

What's the role of asphalt paper in hive building, and what can be used instead?

Here's a general rule for building wood-frame houses that we also apply to building hives: interior lining, vapor barrier, insulation, wind barrier, and siding. These are the layers, moving from the inside out. In our case, plywood used as the interior lining also works as a vapor barrier, so all that's needed is a layer of wind barrier beneath the weatherboard. Its role is to decrease the movement of air through the insulation, and, especially to limit the wind pressure, which can "blow" warmth out of the wall. But, at the same time, the outer layer must allow moisture to pass through, instead of trapping it in the wall—that is, it must "breathe." Those are the basics, in short. In the old days, the only such material was asphalt paper (kraft paper soaked with tar), but today many other synthetic materials have become available. These include Isospan, Tyvek, and others. In our case, any of them will do, but under no circumstances should polyethylene or various kinds of polyethylene foam be used, since they're completely unable to "breathe." Asphalt paper (also called "roofing paper" or "roofing felt") is generally the cheapest option, and can be found in any home improvement store.

Which direction should the hive entrance face?

I position the entrance to face east. That way, the morning sun quickly warms it, while the hot afternoon sun no longer hits it. I get the sense that facing the entrance due south tends to provoke swarming; I've tried having it face north, but the results are so far inconclusive. If the hive is in full shade, then it seems to me that the direction of the entrance has no impact whatsoever. In this case, you should take into account the direction of the prevailing winds, and turn the entrance to face in the opposite direction. The latitude of your apiary is also important: farther south, it's best to turn the entrance as far away from the sun as possible, but farther north this is less important.

What do you use to cover the entrance?

I use jute roll, which is used when building log houses. I use scissors to cut it into strips, roll it into a rope, and use a hive tool to push it into whatever portion of the entrance I need to cover. Whenever the cover's no longer needed, it can easily be removed. If a wooden board is used to cover the entrance, the bees may glue it so tightly with propolis that it can be hard to remove. They also glue jute roll, but it's easier to take out.

Is a landing board necessary?

If the entrance is positioned 4 inches (10 cm) above the bottom of the hive, then a portion of the front wall of the hive is left beneath it where the bees can land easily. In this case, judging from what I've seen, a landing board isn't necessary. If the entrance is located just above the bottom of the hive, then a landing board is preferable. Just think in terms of a tree hollow, where bees can land on the trunk both above and below the entrance. Therefore, if there's no "trunk" beneath the entrance, then a landing board can stand in for it.

Do you try to prevent drones from being born? Do you cut out drone brood, or, perhaps, use other comparable methods?

No, I don't do anything of the sort.

What woodworking equipment do you suggest for building hives?

There's a standard assortment of woodworking equipment that's needed for any sort of woodworking project, up to and including making complicated pieces of furniture. Basic woodworking machines include: a table saw, a planer, a thicknesser, a wood shaper and a miter saw. It's convenient if all of these items are mounted on separate stands, but you can buy a multi-purpose machine with all of the functions listed above. When buying a machine, pay attention to its convenience for work and its dependability, avoiding various kinds of equipment that lack durability, even if it's rather expensive.

But this is the maximum. In theory, all you really need is a good table saw and a planer; you can also get by with hand-held electric tools. It's a question of the speed, quality, and convenience of your work.

Does it make sense to buy swarms?

Buying swarms is like playing the lottery. Does it have a good queen? Will it survive the winter? The ideal option for purchasing (and selling) is a swarm that has wintered successfully with a young queen (a second or third swarm).

What's the best time for moving hives from one place to another?

When this is necessary, I do it early in the spring, when the bees have already completed their cleansing flight but haven't yet begun foraging. But it can also be done late in the fall, once the colonies have already set up for the winter. But I prefer not to bother the bees in the fall.

When should the ventilating openings be opened?

The round openings located in the lower section of the hive's back wall are intended for summer ventilation. In theory, these openings aren't absolutely necessary. However, during hot weather they can go a long way in helping strong colonies ventilate their nest by creating a through flow of air. So that's the only time I open them. The summer of 2010, when the temperature reached 104°F (40°C), proved to be a serious test for my bee colonies and hives. I was very pleased to see that none of my colonies began "bearding" (clustering) outside the hive, which speaks to effective temperature regulation inside.

How do you feel about nadiring (adding boxes on the bottom) and the Warré hive system?

The thing is, I can only tell about my own personal experience, and wouldn't want to analyze or critique other systems. If they work, then why not use them? However, certain things are very important to me—especially keeping local-race bees, and refusing to feed bees sugar or use artificial methods for producing new colonies. I share these views with a great many beekeepers, which is heartening. So the structure of the hive itself is, in many ways, a question of personal preference and custom.

Why don't bees always draw comb on the lower portion of the frames?

Both strong and weak colonies begin at the top—that is, they work their way along the top of the frames, moving as far to the side as possible. The closer the frames are to the nest, the more completely they are filled. However, weak colonies, including swarms and nucs, often don't make it to the bottom of the frames, drawing comb in the upper portions only. This is especially evident on frames formed by joining a Dadant brood frame on top with a super frame on the bottom. However, strong colonies will fill out these frames too, and use all of them from top to bottom. Generally, the horizontal bar in the middle of the frame does act as an obstacle, especially for weaker colonies that are more prone to develop laterally than downwardly. Therefore, frames with an uninterrupted wax field will work better, even though colonies often only partially fill them with comb.

What is empty comb used for?

Empty comb acts as a "container" for storing honey reserves. Drawing comb requires much greater effort from a bee colony than filling it with honey. Therefore, the availability of empty comb sharply increases the honey crop, and with it the beekeeper's "remuneration." A colony also needs a maximum number of empty cells during the honeyflow because smaller amounts of nectar are stored there initially, and only after processing and evaporation of excess moisture is it permanently stored and capped.

The presence of a large number of frames in a hive certainly doesn't mean that they'll all necessarily be filled with honey, as we'd prefer. A hive with 25 extra-deep frames is capable of holding up to 220 pounds (100 kg) of surplus honey, but in reality a colony will gather much less than that. Our task is to give bees as many frames as possible by the time honeyflow begins, but the "harvest" will depend on a number of factors, including the colony's strength, the nectar-bearing plants, and the weather.

What's your opinion on keeping bees in a log hive?

You can keep bees in a log hive (Photogrph 19, p. 336), but:

- The log should be of high quality—that is, warm and sufficiently spacious.
- Only a strong, local-race bee can survive in a log hive.
- The location should be as "wild" as possible—that is, with a wide variety of plants with varying blooming periods.
- Only a strong spring swarm should be installed in a log hive.
- Anyone who keeps bees in a log hive should have a clear grasp of the techniques involved and understand all of the subtleties of his trade.

What's the best honey extractor: an ordinary one, or one made of stainless steel? Does an electric motor help?

Stainless steel is better, of course, but there's no real difference. An electric motor is convenient, but if the honey volumes aren't too high, the added benefit isn't decisive. When choosing a honey extractor, it's important to pay attention to quality of manufacture, especially for the gearbox. Sometimes manufacturers install short-lived plastic pulley wheels and gears that wear out in no time. Some electric motors are also extremely unreliable and don't take long to break down.

Do you fight wasps and hornets?

If wasps become numerous, I set traps for them—jars or plastic bottles with water sweetened with sugar, jam, or any available sweet syrup. Wasps die in these traps in great numbers. I destroy any hornet nests I find near my apiary.

How do you control mice?

In the fall, once the bees have stopped leaving the hive, I cover the open portion of the entrances using strips of $^3/_8$-inch square (10-by-10-mm) metal screen. A mouse can't get through it, but a bee is free to leave the hive. There was one case when a mouse got into a hive by pulling the jute roll out of the sealed portion of the entrance. But this only happened once. There is a more radical method: smearing all around each leg of the hive stand, at the height of approximately 12 inches (30 cm) from the ground, with oil-based gear grease or some other thick lubricant.

Doesn't the plywood used to line the interior of the hive warp during the winter due to moisture?

Generally, no, but there have been cases when it has warped. Most likely, this was due to the low quality of the plywood. But I don't believe plywood to be the ideal material—I just haven't found anything better yet. One could line the hive with thin boards, but that would be more labor-intensive; hive construction would be more difficult, and the hive would become more cumbersome. In general, I agree that the techniques for building these hives need further refinement.

Why has the thickness of the hive bottom been reduced to $^3/_4$ inch (20 mm) in the latest plans?

To save money and to make building the hives easier. In the summer, this thickness is sufficient; during the winter, the bottom is lined with a pillow with some sort of water-absorbing material; on top of that, the air space also helps preserve warmth. But all of this is only true of hives with increased open space beneath the frames; if that space is standard-size—that is, about 1 inch (2–3 cm)—then the bottom should be made thicker and with better insulation.

When installing a standard nuc into a hive with extra-deep frames, is it possible not to make "add-ons"—that is, not to increase the frames' depth?

Yes, it's possible, but the bee colonies will inevitably begin to draw comb under the bottom bar of the frames. You'll have to trim them during the next spring inspection, which could prove difficult. On top of that, this means wasting empty comb. However, this technique for installing nucs is acceptable, but down the road you'll have to shift the open section of the entrance to force the bees to transition to the extra-deep frames, and remove the old frames with the hanging comb from the hive.

Have you had cases when you've had to locate a queen?

Not yet. I judge the queen's presence and quality by the brood. It must be said that locating the queen in a throng of bees is no easy task, especially in a European dark bee colony. Even highly experienced beekeepers can take some time to do it.

Is a smoker really necessary?

In many cases, I refrain from using a smoker—for example, when expanding colonies with foundation and empty comb. However, I prefer to always have a smoker close at hand. During the spring inspection and in certain other cases, you simply can't do without a smoker—for the bees, smoke signals the threat of fire; they quickly fill their honey stomachs with honey, and are distracted from the secondary danger—the beekeeper intruding into their domain. But since smoke does cause the bees a good deal of stress, it certainly shouldn't be overused.

During the winter, there are dead bees lying in the snow near the hive. Is this normal?

Bees always die outside the hive so as not to burden their companions with the extra work of emptying the hive of corpses. This is true during the winter as well. So as long as there aren't too many bees in the snow, it's perfectly normal. On the contrary, when the dead bees are accumulating in the hive itself during the winter, forming so-called "die-off" at the bottom of the hive, then you've got a problem.

Is it possible to build a hive out of "mud and straw" (straw soaked with clay mortar)?

Prior to the Russian Revolution, one way of making hives was out of thin boards (one-inch planks), which were then surrounded on the outside with straw panels about 3 inches (7–8 cm) thick. The resulting hives were excellent. There are diagrams in old books depicting a simple device for making straw panels, but it requires long straw. Today, finding such straw isn't easy—once straw has passed through a combine, it's broken.

Hives were also made simply out of woven straw, and smeared on the inside with a mixture of clay, manure, and

birch ash. One prerevolutionary author by the name of Illarion Kullanda referred to these hives as "golden hives"* due to their cost-effectiveness and their convenience for the bees. As for "mud and straw," I'm not sure—I'd have to try it. More than likely, you'd need to coat it on the inside with something similar to that ash-clay-manure mixture.

How much foundation should I buy?

A pound of foundation contains approximately 5 sheets for a Dadant brood frame (12 per kg). One and a half sheets will be needed for each extra-deep frame, meaning that a pound of foundation will cover 3 frames (8 per kg). Two–four pounds (1–1.5 kg) of foundation will typically be required per hive per season.

---

* *Golden hives*—this involves a play on words, as the Russian word *zoloto* has traditionally had two meanings: "gold" and "manure." *Ed.*

Please explain why you went with the horizontal hive, despite the fact that bees naturally live in vertical tree hollows?

A perfectly reasonable question: indeed, a natural tree hollow is vertically oriented, and the colony living in it expands from the top down. Then how should a hive be built? Expanding a colony upward by adding additional boxes and supers is contrary to nature, so there's only one alternative: placing new boxes from below, which means lifting the entire hive (weighing up to 200 pounds or 100 kg and more) vertically. And how should the honey be pulled in the fall? That's also a bit of a mystery. Some beekeepers have tried this system, but as far as I know it hasn't won widespread adoption.

On the other hand, in pristine nature, hollows were found of more than 3 feet (1 m) in diameter—not to mention the fact that bees also settled in fallen trees. How did they behave in those cases? It turns out that a colony that settles in a wide space draws comb approximately 20 inches (50 cm) deep (in order to winter successfully), and then gradually moves to the sides until it has filled the entire volume. This is precisely the natural mechanism we take advantage of.

Therefore, horizontal hives have existed since ancient times (just look at some old drawings!), and many beekeepers considered these hives better and more "rich in honey" than vertical ones. Nikolay Vitvitsky, a luminary of Russian apiculture, wrote convincingly on this topic. The only drawback with horizontal hives is that they tend to get cold (a large, horizontally extended space), but these days that problem is easily solved using a well-insulated, movable division board.

Can bees be kept in a hive with extra-deep frames in southern regions?

To be honest, I haven't yet studied natural beekeeping in southern latitudes in earnest, although I certainly should. Tentatively, I would say that the situation farther south is in some ways simpler than in Russia's central temperate zone. The winter is shorter and milder, and therefore the demands regarding the race of bees are less strict—one can keep more southerly bee races, such as Carpathians or the mountain grey Caucasian bee. But there are also problems: the summer drought, and the more "modern" agricultural techniques, based on monocultures and widespread use of pesticides. Due to the droughts, stationary beekeeping is all but impracticable in many southern regions—almost all beekeepers haul their hives around. And that means beekeeping is a profession, not a hobby, and a horizontal hive with an extra-deep frame is certainly inappropriate under these circumstances.

Generally, everything depends greatly on location, and the principles of the horizontal hive with extra-deep frames are only applicable if the apiary is stationary. One hive can produce up to 200 pounds (90 kg) of honey, and it can bear the heat more easily due to its thick walls and its gable roof. Of course, it's highly desirable to place the hives in the shade (in our area, this isn't mandatory).

Have you kept bees in other kinds of hives?

At first, I kept bees in Dadant hives, but I didn't like it. Now, I have several hives containing so-called Ukrainian frames (Figure 6, p. 110), which maintains the Dadant dimensions ($11\,^{13}/_{16} \times 17\,^{1}/_{8}$ inches; 300 x 435 mm) but is oriented vertically. The tricky part is that if we take a colony's maximum growth to be equal to 36 brood frames (3 Dadant boxes), then the hive would be 53 inches (135 cm) wide, and that's too much. Therefore, I positioned the frames in two rows ("double-wide"), 18 in each, and between them I placed a partition with a 4-by-4-inch (10-by-10-cm) window that I open in the summer once the bees have filled out the winter "compartment." So far, the results are as follows: good wintering (frame depth!), but considerable swarming in the early summer—even colonies with last year's queens began swarming. I chalk this up to the narrowness of the frames, but this must be investigated further. All things considered, the frame 17 $^1/_8$ x 18 $^1/_2$ inches (435 x 470 mm) has proven most suitable.

How do you keep wax moths out of your hives?

Infestations by wax moths usually go hand-in-hand with robbing of weak colonies.

The wax moth is a rather large, whitish moth that looks very much like an ordinary night moth. It flies around the apiary looking for somewhere to lay its eggs. Strong, prosperous colonies don't let the moth in and protect their comb. Therefore, even empty comb stored in strong colonies beyond the division board is also safe. But the moth is able to infiltrate weak or struggling colonies. What the moth loves most of all, however, are hives that have been completely robbed and left without bees. There may be no honey left in them, but moth larvae don't need any—they prefer to feed on old, dark comb. The larvae eat this comb and spin webs that prevent the bees in the hive, if any are left, from reaching the moths and killing them.

Therefore, some beekeepers who haven't tended their apiary throughout the entire second half of the summer may, when they finally take a peek into a colony, make a sad discovery: a hive full of moths, larvae, cocoons, and webs. This means that at least two generations of moths have bred successfully: larvae have matured and spun cocoons, moths have emerged from those cocoons and, in turn, laid more eggs—and a new generation of larvae have enjoyed a feeding frenzy on the remaining comb.

A sad spectacle, yes, but one that can be avoided: make sure that your apiary is full of strong colonies with young queens, and at the end of summer, check on your colonies from time to time to promptly detect any problems. Another word of warning: never store honey frames or empty comb, following extraction, in a warm location for an extended period of time. When I pull honey frames from a hive, I try to extract the honey from them as quickly as possible and return the empty comb back into the hives, into the vacant section beyond the division board. If it's still fairly warm outside, then the bees will manage to dry the comb themselves— that is, to collect any remaining honey—and if not, they'll dry it out in the spring. If honey is pulled in late fall, when the nighttime temperature can fall below freezing, you can store emptied frames in empty hives whose entrances have been completely sealed. Moth larvae can't survive freezing temperatures, and a temperature of less than 14°F (-10°C) can kill moths in any stage of development, including moth eggs. Therefore, combs that have spent a long, cold winter in completely sealed hives will be "safe" in the spring.

Beekeeping literature describes many methods for storing empty comb, but I haven't used them because I haven't had any need to. Two ways of storing empty frames—freezing them over the winter in sealed hives or beyond the division board in successful colonies—has always done the trick for me. But if someone wants to leave some honey in the comb, then it should also be stored in a cold location at a freezing or near-freezing temperature.

PART IV

How Bee Colonies Winter, and How to Make Wintering As Successful as Possible

Introduction

Wintering is one of the most critical topics in beekeeping. This is especially true for Russia's temperate forest region and farther north, where for half the year or more bees are unable to leave the hive, replenish or redistribute their reserves of honey and beebread, rebuild their nest or purge their intestines. Moreover, during this period, the colony is in "standby mode," and has a very limited ability to maintain the necessary microclimate inside its hive, which often leads to an accumulation of moisture, not to mention other adverse (and often deadly) consequences. Therefore, it's hardly surprising that most deaths—or, as beekeepers put it, "die-off"—of colonies and even entire apiaries come during the winter. Ivan Shabarshov, who studies the history of beekeeping, puts it this way: *"Indeed, winter has often reduced all a beekeeper's efforts to naught. Annual deaths from hunger of bee colonies, and sometimes of entire peasant apiaries; high die-off; diarrhea; moisture and mold in the nests; and low productivity among weakened colonies—these are the main misfortunes caused by winter"* (*A History of Russian Beekeeping*, 1996). This quotation refers to how things were in the 19th century, but, strange as it may sound, little has changed in the century and a half since.

What are we to make of this? Well, the understanding that everything is in our hands. Ever since man dragged the bee colony from its natural home, the tree hollow, and resettled it in artificial dwellings, the responsibility for the life of "God's little fly" (as bees were once called in Russian) has fallen upon man's shoulders, and upon his conscience. The preconditions for a successful (or unsuccessful) winter depend almost entirely on what the beekeeper does throughout the entire season—on how he's prepared the colony for this critical period, and, of course, on the design and quality of the hive itself.

The theory surrounding wintering is quite likely the most complex topic in applied beekeeping, and it often remains an enigma for beginning amateur beekeepers—all the more so since the recommendations provided by popular beekeeping manuals are typically of a rather empirical nature and, quite often, contradict each other. As an example, take the question of which of the hive entrances to leave open during the winter. Some authors recommend leaving both entrances open; others, only the bottom one; and still others insist that it's the upper entrance that should be left open. Where does that leave us?

Luckily for us, we now have a number of high-quality websites (many thanks are due to the people who created them!) that provide a wide selection of rare and extremely interesting studies dedicated exclusively to wintering. The information gleaned from these studies, combined with my own thoughts and experience, has been of inestimable value to me in assembling a more or less clear picture of what wintering looks like—one I'd like to share with you now.

This part of the book contains no new or original information; rather, its goal is to synthesize a large amount of material and create a more or less comprehensive and carefully supported picture of how bee colonies winter, and of the processes that unfold during this period. It is written for beekeepers (present and future) who love and care for their bees, but simply don't have the time to study and analyze

Introduction to Part IV

the considerable amount of literature on this topic. The text contains a number of necessary calculations and formulas, but if such theoretical considerations strike you as too long and boring, you may certainly skip them, focusing your attention on the practical conclusions alone. So let's get started!

What You Must Know
...the Wintering Process
Of an Individual Bee and of the
Colony as a Whole

On the individual bee:

1. Each individual bee is incapable of enduring lengthy periods of excessive cold. This distinguishes bees from many other insects that hibernate for the winter. The activity level of a particular bee depends directly on the external temperature (these data have been taken from various sources):

• The bee is comfortable in temperatures ranging from 57–100°F (14–38°C).

• When the outside temperature drops below 54°F (12°C), bees stop exiting the hive (for the northernmost populations, this limit drops to 45°F or 7°C).

• Between 43–48°F (6–9°C), the bee becomes lethargic and falls into a slight torpor from which it can emerge independently by triggering an "internal heating" mechanism (vibration of its flight muscles).

• *Below 43°F (6°C), the bee will fall into a complete torpor from which it cannot independently emerge, and within a certain time it will die. The lower the temperature, the shorter the period of time following which the bee can still be revived by an increase in the ambient temperature.*

Namely, the maximum length of cold-induced torpor is 48–60 hours at 32°F (0°C), 3–6 hours at 23°F (-5°C), and 30–70 minutes at 14°F or -10°C (data taken from Evgeny Eskov's book *Wintering of Bee Colonies*, 1992).

2. All of the figures listed above are not exact, since in practice much depends on the bee's race, and on its particular physiological state. Furthermore, slightly different figures are cited by various sources.

3. The following are most capable of enduring low temperatures:
- older bees;
- bees of the fall generation, in comparison with those of the summer generation;
- bees of northerly races (particularly the European dark bee).

4. Individual bees have a number of physiological traits that allow them to better endure the winter period. These include:
- the ability to lower the amount of moisture in the organism by winter;
- the ability to accumulate reserves of nutrients in the body, such as carbohydrates (glycogen), fats, and nitrogen;
- the ability to store up to 47 mg of waste product in the intestine over the course of the winter (which can account for up to one half of the bee's total body mass);
- the ability to prevent decay of intestinal contents with the help of the catalase enzyme secreted by the rectal gland.

5. All of these adaptive traits are much more pronounced among northern bees—above all in the European dark bee.

6. Given a comfortable ambient temperature, bees can long remain in a state of rest, lowering their metabolism to a minimum. The proportion of the bee's minimum metabolism to its maximum is 1:140, while that of humans does not exceed 1:10 (Vladimir Alpatov, 1930, cited in Ardalion Semenenko's article "Thermal Regulation During Winter"). The bee's optimal temperature when at rest is 73–82°F (23–28°C).

7. While remaining motionless, a bee can quickly raise its body temperature using a special mechanism for internal heating: vibrating its flight muscles. While doing so, it rapidly consumes the honey reserves stored in its honey stomach.

8. The processing of honey leaves "waste" that accumulates in the intestine over the course of the winter. The bee can only purge its intestine in spring, during its initial cleansing flight. Many researchers consider intestinal overflow to be a limiting factor when it comes to successful wintering.

9. However, it's not only intestinal overflow that can cause problems, but also the "spoilage" of its contents as a result of excess moisture in the hive (which leads to excess moisture in the bee organism), low-quality food, and a number of other factors. All of these factors can trigger any number of intestinal problems and certain diseases, such as nosema. Frequently, this results in traces of diarrhea on the comb and on the interior walls of the hive.

10. As we've already mentioned, these processes are held in check by the catalase enzyme secreted by the rectal gland.

11. Only physiologically young bees will easily survive the winter and prove good workers come spring—namely, those bees who did not gather nectar or raise brood during the fall, the bees who were "born" in late summer or early fall. For Russia's central latitudes, this means mid-August to mid-September. Bees who were born in time to work during the honeyflow typically do not survive until spring. By the same token, bees that are born too late and do not manage to leave the hive to purge their intestines before winter also do not survive the winter.

Concerning the winter cluster:

1. When the outdoor temperature falls below 45–55°F or 7–13°C (depending on the condition of the colony), bees in the hive begin to gather in a tight, compact formation referred to as the winter cluster. The purposes of the winter cluster are obvious: shared body heat, lower overall heat loss, and, consequently, lower consumption of honey reserves. Even a group of bees numbering 50 individuals is capable of auto-regulation (Mikhail Zherebkin, *Bee Wintering*, 1979).

2. Bees almost always form a winter cluster opposite the hive entrance. This is why two entrances were usually made in horizontal hives (and in log hives before them), one near each end of the hive. One entrance was covered; here, the bees would store their surplus honey. The other was left open; here, the colony would hunker down for the winter.

3. A typical cluster forms on empty comb; furthermore, the bees occupy both the empty space between the comb and the empty cells (Figure 1, p. 35).

4. When the outside temperature drops, the cluster tightens; when the temperature rises, the cluster loosens. When spring temperatures stabilize, the cluster breaks up and the bee colony gets to work.

5. Throughout the summer and fall, the bees store the bulk of their winter honey reserves, which are the most important reserves for wintering successfully, above and behind the cluster location (farther away from the entrance).

6. During the winter, the cluster gradually moves upwards and backwards, consuming the honey reserves. Speaking very roughly, the average speed over the course of the winter is estimated at 1 mm per day. That means that bees need at least 6 inches (15 cm) of honey reserves "above their heads," and preferably more.

7. The cluster occupies a narrow band of the honeycomb located to the top and to the back. The bees gradually uncap the comb (biting through the caps) and prepare its contents for consumption. The thick, mature honey in the cells is warmed by the warm, moist air proceeding from the cluster and, due to its absorbency, takes in the water vapors. It is in this watered-down form that the honey is consumed by the bees.

8. There should be no comb in the winter nest that was not capped during the fall, since any honey stored in uncapped comb would quickly absorb moisture and ferment.

9. On the other hand, when bees winter in an excessively warm and dry indoor space, the colony may become thirsty. This results from a lack of the moisture needed to liquefy the honey. In this case, the bees begin to make noise, become restless, and exit the hive. This is why many 19th-century authors recommend providing drinking water for bees that are wintering indoors, using special troughs inserted into the log or hive. The same authors note that bees wintering outside don't experience such problems.

10. During the winter, bees don't pass honey to one another, which means that each individual bee must, from time to time, reach the reserves itself and replenish the contents of its honey stomach. This is one reason why bees are constantly, though slowly, changing their position within the winter cluster.

11. As a rule, the winter cluster is divided into the exterior "crust" or "mantle" and the interior "core," although some researchers distinguish a third layer in between, the "loose core." The crust consists of older bees, and the bees in the crust move very little. The crust is 1–3 inches (2–8 cm) thick, depending on the colony's strength, the hive's warmth, the external temperature, and other factors. As a rule, the core consists of younger bees who move much more actively than those in the crust.

12. The crust consists of bees packed together very tightly, along with two looser areas: one to the bottom (to allow fresh air to enter the cluster) and one at the top, to allow old air, saturated with carbon dioxide and water vapor, to exit. The bees regulate the air inside the cluster by either tightening or loosening the crust formation in those areas.

13. If we picture the winter cluster in the form of a ball, then its volume will be intersected by planes of comb, resulting in multiple "circles." It is believed that bees do not pass from one "circle" to another, spending the entire winter within a single "beeway"—the space between two adjacent planes of comb. This means that each individual "circle" has its own crust and its own core, while also being heated from both sides by the bees in the neighboring beeways. Only the two outer "circles" will consist exclusively of crust bees, shielding the entire cluster from the cold (Figure 1, p. 35).

14. However, this picture is a bit less than perfect. For example, this author believes that bees may indeed move from one beeway to another during the winter, although in all likelihood they don't do so very often. For this purpose, they have openings in the comb, made ahead of time (during the summer); of course, there is also the option of biting through the bottom of an empty cell and passing through it into the neighboring beeway. For bees, this is no more difficult than biting through the waxen top of capped honeycomb. One piece of evidence supporting this idea is the small, cell-sized holes that any beekeeper can find if he looks carefully at finished comb taken from the nest section of the hive.

15. During the winter, the bees can only use honey from the comb on which the cluster is "perched." They cannot access any comb located off to the side during this period; therefore a colony can die during freezing temperatures if it depletes all of the honey located "above its head" and behind it, even if the comb located off to the sides is still full of honey.

16. The colony begins using the honey stored in the side comb in early spring, when the cluster has already broken

up, but there is not yet any honeyflow outdoors. It is during this time that the bees are most actively flying to fetch the water necessary for thinning the thick honey stored in the comb. During the summer, during the thick of the honeyflow, the bees have almost no use for water, since fresh nectar contains significantly more water than mature capped honey, and, in this "pristine" state, it is ready for immediate use.

17. During the winter, the bee cluster emits a characteristic noise that you can detect by pressing your ear against the open hive entrance (or using a special tube for listening in on the colony). The colder it is outside, the louder the bees will get. Based on this noise, an experienced beekeeper can determine the colony's condition and whether or not it is having any difficulties.

18. Beginning in late winter (February to March), the bee colony has something new to worry about: raising a new generation of young bees. At first, there will be very little brood; but as spring approaches, the more actively the queen will lay eggs, and the more resources will be required for raising the brood. Beyond using honey and beebread to feed the larvae, the bees also have to maintain a higher temperature, since the brood requires 95–97°F (35–36°C) compared with the 64–68°F (18–20°C) sufficient for wintering. This is why bees may encounter the most serious problems in February and March, precisely when one would think the winter is behind them.

The Colony's Main Job During the Winter

If we reflect carefully on the information laid out above, we reach a very simple conclusion: *the main job of a bee colony throughout the entire winter period is to maintain a temperature of at least 43°F (6°C) on the surface of the cluster.* Why? Because any temperature lower than that is a threat to the individual bees.

Another job is to use the energy needed to maintain this temperature as efficiently as possible. The primary winter "fuel" is honey, and the honey reserves must be made to last all winter and spring, until the honeyflow begins. Furthermore, as we know, excess honey consumption leads to excess intestinal content.

How does a bee colony cope with these challenges? In the best possible way! It forms a dense, compact structure, the winter cluster; the cluster's core emanates heat, while the densely arrayed crust traps the heat within the cluster. The colder the air outside the cluster, the more heat the cluster's surface loses, and the more intensely heat-preservation mechanisms kick in. Namely, the bees in the crust huddle together more tightly, the crust becomes thicker, and the core generates more heat.

What is the result? There are a number of highly important consequences, and conclusions to be drawn. Let's look at them one by one.

The Thermal Physics of a Wintering Colony

The laws of physics dictate that the larger the cluster is (that is, the more bees it contains), the easier it is to maintain its internal temperature, since its surface area is proportional to diameter squared, and its volume to its diameter cubed. *This means that the larger the cluster is, the less heat loss it experiences per bee, and the less trouble it has maintaining the necessary temperature.* What follows from this?

1. A weak colony, especially one wintering in a thin-walled hive, may simply not cope with the cold during severe freezes, and may perish even if it has abundant honey reserves.

2. In a cluster with a large volume, the core remains at a stable temperature of 64°F or 18°C (but no lower than 57°F; 14°C). A small colony is forced to maintain a higher core temperature, with more abrupt fluctuations.

3. *The average consumption of honey per bee is significantly lower in large colonies than in small ones.* This means that bees wintering in a large colony experience much less physical strain, and accumulate less waste matter in their intestine. Precise data are contained in Evgeny Eskov's book, *Wintering of Bee Colonies*, from 1992: *"A colony of European dark bees that contains 12 thousand*

individuals consumed 29 g of honey per day over the course of a month (during the first half of winter), while a colony containing 30 thousand individuals consumed an average of 37 g of honey per day during the same period, which, on a per-bee basis, is half as much. The corresponding heat losses totaled 10.6 watt/hour and 17.7 watt/hour, respectively."

Next comes another highly important question: where does heat loss from the hive occur, and how can we help the bees to retain that heat? Luckily for us, specialists in thermal physics have studied this problem and made all the necessary, highly detailed calculations. For anyone who wishes to delve into the details, I can enthusiastically recommend Lev Sukhodolets's book, *The Thermal Physics of Bee Wintering* (published by Kolos in 2006); this is the most thorough study of this daunting topic that I know of. We, however, will skip the complicated calculations and simply draw on the results obtained by this and other authors:

1. There are only two ways by which heat escapes from a hive: by direct thermal transfer (through the walls, the top and the bottom of the hive), and through air exchange with the outside (the outside air entering the hive has a lower temperature than that exiting it). Thermal radiation plays a very minor role and can be disregarded.

2. The loss of heat through ventilation depends heavily on the location and sizes of the open hive entrances. But the key factor here is that *as long as we only allow the colony the amount of air exchange necessary for it to breathe, then it will account for no more than ten percent of total heat loss!*

3. This means that the lion's share of heat loss occurs through the hive's walls, top, and bottom! The conclusion is obvious: *we can (indeed, must!) carefully insulate the walls and particularly the top of the hive—and the warmer they are, the easier it will be for the bees to survive the winter deep freeze.* This is particularly relevant, as we've mentioned already, for weaker colonies.

This is why all 19th and 20th century beekeeping manuals are full of detailed recommendations on how to insulate hives for wintering outdoors. Here are a few such tips:

• Walls of logs and hives that are made of solid wood should be built thick, and made from spalted (discolored by fungi) or even partially decayed wood, not fresh wood that is hard and dense (and therefore better able to conduct heat)—especially not wood from a freshly cut tree.

- Hives should be made with double walls filled with any available insulation (sphagnum bog moss, tow, etc.) at a thickness of at least 3 inches (7 cm).

- Build hives with wooden boards, covered on the outside with straw panels.

- Build hives out of straw mats lined on the inside with special coatings made of clay, manure, birch ash, and other components.

To these, Soviet-era literature adds a number of recommendations, such as surrounding hives with special covers and filling the gaps with insulation, or placing the hives next to one another, covering them with snow, or any number of other tips, all aimed at a single goal: heat retention.

Only in the past few decades have voices emerged advocating wintering outdoors in thin-walled wooden hives. Bees can winter just as well this way, they say. Where did such ideas come from? Here's what Edouard Bertrand, a famous European beekeeper who kept bees in a climate much milder than ours, wrote on the topic back in the 19th century, in his book *Managing the Apiary*, published in 1882 (the quote is from A.F. Devrien's edition, published in Petrograd in 1914):

> Some beekeepers claim that precautions against cold are useless. The bees, they say, can even winter in single-walled hives, even those covered poorly on top. We know this full well, and most beekeepers have had the opportunity to conduct such experiments; but when this is done, wintering bees consume a great deal more honey, which is not only unprofitable, but also dangerous; the

brood being raised by the bees may suffer, or the egg-laying process may be slowed by sharp fluctuations in temperature; finally, bees exhausted by working more intensely to maintain warmth in the hive are so weak come spring that they are often incapable of raising their young, and die in great numbers during the initial flights.

More precise data are provided by Vladimir Kashkovsky in his book *Advice for Beekeepers*, published in 1991 (he is speaking here of early spring): "For example, in a single-walled hive without insulation, 3.6 kilocalories are lost per hour, and 13.6 pounds (6.17 kg) of honey are consumed per month to compensate for this loss of heat. In the very same hive with good insulation (a cushion 4 inches or 9.5 cm thick on top, diaphragms and lateral cushions lining the sides, and an insulated bottom), just 1.1 kilocalories are lost per hour, and just 4.5 pounds (2.04 kg) of honey are consumed in compensation—that is, just one third of the amount consumed in an uninsulated hive."

With this, we can bring our discussion of insulation to a close and move on to the following topic, no less important: bees' respiration during the winter.

Bee Respiration in the Winter Cluster

During the winter, bees warm themselves by consuming honey and using it as a kind of sweet fuel. Honey consists of fructose (typically 38%), glucose (31%), water (17%) and other substances (including minerals). Fructose and glucose share the same chemical formula: $C_6H_{12}O_6$; the oxidation reaction looks like this: $C_6H_{12}O_6 + 6O_2 = 6CO_2 + 6H_2O$.

This makes it clear that as bees assimilate honey they take in oxygen from the air through respiration, while emitting carbon dioxide and water. If we translate this formula into hard numbers, we see that for 2 ounces (60 g) of honey consumed (a strong colony will consume this amount during a below-freezing winter day), approximately 10 gallons (40 L) of pure carbon dioxide gas are emitted into the air (under normal circumstances), along with 1.4 ounce (40 g) of water in the form of vapor. These calculations assume that mature honey contains approximately 17% water. The next section will be devoted to water; for now, let's look at oxygen and carbon dioxide.

Studies have shown that in a closed space bees begin to die when the CO_2 concentration tops 9%, or when the oxygen concentration drops below 5% (the usual concentrations of these gases in the air are 0.03% and 21%, respectively). Since the same amount of oxygen is consumed as the amount of carbon dioxide emitted, the decisive factor here is the rise in the levels of CO_2. Bees can handle a carbon dioxide concentration of up to 4%; moreover, specialists believe that this level may promote more successful wintering, although it may possibly accelerate aging. When the CO_2 level in the hive exceeds 4%, the colony becomes agitated and begins ventilating the nest.

Using these figures, we can easily calculate that on an average winter day approximately 35 cubic feet (1 m³) of fresh outside air should pass into the hive, and the same amount of processed air should pass outside. This isn't very much air—less than a quart (0.7 L) per minute (during the summer, air exchange can reach one quart per second). But this is in the case of actual ventilation. *If, however, just one entrance is left open in the hive, then there will be practically no thermal convection of incoming and outgoing air, and most of the air exchange will happen by diffusion.* And this is very important! Diffusion (that is, the leveling out of gas concentration in a given volume as the molecules of a gas spread from an area of high concentration to one of lower concentration) plays a crucial role in the process of winter air exchange within a hive! In particular, diffusion helps reduce overall gas exchange between the hive's interior and the surrounding air several times over. This is due to the fact that all the gasses that make up air behave independently; therefore, nitrogen—the primary component of air—is not involved in the exchange. And this means direct heat economy.

The thoughts developed above help to explain a fact familiar from the literature: that a single small entrance, even one located significantly lower than the bottom of the winter cluster, is more than enough for bee respiration. Given how crucial this factor is, I decided to conduct some simple experiments during the winter by placing an oil lamp in an empty hive. I arranged the lamp's wick so that it would consume approximately 3 ounces (100 g) of oil per day—more than the maximum daily consumption of honey during the coldest winter weather. The entrance was situated very close to the bottom, 20 inches (50 cm) from the top of the hive, and the lamp was situated as high up as possible (the flame from the wick was 10 inches or 25 cm from the ceiling). The hive's top was hermetically sealed using polyethylene film. Two days later, when, according to the calculations, all the oxygen in the hive should have been burned already, the lamp continued burning just as it had at the beginning of the experiment.

All of this leads to one conclusion: *a beekeeper would have to screw things up royally—by all but completely sealing off the hive's interior—to cause the bees to suffocate during the winter.* And that, of course, is a very rare occurrence, save for instances when excessive die-off blocks up the single lower entrance. But some say that the other bees still survive quite often even when this happens.

History provides one example in the form of the theory of August Berlepsch, a luminary of 19th-century European beekeeping. He ardently recommended completely sealing up all the hive entrances for the winter! And a great many beekeepers, both European and Russian, followed his advice—including (early in his beekeeping career) Alexander Butlerov, a famous chemist and no less famous beekeeper of the late 19th century. This isn't hard to explain: back then, hives tended to be made of wooden boards, and the colonies had enough air passing through the tiny cracks that inevitably exist in wood. By the way, Butlerov himself later stopped sealing all the entrances, recognizing that not every "leading European innovation" should be followed blindly. But we'll get back to that later; for now, here are a few simple conclusions to be drawn from this section:

1. A colony does not require much fresh air during the winter, and a single, small entrance is more than sufficient in this respect;

2. Moreover, bees don't need excessive air exchange with the outdoors, since, first of all, their heat escapes along with the hot air that leaves the hive; and, second, carbon dioxide also escapes, and most specialists believe that higher carbon dioxide levels (no more, however, than 4%) improve wintering;

3. When the hive has a single open entrance, diffusion begins to play a significant (if not primary) role in the exchange of gases between the hive's interior and the outside air. This exchange results in a leveling off of the partial pressures of the gases that constitute the air inside and outside the hive. In other words, if, for example, the concentration of oxygen in the hive is lower than in the outside air, then oxygen molecules will pass from the outside into the hive even without an actual air flow;

4. When there is a steady vertical cross-ventilation (two open entrances, an upper and a lower), it makes little sense to insulate the hive's walls.

The last point can be easily illustrated with an example from real life. Let's imagine a house (or apartment) with a crack left in the window during the winter for ventilation. A small amount of fresh air will enter through the crack, and the air in the home will feel more pleasant. But if we open a second window, or the front door, we'll immediately feel a draft. The home will become cold and uncomfortable, and we'll feel like closing one or the other (the door or the window). The same thing happens in the bee's home.

But experienced beekeepers are sure to ask: why, then, when a hive has two entrances, don't bees always seal up the top entrance completely, but instead leave gaps of various sizes in it (depending on the strength of the colony)? Here, I think, the bees somehow "understand" that in this particular situation there's simply no other option. As we know, during bees' respiration process, a decent amount of moisture forms, and, given the smaller volume of the modern hive and the minimal space beneath the comb, this moisture simply has nowhere to escape. This leaves the colony with only one way to get rid of the excess moisture inside the hive: cross ventilation. After all, dampness in the hive is much worse than cold!

The next section is entirely devoted to this highly important topic.

The Role of Water in the Wintering Process

Based on the chemical reaction for the oxidation of honey, it's not hard to calculate that for every pound of honey consumed, approximately 11 ounces of water are produced (680 g of water for 1 kg of honey), which results in an average total of 22 pounds (10 kg) for the entire winter. That's a considerable figure! To understand its consequences, we need to recall a few simple details from high school physics. Here they are:

Water in the air occurs in gas form—namely, as water vapor. Water vapor is invisible to the eye, and shouldn't be confused with "fog," which actually consists of droplets of water. Under certain conditions (of temperature and pressure), a given volume of air is capable of holding a very definite, limited amount of water. And the lower the air temperature, the less water can be "held" in a given volume. Precise data can be easily found in any science reference book. For example, a cubic foot (7.5 gallons) of air can hold a maximum of 1.13 g of water at 95°F, 0.48 g at 68°F, and 0.22 g at 45°F. (I.e., 1 m^3 or 1,000 L of air can hold a maximum of 40 g of water at 35°C, 17 g at 20°C, and 7.8 g at 7°C). This is a significant difference! A commonly encountered term—relative humidity—expresses the ratio of the actual water content to the maximum possible content.

This theory leads to a number of simple conclusions:

1. When air is heated, its relative humidity falls, and when it is cooled, its relative humidity rises.

2. When air is gradually cooled, at a certain moment its humidity reaches 100%, and as it is cooled further the vapor begins to condense, and "fog"—tiny droplets of water—appear in the air.

3. These droplets begin to gather on any surfaces; inside a wintering hive, this means its interior walls and the comb.

4. If there are two surfaces in a small volume of moisture-saturated air—one cold, the other warm—then the relative humidity near the cold surface will be 100%, and less near the warm surface (say, 90%). Quite understandably, then, condensate will form on the cold surface.

And here's where things get interesting. We already know that during the oxidation of honey, approximately 0.7 ounce (20 g) of water is produced for every 0.7 cubic foot (20 L) of carbon dioxide gas. From the figures cited above, we know that at a temperature inside the cluster of 64–68°F (18–20°C), this water will saturate the air to 100%. In the same volume of air, 0.7 cubic foot (20 L) of carbon dioxide will bring the carbon dioxide level to a bit over 2%, which is half the permissible level. *This means that the bees will be forced to "freshen up" the air inside the winter cluster not because of the accumulation of excess carbon dioxide or the consumption of oxygen, but in order to get rid of excess moisture!*
In order to free the hive of 1.4 ounce (40 g) of water produced by the colony over the course of one winter day, approximately 100 cubic feet (3 m³) of air will be required,

assuming the air leaving the hive is at a temperature of 63°F (17°C); but if the temperature is 32°F (0°C), which is much more likely in reality, around 350 cubic feet (10 m³) will be needed. These simple calculations confirm what the specialists say: *in order to remove excess metabolic moisture from the hive, a colony needs approximately 10 times more air than the amount needed for respiration alone!* What does this mean?

Well, it means—as we well know from practice—that *a single small entrance, which is more than sufficient in terms of providing the colony with fresh air, is certainly not sufficient for removing from the hive the moisture that forms during the respiration process!* However, if we create cross ventilation in the hive (two open entrances), thus eliminating excess moisture, then the resulting heat loss will be considerable, and could exceed the heat loss that occurs through the hive walls. We already know the consequences; we'll speak about how to prevent them a bit later. But now is the time to say a word or two about moisture condensation.

As we've already mentioned, the winter cluster emits warm air saturated with moisture, which begins to condense even with moderate drops in temperature. The key issue here is where this condensate will gather. Obviously, the prime candidates are the hive's interior walls—and the thinner (colder) they are, the more intensive this process will become. The better insulated the hive's wall are, the lower (that is, the farther from ceiling level, toward the colder area) the dew point will fall.

But in any case, *if we have two surfaces—a warm one (the surface of the bee cluster) and a cold one (the interior walls of the hive), then the moisture should gather on the colder one. That is, the hive walls should get wet, but not the surface of the cluster. So why is it that bees suffer from dampness during the winter?*

And suffer they do—quite often, in fact! Dampness has become the primary threat to bees during wintering, ever since the colony was moved from its natural habitat, the tree hollow, into artificial habitats—log hives and box hives.

But our line of thought suggests that even if the hive walls and the comb beneath the cluster become completely wet, then the cluster itself, with its warmer surface temperature, should not suffer from dampness! One beekeeper has described a situation in which, on an extremely cold winter day, he (for reasons I don't remember) took the top off of a hive, peeked inside, and found that the colony was sitting quite literally in a snowdrift of hoarfrost! The next spring, much to his surprise, the bees were feeling great, and there was very little die-off. Confirmation of this can be found in old books whose authors, peeking into their hives during periods of severe cold, found a thick layer of hoarfrost on the interior walls; and despite this fact, the bees were doing fine come spring. We already know the explanation: even if the relative humidity inside the hive reaches 100%, it should be lower near the warm surface of the cluster, and there shouldn't be any condensation on it! *So why do the bees get wet?*

In thinking about this issue, I reached a very simple conclusion: *the reason bees in a winter cluster get wet is poor top insulation. If the top is poorly insulated, the condensate will be less likely to gather on the interior walls of the hive, but rather above the cluster (where the processed air initially rises); and at a certain moment the water simply begins to drip down onto the bees from above! And there's nothing they can do to fight it.* When water falls directly onto the bees that form the cluster's crust, they get wet, grow numb from the cold, and drop to the bottom of the hive. The water, which causes their wings to stick together, leaves them unable to fly out of the hive and die outside it, as old or sick bees will typically do, including in winter. This likely explains the large amount of die-off at the bottom of the hive, which is practically unheard-of in natural tree hollows.

About a year after these thoughts occurred to me, I found them confirmed in a book by Julian Lubieniecki (*A Complete Practical Guide for Beekeepers*, 1859):

> During severe cold, both the walls and overhead of the hive sweat, freeze over, and become covered with snow. The stronger the colony is and the colder the walls and overhead are, the more they sweat and freeze, starting in the middle. Then, as the cold subsides and the hoarfrost in the overhead of the hive begins to melt, water drips into the nest, among the bees, causing them to get wet, fly out of the nest, and freeze to death—or they swallow the water and, in a state of constant distress, grow ill and drop to the bottom of the hive. This is why we usually find many bee corpses in the spring following harsh winters.

And now, armed with theory, let's find an answer to this question: What are we to do with the ten liters of water that forms during the winter?

First option: remove the moisture using cross-ventilation. In practice, there are three basic methods available that make use of cross-ventilation.

1. Two open entrances, an upper and a lower. The cold outside air enters through the lower entrance, and the warm, moisture-saturated air leaves the hive through the upper.

2. Bottom ventilation. A lower slit-shaped entrance opened across its entire length, and ventilation openings on the opposite side, positioned right near the bottom of the hive. In this situation, the winter cluster is located in the warm upper portion of the hive, and fresh air circulates underneath it. This option includes the so-called "bottomless wintering," when all entrances are sealed, and a fairly large opening is cut into the bottom of the hive, protected against mice by a wire mesh. Bottom ventilation may also involve a number of other recommendations, such as inserting $^1/_8$-inch-thick (3–4-mm) wedges in between the bottom and the box for the winter (this is often found in 19th-century books on beekeeping).

3. Drawing the processed air from the space underneath the frames. To do so, special vertical channels are made on both sides of the nest, passing through the upper insulation and connecting the space below the frames with the outside air. This option is rather complicated, technically speaking, but they say it's very effective. All three of these options are used in practice, but the last two strike me as much more desirable, since they avoid creating any drafts near the cluster, and, thanks to the pocket of warm air in the top of the hive, there will be less air circulation, thus preserving more heat.

Second option: leave the moisture in the hive. In the fall, place some hydroscopic (water-absorbent) material inside the hive, which will absorb excess moisture throughout the winter.

This option includes the commonly heard recommendation to place a cushion above the frames for the winter, filled with moss, cotton, tow, or any other water-absorbing material. To allow air to pass upward freely, they recommend bending the cloth back one or two centimeters on one side, or replacing it, right before the wintering period begins, with a new cloth not sealed up with propolis. This system works well in practice, but has an obvious disadvantage: as the cushion becomes wet, its insulative quality falls dramatically, with all of the expected consequences.

Another recommendation (a more "natural" one) is to place water-absorbent cushions off to one side, or, even better, off to both sides of the wintering nest. A third tip is to place water-absorbent materials to the bottom, beneath the wintering nest.

Today, many researchers believe that keeping the moisture inside the hive using water-absorbing materials is the best and most promising method, since it sharply decreases the exchange of air with the outside (leaving only the air necessary for respiration), thus minimizing the heat loss associated with ventilation.

Using water-absorbent materials to "trap" moisture inside logs and hives is an age-old practice. Most recommendations found in 19th- and 20th-century literature on the topic describe using straw. Straw was used to make thick partitions in horizontal hives, and it was recommended to fill the empty space behind the partition with straw for the winter. In vertical hives, straw was spread across the bottom and used to fill up all empty spaces left when comb was cut out or frames were removed. By the way, even back in the 19th century, there was nothing new about these methods; even before the first beekeeping manuals were published, straw was used for these purposes by beekeepers who filled empty space beneath the comb in their artificial tree hollows.

Why did they use straw, of all things? Most likely, they used it due to its wide availability. However, the all-time "king" of water-absorbent materials is dried sphagnum bog moss, which, on top of everything else, has powerful germicidal properties and can therefore be used repeatedly. But bog moss wasn't available everywhere, so straw was used instead, as well as wood shavings, coal and other materials with similar properties. Now the list of these materials has become considerably longer, including everything from silica gels to disposable diapers.

Generally speaking, when it comes to trapping moisture inside the hive throughout the winter period, there are any number of unexploited possibilities, but here we'll leave this interesting topic to the reader's creativity. We still need to add a word or two about the open space underneath the frames.

The overwhelming majority of authors agree that an increased space under the frames (at least 1–2 inches or 3–5 cm deep) considerably improves wintering—provided, of course, that the bottom is well insulated. But many thoughtful researchers go even further, recommending leaving an open space of 6–8 inches (15–20 cm), or even more, beneath the frames (and, consequently, beneath the lower slit-shaped entrance!). It is filled with straw, bog moss, tow or some other material with similar properties. What does this do for us?

- The bottom of the hive becomes significantly warmer due to the still air below the entrance, even absent any materials filling it, but all the more so when materials are present.

- The additional volume of air located beneath the frames promotes more effective air exchange in the nest portion.

- The materials filling this space will absorb excess moisture during the winter.

- *Many practicing beekeepers believe that an additional space at least 5 inches (12 cm) deep located beneath the lower entrance promotes the colony's ability to deal with mite diseases completely on its own!* It turns out that when the mites (we're speaking primarily of the Varroa mite) fall to the bottom of the hive, they're unable to climb back up, and die. When the lower entrance is situated at the very bottom of the hive, the bees come into contact with the mites as they enter and exit the hive, making the colony vulnerable to repeated infestation.

And now, with this important addition, we can move on to our most important topic: to searching for the ideal "home" for a bee colony.

The Search for the Ideal Home For a Bee Colony

In light of everything we've said above, a rough outline of an ideal home for a bee colony begins to emerge. And it turns out, as it so often does (not surprisingly!), that its features are shared by the bee's natural home: the tree hollow. Let's list them once again:

1. Warm walls. Tree hollows in old-growth forests had walls with a thickness of 4–6 inches (10–15 cm) or more.

2. A very warm top that prevents the condensation of moisture above the winter cluster. In a hive, the top should be significantly warmer than the walls. In a tree hollow, the entire tree trunk is located above the nest.

3. The hive should contain hydroscopic, moisture-absorbing materials. The bottom of a tree hollow always contains loose, decayed wood. By the way, this is what distinguishes a natural tree hollow from an artificial one hollowed out by man.

4. A single entrance located no higher than the lower extremity of the winter cluster (14–16 inches or 35–40 cm from the ceiling). In tree hollows, there's almost always just one entrance, which is rarely very large. In most tree hollows studied by beekeepers, the entrance is located

beneath the lower extremity of the winter cluster, sometimes even 5–6 feet (1.5–2 m) from the ceiling.

5. An airproof, insulated pocket in the upper portion of the nest. Bees always use propolis to seal up the upper area of a tree hollow where the nest is located, especially the ceiling.

6. The presence of sufficient space under the frames. Such space is always present in a tree hollow—and often a lot of it. In the "old days" they'd find bee-inhabited hollows up to 16 feet (5 m) or more in depth.

7. A comb (frame) depth of at least 18 inches (45 cm), that is, for areas with a climate similar to that in the temperate forest region of Russia. A colony needs a comb this deep in order to prepare effectively for winter and to weather it with flying colors. Along with the space under the frames, the total hive (log hive) depth comes to at least 20 inches (50 cm). These are the recommendations found in the guidelines for building log hives written by Petro Prokopovych (1775–1850), Nikolay Vitvitsky (1764–1853), and other prominent beekeepers from days gone by.

The experience of these same 19th-century authors showed that a vertical log hive (referred to as a "gum" in popular parlance) is great for wintering, but in summer its bees show a strong tendency to swarm. A horizontal log hive is cold in the winter, but in the summer its bees develop well and swarm much less often—hence its reputation for being more "honeyful."

Therefore, the invention of the movable-frame hive led to the idea of combining the advantages of the vertical and horizontal hive by creating a horizontal hive with an extra-deep frame and outfitting it with an insulating division board. In fact, one of this hive's creators, Kazimierz Lewicki, called it the "horizonto-vertical" hive, since during the winter it effectively became a vertical hive, thanks to its extra-deep frame and insulated division board, while during the summer it turned back into a horizontal hive (Figure 5, p. 104). I too adopted this same approach.

Still, regardless of how good the hive may be, it alone can't provide any absolute guarantee of a successful winter, since there are a number of other factors that are just as decisive. These include the physiological condition of the colony as it enters the winter period, the quality of the winter honey reserves, the bee race, and a few others.

Let's look at them one by one.

The Physiological Condition of a Colony as It Enters the Winter Period

Fall brood buildup

As we've already mentioned, only physiologically young bees will winter well and work for an extended period in the spring—that is, those who did not participate in gathering nectar or in feeding the young during the fall. Such bees emerged from their cells at the very end of summer or in early fall. They appear as a result of the second peak in egg-laying, which begins after the main honeyflow. In Russia's temperate forest zone, this comes in the middle of August. The first egg-laying peak comes during the period before the main honeyflow.

For a successful fall buildup, you need a strong colony, the availability of free cells to hold the eggs, good reserves of honey and beebread in the hive, and, preferably, at least some honeyflow outside.

The most frequently encountered problem is a lack of free space in the hive. This is especially widespread if there is still abundant honeyflow, when competition arises between the queen, who needs empty cells for laying eggs, and the foraging worker bees bringing nectar into the hive. Preference is naturally given to the nectar, which means that the queen is often left with no free space at all!

The classic example of this problem occurs when a good strong swarm settles into a small swarm trap. During the main honeyflow, it quickly builds up its nest and fills all available comb with nectar. As a result, when the time comes for the fall buildup, the queen simply does not have enough open cells to lay eggs in; and then, during winter, the predominantly older bees, their life's work complete, gradually die off. Come spring, the beekeeper finds that the colony has perished.

Another possible problem arises when a swarm colony that is weak or swarms too late simply lacks the time needed to build sufficient strength by winter. A third problem is an old queen who is simply unable to lay the necessary number of eggs.

Queen quality

No two queens are alike; some function well for six years, or even longer. But all queens are most productive during their first three years. All beekeepers therefore agree that the younger the queen is, the better her colony's chances of making it through the winter successfully. Why? There are three main reasons:

1. The younger the queen, the longer she continues laying eggs during the fall. One-year-old queens complete their fall egg-laying an average of ten days later than two-year-olds, and twenty days later than three-year-olds (Nikolay Kokorev and Boris Chernov, *Bee Wintering*, 2005).

2. A young queen lays eggs at a faster rate during the fall buildup. Studies have shown that colonies with

one-year-old queens raise an average of three times more fall brood than those with three-year-old queens (Mikhail Zherebkin, *Bee Wintering*, 1979).

3. The older the queen, the more likely she is to die during the winter. The same author has shown that 0.2% of one-year-old queens, 2.9% of two-year-olds, and 10% of three-year-olds die during the winter.

A colony left without a queen during the winter period becomes deeply agitated, and thus begins to consume more honey, with all of the expected consequences. But even if it does make it until spring, it is unable to produce a new (emergency) queen, since there aren't any freshly laid eggs in the colony. The only thing that can save it is the addition of a reserve queen. But not every beekeeper is likely to have one on hand—and finding a young queen during the early spring is no easy task.

However, there's no consensus when it comes to the ideal age of a queen. Some believe that in Russia's temperate forest zone colonies with two- or three-year-old queens winter more successfully than those with young queens (produced that same season); therefore, beekeepers tend not to replace them too frequently (Nikolay Kokorev and Boris Chernov, *Bee Wintering*). Nevertheless, practically all beekeepers agree that the likelihood of a successful winter falls noticeably with queens beyond three years of age.

Colony strength

We've already dealt with this topic; all that remains is to provide a few numbers. A strong colony refers to a winter cluster that occupies the beeways between 8–11 extra-deep frames—that is, 5–6 pounds (2.5–3 kg) of bees. An average colony occupies 6–7 frames, and a weak one occupies 4–5 frames, weighing 2–3 pounds (1–1.2 kg). It makes sense to combine two weak colonies in a single hive for the winter, separated by a division board, or to install a weak colony alongside a strong one. Otherwise a weak colony will have little chance of survival. At the same time, experienced beekeepers will tell you that there's little sense in creating excessively large colonies—that is, weighing more than 6–7 pounds (3 kg).

Winter Reserves

An average-strength colony that is left to its own devices will consume up to 30 pounds (15 kg) and more of honey during the winter. Moreover, most of this consumption can be chalked up not only to the months with the coldest temperatures, but to early spring as well, when the colony has already begun to raise its brood but no nectar is yet available in nature. After all, as we know, the brood requires much higher temperatures in the nest area, as well as "baby food"—honey and beebread.

However, practicing beekeepers have seen that if a colony is left with "just enough" honey in the fall—just enough, that is, to last until the first honeyflow next spring—then when spring does arrive the colony will struggle to grow and will be unlikely to build up sufficient strength in time for the main honeyflow. In the spring, the queen will only lay eggs effectively if the hive contains reserves of at least 20 pounds (10 kg) of honey and the bees are certain that the "kids" won't lack for warmth or food. That's why conscientious beekeepers are in the habit of leaving at least 50 pounds (25 kg) of honey in the hive in the fall, and those who are especially caring keep another 20 pounds (10 kg) for each colony around as an emergency reserve to be used for supplemental spring feeding, if necessary. And although the question of spring feeding is only tangentially related to our topic at hand, we can't avoid saying a bit about it here.

Theoretically, the need for feeding a bee colony in the spring is based on the assumption that the queen, as the accepted theory has it, will only accelerate her egg-laying when there is a consistent flow of fresh nectar into the hive. And good egg-laying is essential for building up the colony. That's why most industrial beekeepers place such unrivalled emphasis on spring feeding and why detailed recommendations on how, when and what to feed the bees can be found in almost all beekeeping manuals.

Nevertheless, despite the abundance of literature dedicated to this topic, the question of whether or not artificial supplemental feeding is necessary still remains an open one. Many beekeepers believe that a successful colony itself "knows" when and by what time it has to build up its strength—the main thing is to have honey and beebread reserves in the hive. Furthermore, no two summers are alike, the honeyflow always varies in intensity, and the timeline

for the main honeyflow can shift by two weeks or even more. And sure enough, at winter's end, for example, when there's still snow on the ground, the queen begins laying eggs without any inflow of nectar whatsoever, simply "sensing" that the right time has come. And she does it at a different point in time each year.

To this, advocates of supplemental feeding understandably object that the conditions that hold in nature are now very different from those that held sway in days gone by— that the abundance and variety of nectar-bearing plants have dropped dramatically due to human activity, that the bees today are very different from what they used to be, etc. On the other hand, even in the past, the areas bees lived in varied widely in terms of their natural wealth; luckily, pesticides and genetically modified organisms still aren't used everywhere by any means; and, finally, we need to restore the population of the European dark bee in any event.

Of course, this entire discussion is purely theoretical, and potentially never-ending. But has anyone conducted close studies of the effect of supplemental feeding on bee colonies? It turns out that they have, and some time ago. We can find the results in the previously mentioned book by Vladimir Kashkovksy.

In order to increase the brood during the non-honeyflow period, some beekeepers provide supplemental food for their colonies, in small portions of diluted honey (one cup of water for every pound of honey), or liquid sugar syrup (1 pint of water for every pound of sugar). This food is served once per day or every other day, in servings of half-a-pound (200–300 g) per colony. Previously, this feeding was referred to as speculative; today it's referred to as stimulative.

In the 1920s, Anatoly Butkevich conducted experiments at his apiary and reached the conclusion that such supplemental feeding is not economically justified. His results were so conclusive that speculative feeding fell out of use until the 1940s. Then, in 1944, at the Kemerovo Experimental Station for Apiculture, L.I. Perepelova experimented with feeding bee colonies using various methods.

The experiment showed that feeding colonies in small doses did not increase the number of brood—that is, the expenditures of labor and syrup did not prove justifiable. This confirmed the results obtained by Anatoly Butkevich. The best results were obtained in the test group in which a portion of the honey cells on the outer frames was periodically uncapped. This method was used by the famous Siberian beekeeper Daniil Naichukov.

The only thing in this quotation that might remain unclear is the very end: why add comb in the spring? Why not simply leave sufficient reserves in the hive during the fall and forget about it? This objection is certainly well-grounded, as long as we take into account one important factor.

Namely, honey reserves—even those stored in capped comb—can spoil over a winter spent in the hive. First, honey—especially honey gathered from cruciferous plants—may crystallize; and second, when the hive is very damp, the honey may absorb moisture and turn sour (the wax caps don't completely protect it). In both cases, the reserves stored in the comb become of little use for the bees. In addition, several frames full of honey increase the volume of the winter nest (and thus make it colder), and, since they're located off to the sides, are more likely to suffer from moisture and the resulting mold.

Therefore, the best results are assured by storing some portion of capped honey in specially constructed, cool storage units, and then adding them to the hives in the spring when the need for them arises. To do so, the comb is warmed, opened using a special knife, and sprayed with water. This is the method that was used by Daniil Naichukov, mentioned in the quote, who achieved record honey harvests in the harsh conditions of Siberia for several decades on end.

But there's a simpler, more "natural" path to follow: creating conditions in the hive in which the honey won't spoil, or spoilage will be kept to a minimum. We've already said enough about such conditions, and there's no sense in repeating ourselves. Only when we create these conditions can we take advantage of the recommendations of certain authors to leave up to 75 pounds (35 kg) of "reserve" honey in the hive of a strong wintering colony. They believe (and not without reason!) that extra honey "spent" in the fall will pay great dividends the following year. In practice, of course, few actually follow this advice (the beekeeper, too, needs to be well fed through the winter!), but one must certainly leave 50 pounds (25 kg) of honey per colony. And those colonies should be kept in hives that don't allow honey reserves to spoil.

The Location of Winter Reserves

Now for the next question: the location of winter reserves. In what order should comb be placed in the nest section, and how much honey should each contain? Detailed instructions on this score can be found in almost any book on beekeeping. There are several commonly accepted systems for arranging the nest, which beekeepers follow when "winterizing" their bees, and almost every individual keeper has his own unique experiences in this sphere and his own little tricks. Although quite often even experienced beekeepers spend their whole life experimenting, continuing to search for the most reliable way to help their bees get through the winter.

At the same time, most beekeepers know full well that no one is in a position to better prepare a nest for winter than the bees themselves. Moreover, following the beekeeper's "help," the bees typically expend a great deal of effort on re-arranging their winter reserves as they see fit. It was with good reason that Alexander Butlerov, who dedicated a great deal of attention to the subject of wintering, advised *"shuffling comb around as little as possible; indeed, one should strive for the nest to remain—to the extent possible—just as the bees themselves arranged it."* Gennady Kondratiev, a prominent beekeeper and researcher in the 19th century, who considered the brood nest and everything in it to be strictly off limits, also wrote on this topic: *"Disturbing the arrangement of food reserves in the hive especially makes itself felt during the winter, and often becomes the reason why a colony dies from hunger, despite the fact that the hive still contains comb filled with honey—comb that is in fact inaccessible to the cluster. This is no place for playing around."* (Both citations taken from Ivan Shabarshov's book, *A History of Russian Beekeeping,* 1996).

This is why contemporary beekeeping literature so frequently recommends leaving the order of frames unchanged during the fall inspection, and not removing frames from the nest that contain sufficient amounts of honey. Some authors go even further, recommending that the hive be assessed based on weight to make sure that it contains sufficient honey, without even looking inside it.

Is there a contradiction lurking here? Of course not. Despite several centuries of domestication, bees have retained their ability to independently arrange their winter nest and winter splendidly in it. All they need to do so is an appropriate home and the ability to work freely throughout the summer. But if, during the summer, the beekeeper repeatedly disrupts the nest the bees have constructed (for example, by reversing brood boxes), or removes honey supers, then in the fall he'll also need to "winterize" the bees. But if he refrains from such disruptions, then in the fall he won't even need to glance into the nest portion of the hive. The bees will do everything themselves. In this case, there are a few crucial conditions: there should be at least eight frames with comb in the nest portion, and they should be at least 18 inches (45 cm) deep, allowing the colony to sit, come fall, on empty comb, having positioned its honey reserves along a 6–8-inch (15–20-cm) "overhead."

This figure—at least eight frames of comb at least 18 inches (45 cm) deep—is supported in numerous 19th-century recommendations on building horizontal hives. The world's most common hive systems are built to accommodate between eight and twelve frames, and natural beekeepers from both the 19th and 20th centuries used frames approximately 18 inches (45 cm) deep.

In the nest section of the hive, starting in early spring, the queen is busy laying eggs—first and foremost in the "warmest" upper cells, which have been freed of their honey during the winter. When warm weather sets in and the queen begins laying farther down on the comb, the upper area of the comb, once free of brood, is filled with the best honey—the honey resulting from the main honeyflow. This is the make-it-or-break-it period in terms of the success of the coming winter. But the bees won't get down to their final "winter prepping" until the fall, when the final brood emerges. During that period, they'll partially shift around their reserves, arranging them so that they'll feel as comfortable as possible during the winter, and carefully seal up the tiniest cracks with propolis.

Around this same time—namely, in mid-September in Russia's temperate forest zone—it was recommended to

harvest ("break off") comb honey from log hives and prepare the bees for winter (see, for example, Stepan Krasnoperov, *The Beekeeper's Rulebook*, 1895).

Modern recommendations to pull honey no later than mid-August are dictated by the fact that throughout the summer the beekeeper collects the best reserves from the bees, out of the supers, and is therefore forced, come fall, to get them ready for winter with supplemental feeding by sugar syrup. But the processing of sugar can't be entrusted to the young bees readying for the long winter, since they would be exhausted by such work and might not live until spring. Hence, the earlier timeframe for feeding.

In extra-deep frame hives, without supers or boxes, the bees themselves take care of all preparations for winter; all that's left for us to do is to pull the "surplus" honey, as a token of the bees' gratitude to man for providing such a cozy home, and for all the other little things he does for them. The comb is removed, of course, during the same time as it was by beekeepers of old—no earlier than mid-September, when all of the brood has emerged and the winter reserves have been redistributed.

With the natural approach, there's also no longer any need to worry about the quality of reserves. The kinds of honey that are less favorable for wintering (honey from cruciferous plants, honeydew honey, and certain others) typically are not to be found among a cluster's winter reserves. The only time when this must be paid attention to is when preparing weak or late swarms for winter. But if we only install early and strong swarms by themselves, and unite later and weaker swarms with existing colonies, then this too ceases to be a concern.

One very important point remains: only local-race bees can prepare independently for wintering. At our latitudes, that means the European dark bee.

The European Dark Bee

This book has already said quite a bit concerning our local bee race, the European dark bee. But it is well worth summarizing its unique traits once again:

- As a rule, the farther north the honeybee, the larger it is. The European dark bee is the world's largest. Measurements taken in Novosibirsk showed an average weight of 127 mg per bee, compared to 102 mg for southern bees (Mikhail Zherebkin, *Bee Wintering*).

- In the European dark bee, the individual wintering-related adaptations listed in the first section are considerably more pronounced than in bees of other races. For example, winter-resistant bees accumulate an average of 30% more fat than those that are less winter-resistant (ibid.).

- The catalase enzyme (the rectal glands) is twice as active in northern bees as in southern ones! This enzyme is responsible for preserving fecal matter in the rectum and preventing it from decaying. There is an established correlation between the activity level of catalase and the level of diarrhea in bee colonies (ibid.).

- Given colonies of equal strength, the interior of northern bee clusters contains more carbon dioxide and less oxygen than those of southern bees. For example, in 4-pound (2-kg) colonies of European dark bees, the percentage is 3.56%, and just 1.73% for Caucasian bees (data reported by Gurgen Avetisyan, 1971, cited in Ardalion Semenenko's book, *Thermal Regulation in Winter*).

• For the reasons listed above, the European dark bee is much less prone to disease, particularly nosema.

• The European dark bee stores its reserves "above its head" first and foremost. Southern bee races "scatter" them throughout the nest.

• The European dark bee builds up strength in time for the main honeyflow and makes maximum use of it.

• The European dark bee is well adapted to a lengthy period without honeyflow, and, generally speaking, to the rhythms of our fairly harsh natural environment.

In light of all these distinguishing traits, we can confidently allow European dark bee colonies to winter outdoors (provided that the conditions described in this chapter are met), which is practically impossible with more southerly bee races. It seems that the commonly heard recommendations regarding "winterizing bees" and wintering in specially built sheds are directly linked to the widespread distribution of southern bee races in our country.

Wintering Indoors

In all fairness, we should note that wintering in special sheds, in which a stable temperature of 37–39°F (3–4°C) is maintained, along with the necessary air humidity, does indeed seem to go more smoothly and successfully than wintering outdoors. This is especially true of weaker colonies, which have a real chance of wintering well indoors. This is easy to explain: in warmer temperatures, the bees consume less honey, and much less moisture gathers in the hives. Moreover, this moisture can be driven out of the hive with cross-ventilation, without any fear of the excessive cooling normally associated with it.

At the same time, wintering indoors also has some serious drawbacks:

• The winter shed has to be well constructed and outfitted for ventilation and for maintaining the appropriate microclimate. Otherwise there is no sense in using a shed in the first place.

• The hives must be moved to the shed on time and, much more importantly, removed from the shed on time in the spring.

• *Bees wintering indoors do not have the advantage of being "toughened up" by surviving the winter; they therefore*

318

have a much weaker immune system and are more suscep-tible to various diseases.

And this final point turns out to be the most important one! Even Nikolay Vitvitsky pointed to it in his day, dividing bees into three distinct categories: "wild" bees who lived in a tree hollow (the best), "log hive" bees (a bit worse), and peasant-kept bees wintering indoors, which he claimed had "now become completely feeble." Even back in his era, many bee colonies wintered "indoors"—not because of some in-flux of southern bees (no one had even thought of that yet), but due to the low quality of artificial hive structures.

In the 19th century, Russian bees were primarily kept in so-called "bottomless" hives (or "gums"), distinguished from the old-fashioned log hives by their thin walls, small interior space, and the lack of a bottom. In the summer, they were set up on a piece of board, and in winter they were taken indoors, into places that were often not suitable for this purpose in any way—for example, into a cellar or basement. This is apparently why nosema became so common at the time, while the "log hive" bees had never suffered from it to the same degree. By the way, these "bottomless" gums were associated with the system by which a colony that had filled the cramped space entrusted to it with comb was simply smoked to death with poisonous gas in the fall. And swarm colonies were left to endure the winter, since, thanks to the cramped hives, there was never a shortage of swarms.

As for genuine, large-volume, thick-walled log hives, with useful lives of a hundred years or more, no one, of course, carried them into winter enclosures. This seemed complete-ly obvious to all the authors of the day; for brevity's sake, we'll provide a single quotation from the aforementioned Julian Lubieniecki:

It's not even worth mentioning large log hives and artificial tree hollows—no one would think of storing them in a winter enclosure or in any other space, since they do perfectly well outdoors.

And with that, we can bring this chapter to a close, wishing our bees a "happy winter outdoors." The only thing left for us to do is to draw a few practical conclusions.

Conclusions

1. Good hive insulation is of great benefit to bees wintering outdoors. Insulation also doesn't hurt during the summer, since it prevents the nest area from overheating.

2. A wintering nest absolutely must be well insulated up top. This prevents condensation of moisture above the cluster that might drip directly onto the wintering bees.

3. Absent the ability of accumulating (absorbing) moisture inside the hive, cross-ventilation gives good results. It is created using two open entrances, an upper and a lower one (the bees will tend to partially seal the upper entrance themselves depending on the colony's strength). The other option—which is more "natural" and lowers honey consumption during winter—is bottom ventilation, which consists of an open lower slit-shaped entrance and openings on the opposite hive wall near the bottom.

4. Placing hydroscopic (moisture-absorbing) materials inside the hive can sharply reduce the amount of air exchange with the surrounding environment, and thereby significantly reduce heat loss. In this case, the need for respiration is satisfied by a single small entrance located below the winter cluster.

5. One solid option is to fill an open space under the frames—5 inches (12 cm) deep or more and located below the entrance—with water-absorbent material.

6. Another option is to place the absorbent materials off to one side, or, even better, to both sides of the wintering nest. At any rate, the space under the frames should not be any less than an inch (3 cm).

7. Successful wintering depends on the strength and physiological condition of the colony as it enters the winter period.

8. A colony belonging to the local bee race (in our case, the European dark bee) is best equipped to independently prepare for winter and to get through it successfully.

To conclude this discussion, I'd like to say that my journey, when it comes to this issue, has been neither simple nor easy. At first, like many other beginning beekeepers, I didn't pay due attention to the issue of wintering, and ended up stepping on the proverbial rake. When spring came, I found moisture in my hives, and excessive die-off. And, I must openly admit, there were colonies that had been dramatically weakened, or had even perished, due entirely to my own fault.

But all it took was addressing the wintering problem head-on, and the situation changed dramatically for the better. And for that I'd like to thank, first and foremost, the authors of the many books and studies on wintering that have provided me with such desperately needed information, and inspired me to my own reflections and conclusions. I am tremendously grateful to them!

I sincerely hope that this discussion will also help you hit upon your own path to success in beekeeping.

Afterword

A man returned home to India after spending many years in Russia. His relatives all asked him:
"Well, how did you like the Russian winter? Was it rough?"
The traveler answered:
"Actually, Russia has two winters. One with green grass and green leaves on the trees—which is bearable—and another one with snow, which is absolutely horrible!"

A popular joke

When, once upon a time, I became interested in bees, I had no idea of how important a role they would come to play in my life. I simply wanted to keep a few bee colonies on my land to provide my family with our own honey, and to pollinate my plants (Photographs 27–28, p. 340). And, of course, I didn't plan on dedicating much time to it, since I was sure, from the very start, that bees were perfectly capable of taking good care of themselves. After all, books will tell you (and as much is obvious even without them) that bees haven't changed at all since they were "tamed" by man. Any swarm that has flown from an apiary can effortlessly (and sometimes even with great pleasure!) settle in a good tree hollow—or, vice versa, move from a tree hollow into a hive.

And I didn't understand why the life of a beekeeper at his apiary should turn into constant, and at times quite arduous, work. Why do bees die so often, despite all the treatment and preventative measures directed against all kinds of diseases? So I found myself driven to undertake a serious study of this very complex issue, and that study culminated in this book.

This book is free of fiction. It is exclusively concerned with what I've done firsthand, many times over—from building beehives in my workshop to raising nectar-bearing trees in my nursery. In my many years of beekeeping experience, I haven't used a single gram of medicine, have only propagated my colonies through swarming, and have never fed bees sugar. And I've been convinced through experience that it all works! However, everything presented in this book isn't a dogma, or some action plan; it's just food for thought! Work out things for yourself, with your own intelligence and feelings as your guides!

Besides, the joke above is as good an illustration as any of the difference in climate between the temperate belt of Russia and the temperate zone of the United States or Europe. Personally, I feel right at home in our climate, but it may be hard for someone from France—not to mention California—to even imagine that our snow cover may last from late October through early April, and January temperatures of thirty degrees below zero are no rare occurrence. We, in turn, have a hard time believing that it's possible to complain of the heat in March.

My apiary is at the same latitude as northern Germany, northern England, the central portion of Canada, and southern Alaska, but the climate is similar to that of Scandinavia, the northern US states (Minnesota, Wisconsin, and Vermont) and many areas of Canada. So, to what extent is the practical advice provided in this book applicable to more southerly regions?

I have kindred spirits in the most far-flung corners of the planet—beekeepers who follow the same principles presented in this book, and strive to keep their bees just as they once lived in nature, before extensive human interference in their life. And if natural beekeeping is possible even in such difficult conditions as exist in Russia's forest zone, then it should certainly be no problem in a warmer climate! Therefore, I'll be very glad if this book inspires those who are still only dreaming of natural beekeeping and encourages those who have already headed down this path. As for the climate-related details—the position of the hive entrance, the ventilation system, the dimensions of the frames—the best thing is to turn for advice to experienced natural beekeepers in regions whose climate is most similar to that of your area.

For my part, I'll welcome any kind of constructive criticism, additional information regarding natural beekeeping, or any interesting practical experiences. I promise to gather any information you share and make it widely available, so we can progress together. And I'll look forward to working with you to track down and restore the population of our genuine local bee, the European dark bee.

I do dedicate a great deal of attention to restoring the local bee race. This is truly of vital importance for us natural beekeepers in northern regions, where more southerly bee races simply won't survive with natural beekeeping methods. But is the question of bee races as important for areas farther south, where bees can leave the hive even in January for a cleansing flight, and where the colony doesn't necessarily have to store its reserves in the upper portion of the nest frames? And what race is best suited for those areas where honeybees were simply not present historically?

An answer to the latter question can easily be found based on the logic of natural beekeeping: bee colonies can be taken from areas with similar climatic conditions, and nature will do the rest, gradually creating a genuinely local race—provided, of course, that bee colonies are not treated for diseases, fed sugar, or subjected to other artificial methods prescribed by industrial beekeeping. In all likelihood, new questions may arise in a southern climate—questions that we northerners might never have confronted. But all such problems can be solved.

Today, the only obstacle to natural beekeeping is the activity of man himself. The dominance of monocultures across huge swathes of farmland, the massive use of pesticides and genetically modified plants make survival impossible not only for bees, but for all the other living creatures that once filled our Earth. Unfortunately, modern man has long since swapped the boundless joy of interacting with living nature for the fleeting satisfaction of owning the latest stylish knick-knack.

But times are changing! More and more people are beginning to reflect on the course of civilization and are making a personal choice in favor of purposeful living and awareness. And I believe that the future belongs to such people!

Thank you for your interest in natural beekeeping—an essential part of a natural human existence on our Planet Earth. I heartily wish you success in keeping bees with a smile!

Fedor Lazutin
Kaluga Region, Russia
www.medvinka.ru
www.eco-bee.ru
E-mail: fedor-kovcheg@yandex.ru

↑ Photo 1. This honeycomb is 18 inches (470 mm) deep! Please meet my wife Lena.

↓ Photo 2. Horizontal hives with twenty-five 18-inch-deep (470-mm) frames each.

↑ Photo 3. Nectar plants are key to beekeeping. Field mustard (*Sinapis arvensis*).

↓ Photo 4. Bees visit hundreds of wildflower species. Brown knapweed (*Centaurea jacea*).

↑ Photo 5. Borage (*Borago officinalis*) is easy to grow. It's pretty and you can eat it, too!

↓ Photo 6. Trees can produce gallons of nectar. Black locust (*Robinia pseudoacacia*).

↑ Photo 7. Inspecting a horizontal hive only takes a few minutes... once per year!

↓ Photo 8. Inside the hive. Sealed brood, pollen, nectar, and drone larvae (top right).

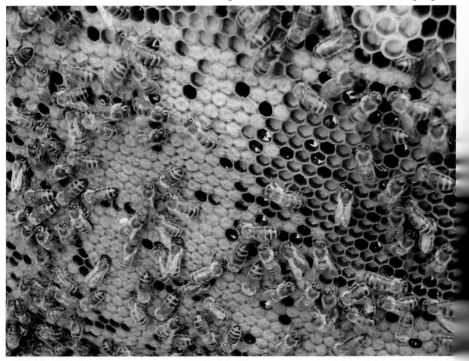

↑ Photo 9. Sealed brood (center), empty comb, and capped honey.

↓ Photo 10. Sealed brood (center), pollen, and capped honey (top right).

↑ Photo 11. See the swarm perched on a bush stem, right behind the swarm box?

↓ Photo 12. Swarm bees are docile and easy to collect. But they may fly off, so be quick!

↑ Photo 13. Once collected, the swarm will be installed in the hive in the evening.

↓ Photo 14. The bees are dumped on a piece of plywood and enter the hive. Done!

↑ Photo 15. These swarm traps accept eight 18-inch-deep (470-mm) frames.

↓ Photo 16. Hung on a tree come May, traps are an excellent way to get free local bees.

↑ Photo 17. Shaded visible sites are best. This swarm trap was discovered by bees.

↓ Photo 18. It worked! A swarm of bees is entering the swarm trap. Welcome!

↑ Photo 19. In the north, only strong local-race colonies can thrive in a log hive.

↓ Photo 20. New queens were reared in these queen cells during the previous season.

↑ Photo 21. A frame feeder. The little raft with holes prevents bees from drowning.

↓ Photo 22. No more heavy supers! A frame of honey is the heaviest thing you lift.

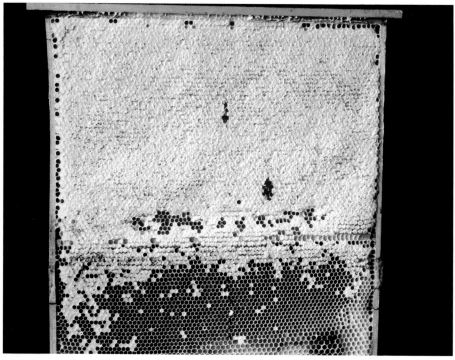

↑ Photo 23. Eighteen-inch-deep (470-mm) honeycomb is a sight to behold.

↓ Photo 24. And it is as delicious as it is beautiful.

↑ Photo 25. Not all combs are fully filled. But, then, a half-full frame is 8 lb of honey!

↓ Photo 26. Queens *love* extra-deep frames! Darker cells were occupied by brood.

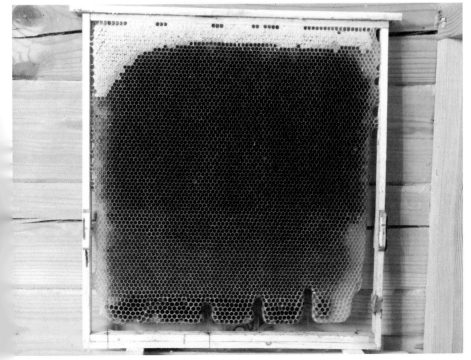

↑ Photo 27. Good pollination, loving hands, and mixed permaculture plantings.

↓ Photo 28. Are *you* ready for the pumpkin bread season? My wife Lena and son Misha.

↑ Photo 29. As our apiary grew, so did our family! That's Misha on the front cover, too.

↓ Photo 30. We've hosted dozens of hands-on workshops. Can you spot the author?

↑ Photo 31. Ten years earlier our homestead site was just an empty old field.

↓ Photo 32. With 20 inches of snow, winter is the right time to enjoy tea with honey!

Appendix 1
How to Make Swarm Traps and Capture Swarms

Catching swarms is an efficient, inexpensive, and natural way to start or expand your apiary. As discussed throughout the book, natural swarms are in many respects superior to purchased nucs or package bees. The procedure of setting up a swarm trap is described in Part II, section "How to capture a swarm in a swarm trap." The instructions below offer a bit more detail. See also Photographs 15–18, pp. 334–335.

Making swarm traps

A swarm trap, used for capturing swarms, is a box capable of holding frames, built according to taste. Good swarm traps can be made from $^1/_4$–$^5/_{16}$-inch-thick (6–8-mm) plywood, but $^5/_{32}$-inch (4-mm) will also do. If there's no plywood available, boards can also be used ($^3/_4$ to 1 inch thick; 20–25 mm), but make sure the finished box isn't too heavy, since you'll have to lift it for mounting on a tree and, later, get it back down again.

The ideal volume is 7–8 extra-deep frames. My frames are $17^1/_8$ x $18^1/_2$ x $1^1/_2$ inch (435 x 470 x 37 mm). The internal dimensions of an 8-frame box will be $17^3/_4$ x $11^{13}/_{16}$ x $19^{11}/_{16}$ inches or 450 x 300 x 500 mm (the final figure is the depth).* Make a rabbet (groove) $^7/_{16}$ x $^7/_{16}$ inch (11 x 11 mm) on the top inner edge of the short side to hang the frames from.

The box is closed on top with a removable top covered with two layers of roofing felt to protect it from rain.

An entrance is cut into the front wall, consisting of a horizontal slit $^1/_2$ inch (12–13 mm) high and 4–5 inches (10–12 cm) wide. The ideal position is 14–16 inches (35–40 cm) from the top of the frames. You can also attach, with a screw on one side, a strip of wood to close the entrance when removing the swarm trap from the tree.

How to equip the swarm trap

The best option is to completely fill the trap with frames, which allows you to leave it for a long time without worrying that the bees might begin to draw their comb beyond the confines of the frames. If you'll be able to check the trap at least once every few days, then 2–3 frames will suffice, and $^3/_8$-inch-thick (10-mm) top bars can be used to fill out the rest of the volume.

Any frames will do for a swarm trap, including discarded frames—that is, the very lowest quality. There should always be 2–3 frames with foundation (starter strips are also

---

* In Russia, frame's standard length is 17 $^1/_8$ inches (435 mm), excluding frame's "shoulders." In the US, frame's standard length is 17 $^5/_8$ inches. Therefore, to be compatible with the US standard, the swarm trap's internal length would be 18 $^3/_8$ inches (frame length plus $^3/_8$-inch bee space on each end). Likewise, the standard frame length is different: 1 $^3/_8$ inch in the US compared with 37 mm (just shy of 1 $^1/_2$ inch) in Russia. Accordingly, the width of a US-standard 8-frame box would be 11 inches (eight times 1 $^3/_8$). *Ed.*

possible) in the trap to give the young colony enough room for building, and 1–2 frames with old, blackened comb, which swarms especially love.

Where to place the swarm trap

Preferably, one should look for the largest trees one can find (since this is where bees look for hollows)—trees standing alone or located at the edge of a forest are best.

There's no need to elevate the trap too high; 10–14 feet (3–4 m) is sufficient. If you want, you can always raise it higher, but don't forget that it will weigh significantly more once there are bees and honey inside, and getting it down again safely will be no easy task.

It's easiest to install the trap on a thick branch, attaching it to the tree trunk, but you can also hang it from a branch or from the trunk.

If you've successfully caught a swarm at a certain location, then you should place the trap at the same spot next time—you can even put one back as soon as you've taken the old one down.

A freshly built swarm trap should be rubbed down on the inside with wax or propolis. Traps that have already been repeatedly occupied by swarms "work" the best at attracting new ones.

How to install a newly caught swarm in the apiary

The key factor here is distance. If the swarm trap is more than 3 miles (5 km) from the apiary, then things are very simple. Late in the evening, once all the foraging bees are back in the box, you can remove it from the tree and transport it to the apiary. There, put the trap where its hive will be located. Or put it right up against the hive in which the colony will be installed. Open the entrance right away, late in the evening or during the night.

It's important not to "cook" the bee colony during transit. During this time, the bees may become highly agitated, thus raising the temperature inside the box. And if there's no ventilation, the colony could simply die.

If the distance isn't as great, then the entrance should be covered with a fine mesh screen, made of metal or plastic, instead of with a solid bar. If the trap will be transported across a very large distance, then another opening, in addition to the entrance, is made during construction, in the opposite wall nearer the top. This opening is sealed right away with a screen, and then from the outside with a wood or plywood cap. During transport the cap is removed to create cross-ventilation (the entrance is also covered with a screen).

If the swarm trap is completely filled with frames and is located far from the apiary, then you can check it once every two or three weeks. Any swarm that settles in it will keep busy, drawing comb and filling the cells with honey, beebread and brood. But you also shouldn't leave it there the whole summer—a large, strong colony could settle in it, and in time it will begin to feel cramped. It sometimes happens that young colonies who have filled up all of the available space begin to cast swarms later that very same summer.

Swarms captured closer to the apiary can be dealt with in various ways. The simplest is to take them to another location at least 3 miles (5 km) away and let them stay there for several days (a week, ideally), and then transport them to the apiary. The rules are the same: transport them late in the evening, and open the entrance immediately.

Another way is to check the traps every day, and once a swarm has been caught, transport the trap to the apiary that same evening. This will prevent the bees from growing attached to their location, and in the morning they'll make an orientation flight around their new environs. The most difficult case is when the trap is located close to the apiary, and a young colony has spent several days in it already. If possible, you should bring the hive and set it right under the tree where the trap is hanging. If you take down the trap and install the colony in the hive, then the forager bees will easily find their new home when they return from their rounds. In late fall or at the end of winter—but once the colony has completed its cleansing flight—you can finally move the hive to the apiary.

Another option traditionally used by beekeepers in such cases is to move the trap to the apiary late in the evening, open the entrance, and cover it with some branches, making it possible—but quite difficult—for the bees to get through. For this purpose, you can use small fir branches, leaning them against the front wall of the hive. The forager bees who leave the hive in the morning will discover that something has changed in the outside world, and will conduct a new orientation flight, noting the location of the hive and its surroundings. In the process, some bees will still get lost by trying to return to their old location—therefore, this method is best reserved for cases when no other option is available.

Installing the colony in the hive

The swarm trap is moved to the apiary late in the evening, and the next day it's best to install the young colony in the hive. The best time for this is the second half of the day, when the bees have already had time to fly around their new area and gather nectar. The procedure itself is very simple: after a puff of smoke into the entrance, move the frames to their new location, keeping them in the same order. If necessary, add more frames with foundation and empty comb. If the swarm has been in the trap for a long time already, check the brood as well, in order to gauge the fertility of the queen.

The remaining procedures with swarm colonies caught in a trap are the same as those used with swarms collected at the apiary. A newly installed swarm should ideally be given 6–9 pounds (3–4 kg) of honey, and if the swarm is small, an additional swarm or two can be united with it. A late swarm that has settled in a trap is best united with a weaker existing colony. Two or three weeks after installing a swarm colony, especially a late one (with a young queen), one should check for the presence of brood. Another option is to add a weak late swarm to the newly installed swarm a week or two after installing it; the swarm will certainly fix the previously in-stalled swarm if it is having any issues with its young queen.

Capturing swarms is an easy and accessible way to obtain new colonies and is a good help for any apiary. I can especial-ly advise those beekeepers who are unable to check their api-ary frequently during the swarming season to use as many swarm traps as possible and to use the swarms they capture to maintain and expand their operations. In this case, captur-ing one's own swarms and swarms from outside the apiary can help to guarantee a sustainable beekeeping operation.

The only remaining problem is the lack of information on the origins of the queens that arrive with new swarms. Here, everything will depend on luck, and on the genetic makeup of surrounding apiaries. In the future, once the local bee race has made a recovery (as we sincerely hope it will!) this problem will become a thing of the past.

Appendix 2
How to Produce, Install, ~~and~~
Unite Your Own Swarms

The following is a summary of the discussion contained in Part III, sections "Various approaches to natural beekeeping" (pp. 203–207) and "Swarming" (pp. 210–212).

The best colonies in the apiary are those resulting from swarms from the previous year and the year before that. They're excellent honey producers, and as long as their hives are promptly expanded they practically never swarm. However, after two years, the likelihood of various problems emerging in the colony rises sharply; for this reason, following the spring inspection, I induce swarming in any colony that hasn't swarmed in the past two seasons. I do so by simply not expanding their nest.

As a rule, such colonies cast their first swarm in late May. I install first swarms in separate hives, since over the course of the summer, in most cases, they'll develop into strong colonies capable of producing a significant quantity of surplus honey. Quite often, first swarms that have settled in new hives change their queen themselves that very same season (a so-called "supersedure")—as evidenced by the presence of empty queen cells during the next spring inspection (Photograph 20, p. 336). But I've also seen the following: after a full summer of hard work, the first-swarm colonies are robbed blind in the fall, usually as a result of having an aging or dead queen. Therefore, if at all possible, I also install a weaker, late swarm with a young queen in the empty section of the hive inhabited by the first swarm, and unite them two or three weeks later. In this fashion, the weak swarm survives, and the stronger first swarm gains a young queen.

Second swarms emerge quite early and are strong enough to form a new and successful colony. Therefore, I install them separately—or, if there aren't enough empty hives available, I install two in each hive. Twelve frames—one half of a hive—is more than enough for such swarms. In the spring I remove one of the colonies and reinstall it in its own hive.

Based on what I've seen, there's little sense in installing third swarms separately. It's best to install them with first swarms, or add them to second swarms. Here's the situation in the latter case: quite often, swarms with young queens (beginning with second swarms) encounter various problems that stem from having a young queen, who may simply not return from a flight, or may prove to be of "low quality." A colony like this, despite emerging so early in the season and its large number of bees, is doomed—it has no way of producing another queen. However, the literature suggests that such a colony continues to draw comb and stock honey and beebread as though expecting another swarm with a young queen to join it. And this is precisely what often happens in nature—which perhaps explains the very existence of late, weak swarms. Once at my apiary, it so happened that a swarm appeared from out of nowhere and settled in with a swarm colony that had formed just two weeks previously.

Therefore, where before I would unite two or three late swarms and install the resulting colony separately, now I've begun adding late swarms to previously installed second swarms. Doing this is a cinch: just as we would do when installing a swarm, we set a sheet of plywood up against the entrance and, having given the colony inside the hive a good dose of smoke, we gently pour the swarm out onto the plywood. As a rule, the swarm will enter the hive of its own accord, but on occasion it helps to nudge it a bit with some smoke from the smoker.

Once the first swarm has been cast, we should expand the colony using foundation frames, but this usually doesn't stop the swarming—another swarm or two will emerge from the hive before the colony calms down. Rarely will a single colony cast more than three swarms. Colonies that stubbornly resist swarming (which is a fairly common occurrence) shouldn't be kept too long in cramped quarters; otherwise, not only will they not produce swarms, they'll also produce less honey. Therefore, in early June I expand all of them with additional foundation frames, and from that point on I treat them no differently than the other "honey-producing" colonies.

Swarms must be given a helping hand. As I understand it, "wild" nature doesn't do that—only the strong survive. In natural conditions, a young colony has to find a good home itself—a tree hollow, say—draw comb, and gather the honey reserves needed to make a start. Even a weak late swarm can survive in a good location with plentiful nectar-bearing plants, but if conditions aren't so good, then natural selection steps in, up to and including robbing by other bees, when the weak colony is discovered and burglarized by its stronger "cousins."

But if we want to save as many young colonies as possible, then we have to help the swarms: instead of installing them on "bare foundation," we have to give them several frames of good empty comb so that the queen can get right down to business and the foraging bees can begin to store away honey. It goes without saying that a swarm should be given a good home; but beyond that, weak swarms should also be strengthened by adding another swarm or two a bit later—and, ideally, they should be given supplemental food, 6–9 pounds (3–4 kg) of honey.

This is all we can do; at the end of the day, the colony's future boils down to "genetics"—the inherited traits of its particular queen. Here there's no avoiding natural selection—and its main instrument, at our latitude, is wintering.

Appendix 3
Nucs: What to Expect and How to Handle Them

If you don't want to catch swarms, where can you get good bees? That's the first question that almost all beginning beekeepers ask me. And there's no simple answer.

Specialized businesses geared toward breeding bees for sale sell their bee colonies in the form of so-called nucs. They're produced as follows: starting in early spring, a colony that has wintered successfully is "juiced up" using artificial feeding, then split into several parts—usually, three—or, a "nuc" is made from the colony by removing several frames, along with whatever bees and brood they contain. By this time, queens have been raised in a separate hive, artificially inseminated, and installed in the resulting nucs. And it's in this form that the bees are sold (this is a very brief description—a lot of subtle details go into it).

The people who work at such apiaries are often enthusiastic about what they do; they love bees and they love their jobs. But we, the buyers, should understand that a nuc with an artificially bred queen is by no means the same thing as a real swarm-produced colony.

Queens that are artificially bred and inseminated, for reasons that remain poorly understood, are significantly inferior to natural queens produced by swarming colonies and inseminated during several "mating flights" by the quickest

353

and most active drones (a queen will "rendezvous" with several drones during any given flight). On to of all this, a nuc, which generally consists of four deep frames, is an extremely weak colony that lacks balance in terms of the age of its bees and brood, and one that has undergone the stress of being split into several parts. If we believe that every bee colony has its own collective intelligence, then that intelligence must be essentially destroyed. And when will it recover?

The experience of many people who have bought nucs suggests that their quality varies greatly, and that they prove "unsuccessful" with great frequency. I know of cases when people have received nucs without queens and without brood, and only discovered these disastrous omissions when they began installing the bees in their new hive. These are just examples of shoddy work; but, generally speaking, only a third of typical nucs are successful; another third result in medium-strength colonies; and the rest simply don't live to see the fall or the spring.

For all of these reasons, the last few times I've bought European dark bee in nucs for my apiary from a breeder, I've gone about it as follows: I kept them just as I did the other colonies until fall, and the next spring I induced them to swarm. Those swarms that were installed and that wintered successfully resulted in strong, promising colonies. This season, one such colony cast four full-fledged swarms, and by fall it had produced 30 pounds (15 kg) of surplus honey. Now that's a strong colony! By the way, nucs that cast swarms also produce new queens and turn into full-fledged colonies themselves.

Rules for handling nucs

1. Don't "cook" the nuc during transport. Make sure the box is cross-ventilated.

2. Once the nuc has reached its destination, leave it until evening in a cool, shaded spot, then set it where the hive will be located, or right next to the hive, and open it very late in the evening, once darkness has fallen. If this is done during daylight, a number of the forager bees may be lost right away.

3. When installing the bees in an empty hive, add a frame with foundation and another with good dry comb—then, as the colony grows, expand gradually.

4. Since nucs arrive with a pitifully low amount of honey (even when the rules are followed, there's no more than 2 pounds or 1 kg of honey) and, as a rule, with a shortage of forager bees, it's a good idea, at first, to supplement their food, particularly when there's no stable honeyflow. Each such colony should ideally be given 6–9 pounds (3–4 kg) of honey right away, and more later, as needed.

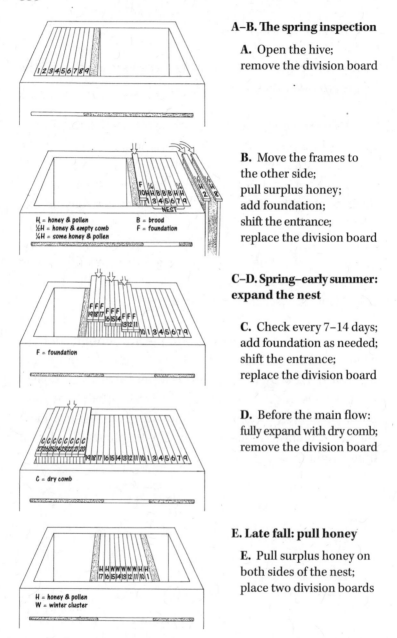

A–B. The spring inspection

A. Open the hive;
remove the division board

B. Move the frames to
the other side;
pull surplus honey;
add foundation;
shift the entrance;
replace the division board

**C–D. Spring–early summer:
expand the nest**

C. Check every 7–14 days;
add foundation as needed;
shift the entrance;
replace the division board

D. Before the main flow:
fully expand with dry comb;
remove the division board

E. Late fall: pull honey

E. Pull surplus honey on
both sides of the nest;
place two division boards

H = honey & pollen
½H = honey & empty comb
¼H = some honey & pollen
B = brood
F = foundation

F = foundation

C = dry comb

H = honey & pollen
W = winter cluster

Figure 11. The sequence of operations (same as Fig. 10, pp. 236–237)

Appendix 4
Operations Throughout the Year

The following is a summary of the corresponding sections of Part III (pp. 224–250).

The end of winter (spring inspection)

As soon as the snow disappears and the bee colonies have completed their cleansing flight, the keeper needs to identify which colonies, if any, have not survived, and remove their honey frames. Otherwise, the honey will be quickly robbed by other colonies, both from your yard and from others. It's best to clean these hives immediately, and treat them with either a blowtorch or a potassium permanganate solution (in the old days, this was done using lye—that is, an ash infusion).

Lately, I've even been trying to conduct my inspection early, during April. If the hive is damp, then I move the nest frames to the opposite, dry portion of the hive and shift the open portion of the hive entrance accordingly (*Figure 11.A–B*). During the inspection, I note the quality of the brood and the presence of honey reserves, and I remove the surplus honey and any empty, damaged frames. For the time being, the bees don't need any foundation, but they do need a well-insulated hive and about 20 pounds (10 kg) of honey in reserves.

Spring (expand the nest for spring buildup)

Starting in early May and through mid-June, gradually expand colonies using foundation frames (*Figure 11.C*). You can also add some good empty comb, but it's foundation that's really needed, since this is right around the time when the young bees need a maximum workload in drawing comb. When the main honeyflow begins, drawing comb will be the farthest thing from their minds. Colonies that have been earmarked for swarming aren't expanded, and the gap beneath their division board should be sealed.

The start of June (collect and install swarms)

The swarming period is the peak season for a beekeeper. He should catch and install swarms while continuing to add foundation frames to his primary colonies. During a given summer, a strong colony will draw an average of eight extra-deep frames. Colonies that were induced to swarm can now be expanded. If a colony is being "stubborn" and refuses to swarm, then there's no point in insisting. This happens with some frequency—as does swarming in colonies earmarked for honey production during the given year.

Mid- to late June (fully expand the hive)

During this period, it's high time to fully expand strong colonies. There's no point in adding more foundation, since by early July bees practically stop drawing comb. Fill any empty space with empty-comb frames (*Figure 11.D*); for this purpose, even frames that aren't of the highest quality will do—just place the lower-quality frames as far from the nest section as possible.

July-August (main honeyflow)

Starting at the end of June, the main honeyflow begins in Russia's temperate central zone. And the apiary is ready for it—all of the colonies are in good working order, and the bees have been provided with the maximum amount of honey storage containers—namely, the frames with empty comb. There's no work for the keeper to do at the apiary, except possibly to check up on first-year swarm colonies to see how they're doing and whether or not they need any additional frames.

The end of August (robbing)

Around the middle of August, the robbing period begins. In days gone by, I'd have narrowed the entrances by now, and monitored the colonies, ready to help if needed. But now, I tend not to do any of these things. Colonies with strong queens—both swarm colonies and "honey" colonies—never suffer from robbing. But even a strong colony whose queen has died or become ineffective cannot be protected from robbing. And even if such a colony is protected successfully, it has little chance of surviving the winter.

Therefore, I keep the entrances open all summer to widths of around 8–10 inches (20–25 cm) opposite the area of the hive where the queen is laying and where the colony will prepare for wintering. And I don't even narrow the entrances for winter! A weak colony will partially seal it itself, and a strong one will leave it open—and I assume that's the way it should be. There's no cross-ventilation in the hive (with just one entrance), so there's no reason to fear excessive cold. As for robbing—well, if you monitor the age of your queens and try to keep strong colonies only, then the likelihood of robbing will be low. If, however, a colony has fallen prey to robbing and there are visual indicators that the robbing is proceeding full speed ahead (the entrance is literally jam packed with bees), then the only thing left for the keeper to do is to pull the honey by removing all frames from the hive. Otherwise, you'll just add insult to injury by losing both the colony and its honey!

Pulling honey and preparations for wintering

In recent years, I've pulled my honey in late fall, starting in mid-October. By this time, the bees have already formed a cluster, and the honey frames can be removed without any trouble. I "make my way" to the edge of the cluster, leaving one extra honey frame beside it, and close the hive. Sometimes, if the bees have "set up" for winter in the middle of the hive, then I remove frames from both sides of the cluster (*Figure 11.E*). There can be difficulties with removing the frame farthest to the edge when it's been glued to the neighboring frame and to the hive wall with propolis. But this is solved easily enough: I loosen it using a hive tool and, prying it free from the side, pull it from the hive.

I don't examine the nest in the fall. If the colony is a good one and there's surplus honey in the hive, that means that the colony was perfectly able to prepare for winter. There are, however, some swarm colonies whose honey reserves are cause for doubt. Such colonies can be inspected and, if needed, honey frames can be added, thus artificially creating a nest. For this, frames roughly one-third full of honey are well suited—that is, frames with 6–8 inches (15–20 cm) of capped comb in the upper portion of the frame.

But I rarely have such situations. To avoid them completely, it's much better to feed swarm colonies that haven't stored up enough honey reserves in early August, when there are plenty of worker bees in the hive. The queen will also do a much better job with the "fall buildup," meaning that the colony will enter the winter with greater strength.

Wintering

Successful colonies that are strong in the fall will winter well. They tend to have little or no die-off, and, strange as it may seem, much less moisture buildup than in weak colonies.

Weak colonies winter poorly. In my experience, the majority of colonies that enter the winter with a "question mark" don't survive until spring. Perhaps it would be better to unite such colonies with other, more prosperous ones, but I've never done this, hoping each time that even the weak colonies will survive the winter. And that does happen on occasion; swarms that have had trouble surviving the winter may even turn into strong colonies during the next summer. But this is the exception, not the rule.

Another issue is winter moisture. Calculations show that an average winter honey consumption of 30 pounds (15 kg) of honey results in 3 gallons (10 L) of water forming in the hive, which either escapes outside through the process of air exchange, or remains in the hive until spring. When warm weather arrives, the bees begin to ventilate the hive

and easily get rid of the excess moisture. Therefore, the issue of winter moisture is key when it comes to the topic of
wintering.

I have hives in my apiary lined on the inside with plywood;
others were made out of boards. There are hives with various
entrance locations: some beneath the frames, some higher
up. But I haven't noticed any direct correlation between
these factors and the amount of moisture. The only correlation comes with the presence in the hive of water-absorbing
materials. Partitions with silica gel work well; they're made
in the form of a box, the same size as an extra-deep frame,
and 2 inches (50 mm) thick. On two sides, the box is covered
with a fine screen or some material that water can pene-
trate, along with laths, spaced out a bit from one another,
filled with silica gel. The partition is hung inside the hive on
shoulders, just like a frame. It holds 13–15 pounds (6–7 kg)
of silica gel, capable of absorbing up to 1.5 gallon (5 L) of water. In the summer, this partition is replaced with a regular
division board and is left to dry in the sun.

The silica gel partition is usually added in place of the
regular division board in late fall, before frosts begin. It is
even better to add two silica gel partitions on either side of
the nest area. But even one is enough to drastically improve
wintering. Another option is to add a bag full of water-absorbing material beneath the frames (if there is free space
beneath them). But, in my experience, the silica gel partition
is even more effective.

Appendix 5
How to Build a Horizontal Hive
With Extra-Deep Frames
(Version 1)

I personally make 25-frame hives, so that (in case of a shortage of hives and a surplus of swarms) I can install two swarms in a single hive, with 12 frames for each swarm, plus a division board. During the swarm's first summer as a new colony, 12 extra-deep frames are more than enough for an average-size swarm, but the next spring one of the colonies will have to be transferred to its own hive.

If you have enough woodworking equipment, anyone who knows how to use it can easily make hives himself. I've deliberately refrained from excess detail, since the precise dimensions of the parts will depend on the materials available, and can easily be calculated by the craftsman himself. One must simply observe the basic internal dimensions and be guided by the principles enumerated below. For additional detail, see this hive's description on pp. 123–127.

Basic internal dimensions

I use frames built to the Russian Dadant standard of length and width: 17 ¹/₈ inches (435 mm) long and 37 mm (just under 1 ¹/₂ inch) wide. I make my frames 18 ¹/₂ inches (470 mm) deep. Therefore, my hives have the following *internal* dimensions (see Figure 12 for the length, width, and depth designations):

- Length: 17 ³/₄ inches (450 mm), that is, frame length plus bee space on each side. IMPORTANT: standard frame length may be different where you live. For example, standard American frames are 17 ⁵/₈ inches long, so you'd have to increase hive's internal length to 18 ³/₈ inches, that is, frame length plus ³/₈-inch bee space on each end.

- Width: 38 ³/₁₆ inches (940 mm), that is, frame width (just under 1 ¹/₂ inch; 37 mm) times 25 (number of frames) plus 0.6 mm margin for each frame.

- Depth: 19 ¹¹/₁₆ to 20 ¹/₂ inches (500–520 mm), that is, frame depth plus 1 ³/₁₆ to 2 inches of space between the frame's bottom bar and the hive's bottom.

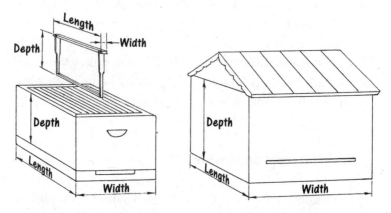

Figure 12. The conventional names of hive and frame dimensions

This is how I build my hives

- The starting material for building a framework is a dry board 2 x 6 inches (50 x 150 mm). After planing, you can end up with a thickness of 1 $^3/_4$ to 1 $^7/_8$ inch (45–48 mm), which is the thickness of the insulation. I use Styrofoam (foam polystyrene) with a thickness of 2 inches or 50 mm (in reality, it's usually a bit less).

- For the bars of the framework, I use the above board ripped into two or three strips (i.e., I end up with "2-by-2s" or "2-by-3s").

- Cut rabbets (grooves), $^7/_{16}$ inch (11 mm) deep and $^1/_4$ inch (7 mm) wide, in the longer upper bars. Once the interior of the hive has been lined with plywood, a rabbet $^7/_{16}$ x $^7/_{16}$ inch (11 x 11 mm) will be formed for the frame shoulders, with a 1-mm clearance.

- Line the interior of the hive with $^5/_{32}$-inch (4-mm) plywood; if possible, it can be even thicker. When building the framework, take plywood thickness into account in order to maintain the desired final interior dimensions.

- The hive walls will consist of the following layers (moving from the inside to the outside): plywood, Styrofoam, roofing paper, and weatherboard.

- The top's height is 2 $^3/_4$ inches (70 mm) plus a perimeter strip made with bars $^3/_4$ x $^3/_4$ inch (18 x 18 mm). Insert fiberboard or plywood into the perimeter strip from below, then fill the top with insulation (I use Styrofoam here as well).

• Rafters are mounted on the top (attached with self-drilling screws), and the rafters are covered with roof boarding and any roofing material. Following installation at a permanent location, the top is attached to the box using hinges. In this way, the top and the roof can be swung forward as a unit (without covering the upper hive entrances), providing quick and easy access to the hive for inspections and other procedures.

• The bottom is made from either tongue-and-groove boards or using the same frame technique. On the sides and the back, the bottom fits into $5/8$-inch-deep (15-mm) rabbets and protrudes in front, thus forming a landing board. The $3/8$-inch (10-mm) gap between the bottom and the front wall of the hive is the lower entrance; the bottom is fastened in the back with hinges, and in the front with latches. This way of building the bottom makes it possible to swing it open, downward, for cleaning and to replace it easily if necessary.

• The upper entrances are 1 inch (25 mm) in diameter and are located approximately halfway up the frame ($9 1/2$ inches or 240 mm from the hive's ceiling). The entrances are located $6 11/16$ and 26 inches (170 and 660 mm) from the internal wall, near which the colony will winter. Vertical bars are located inside the framework at the points where the upper entrances are to be drilled (so that the entrances don't pass through the insulation).

Experience has shown that every craftsman will always bring his own unique touches to a project, but for convenience I have provided an assembly drawing for the hive framework (Figure 13.B) as I make it myself.

The sequence is as follows:

- *Figure 13.C.* Assemble the side walls of the framework. Parts 2 and 3 measure 2 x 2 $^3/_4$ inches (50 x 70 mm) across, while Part 1 measures 2 x 1 $^3/_4$ inch (50 x 45 mm); a rabbet $^7/_{16}$ x 2 inches (11 x 50 mm) is cut into Part 2 for the bottom (once it is lined with plywood, the rabbet will be $^5/_8$ x 2 inches or 15 x 50 mm).

- *Figures 13.E and 13.D.* Join the side walls using horizontal bars. Parts 4 and 5 measure 1 $^3/_4$ x 2 inches (45 x 50 mm) across, while Part 6 measures 2 x 2 $^3/_4$ inches (50 x 70 mm). Rabbets $^1/_4$ x $^7/_{16}$ inch (7 x 11 mm) are cut into Parts 5, as mentioned. A rabbet $^7/_{16}$ x 2 inches (11 x 50 mm) is cut into Part 6 for the bottom.

- *Figure 13.F.* Insert vertical bars where the upper entrances are to be located on the front wall (Parts 8), one on the back wall (Part 7), and bars $^3/_4$ x 2 inches (20 x 50 mm) along the corners (Parts 9 and 10) to attach the plywood.

- *Figure 13.G.* Build the framework for the bottom using bars 1 $^1/_2$ x 1 $^1/_2$ inch (40 x 40 mm)—Parts 16 and 17; I make the landing board separately.

- *Figure 13.H.* Build the top: bars 2 x 2 $^3/_4$ inches (50 x 70 mm)—Parts 11 and 12.

- *Figure 13.I.* Mount the rafters (Parts 15).

You can see finished hives on Photograph 29, p. 341.

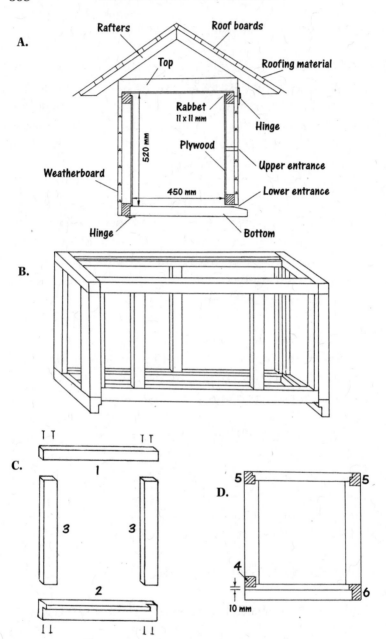

Figure 13. Hive plans (Version 1)

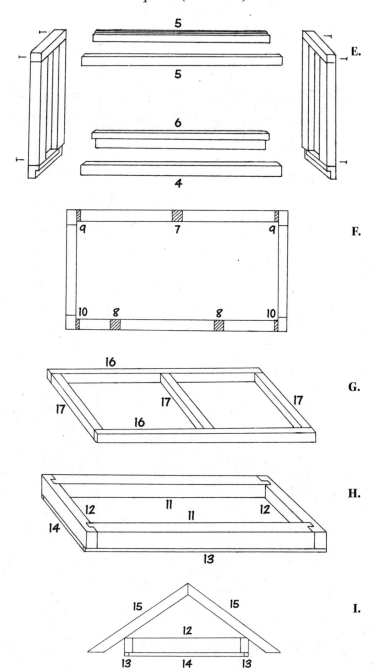

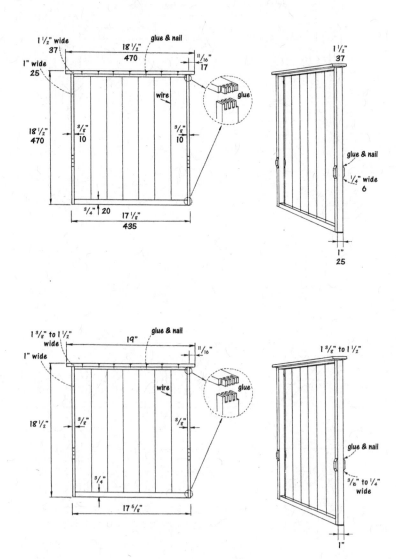

Figure 14. Extra-deep frame plans: Russian (top) and US (bottom)

Making hive stands

I make hive stands by welding metal, with legs from 1-$^1/_2$-inch (40-mm) angles and braces from 1-inch (25-mm) flat bars (Photograph 29, p. 341). The stands are 16 inches (40 cm) high. I place pieces of board beneath the legs (to prevent them from sinking into the ground), while also using them to ensure that the hive is level. A stand like this will last for a long time. You can also mount hives on stakes driven into the ground, but this isn't as dependable and doesn't last as long.

Making frames

As I've said, the frames are assembled from two parts—one standard Dadant brood frame and one super frame (Photographs 23–24, p. 338). I make all my frames from bars $^{15}/_{16}$ x $^5/_8$ inch (24 x 8 mm), cutting finger joints and gluing them together. I make the upper (brood) frame 17 $^1/_8$ inches (435 mm) long and 11 $^1/_2$ inches (290 mm) deep, after which I nail a strip 18 $^1/_2$ x 1 $^1/_2$ x $^3/_8$ inch (470 x 37 x 10 mm) to the top, which serves both as a top bar, a spacer, and as a ceiling for the nest area of the hive. The super frame is 6 $^{11}/_{16}$ inches (170 mm) deep.

I join the frames using connectors consisting of plywood rectangles $^5/_{32}$ inch (4 mm) thick, with dimensions of 2 $^3/_8$ x 1 $^1/_2$ inch (60 x 37 mm), to whose edges I glue bars $^1/_4$ x $^1/_4$ x 2 $^3/_8$ inches (6 x 6 x 60 mm). These connectors also serve as additional spacers for the frames (a width of 1 $^1/_2$ inch or 37 mm). I attach them to the frames using $^5/_8$-inch-long (16-mm) self-drilling screws with as small a diameter as possible.

Of course it's even better to make frames as one whole (Figure 14; Photographs 25–26, p. 339). The only downside is that they do not fit into a standard extractor, so you'll have to modify one.

Appendix 6
How to Build a Horizontal Hive
With Extra-Deep Frames
(Version 2)

Since Parts I and II of *Keeping Bees With a Smile* were first written, there have been some new developments in how the hive described in the book is constructed (Photographs 1–2, p. 327). The main changes are connected with wintering—an issue which, quite honestly, I had not paid enough attention to. Now the hive has a large open space beneath the frames, separated during the summer from the main interior volume with a screen, as well as a removable back panel used for accessing this space. For additional hive ventilation, the removable back panel is outfitted with four openings, 1 inch (25 mm) in diameter, covered on the inside with a finely meshed screen. The bottom is now thinner (a board $^3/_4$ to 1 $^3/_8$ inch thick; 20–35 mm), and the hive itself can now be disassembled, and is easier to build.

It's hard to say whether or not this particular design can be considered final—after all, the human mind is always pushing forward, seeking simpler and more effective solutions. However, the passage of time has only served to reinforce how simple, rational, and natural the single-box horizontal hive with extra-deep frames really is.

Now as before, there is no clear-cut answer to the question of where to locate the entrance, not to mention its dimensions and shape. On this topic, the literature offers a wide range of ideas and theories that need further testing. For the time being, I've settled on a slit-shaped opening $^1/_2$ inch (12 mm) in height, located 13 $^3/_8$ inches (34 cm) from the top of the frames—however, it may be that positioning the entrance farther down (18 $^1/_2$ inches or 47 cm from the top) may prove more effective.

In addition, there's still work to be done in researching optimal arrangements for wintering. In a tree hollow, bees almost always have an empty space beneath their comb, and a hydroscopic bottom of decayed wood that absorbs excess winter moisture. With Nature and some highly experienced beekeepers as our guides, we have increased the space under the frames and made it possible to place moisture-absorbent material beneath the comb during the winter. All that remains is to see which materials work best and determine the necessary level of bottom ventilation (how wide should the entrance and the openings on the removable back panel be left open).

Since beekeeping has always been considered a creative occupation, anyone who owns these hives will eventually have his own observations and develop his own preferred techniques, which we should eagerly share with one another.

Building the hive

To make it easier to build and convenient to transport, the hive can now be disassembled. It consists of a front wall, a back wall, two identical side walls, a removable back panel, a bottom, a top, two sloping roof panels, and some decorative elements (two gables, four corner boards, four boards for covering the gaps between the rafters, and four bargeboards covering the butts of roof boards).

In addition, building the hive requires: roofing material, a division board, and a frame-mounted screen for separating the space under the frames during the summer (to prevent the bees from filling the space with comb).

Hive elements:

1. The front wall: 37 x 24 $^3/_4$ inches (940 x 630 mm). The top interior edge has a rabbet (groove) $^7/_{16}$ x $^7/_{16}$ inch (11 x 11 mm) to hold the frame shoulders, while the lower interior edge has a rabbet $^3/_4$ x 1 inch (20 x 25 mm) to hold the hive bottom. At a depth of 13 $^3/_8$ to 18 $^1/_2$ inches (340–470 mm) from the top of the wall, an entrance is cut, with a height of $^1/_2$ inch (12 mm). Lately, I've been locating it 13 $^3/_8$ inches (340 mm) from the top, but it remains unclear which variant is better.

2. The back wall: 37 x 19 $^{11}/_{16}$ inches (940 x 500 mm). The top interior edge has a rabbet $^7/_{16}$ x $^7/_{16}$ inch (11 x 11 mm) to hold the frame shoulders, while the lower exterior edge has a rabbet $^5/_8$ x 1 $^1/_2$ inch (15 x 37 mm) for joining with the removable back panel.

3. The removable back panel: 37 x 5 $^3/_4$ inches (940 x 145 mm). The top interior edge has a rabbet $^5/_8$ x 1 $^1/_2$ inch (15 x 37 mm) for joining with the back wall, while the lower interior edge has a rabbet $^3/_4$ x 1 inch (20 x 25 mm) for joining with the hive bottom. At distances of 1 $^5/_8$ and 10 $^1/_4$ inches (40 and 260 mm) from the right and left edges, halfway up the panel, drill four 1-inch (25-mm) openings. These openings are

drilled at a slight incline to the outside to prevent rainwater from dripping in through them.

4, 5. Side walls: 22 $^1/_8$ x 24 $^3/_4$ inches (562 x 630 mm).* The lower interior edge has a rabbet $^3/_4$ x 1 inch (20 x 25 mm) that ends 1 $^3/_8$ inch (36 mm) shy of the butts.

All walls and the removable panel have a thickness of $^1/_4$ inch (interior plywood) + 2 inches (framework stock) + $^3/_4$ inch (weatherboard siding) = 3 inches total (6 + 50 + 19 = = 75 mm). If the overall thickness of any of the elements is less or more, then all these measurements will be adjusted accordingly.

6. The hive bottom: 19 $^1/_4$ x 38 $^1/_2$ inches (490 x 980 mm). It is assembled from tongue-and-groove boards $^3/_4$ to 1 inch (20–25 mm) thick.

7. The top: 23 $^5/_8$ x 42 $^7/_8$ inches (600 x 1090 mm). The frame is assembled from bars 1 $^3/_4$ x 2 $^3/_4$ (45 x 70 mm); this may vary slightly depending on the original stock. These can be assembled with butt joints using self-drilling screws, but for sturdiness it's best to cut a rabbet on the shorter bars and a dado on the longer bars, as shown in the diagram. From the bottom, along the outside perimeter of the top's frame, nail strips $^5/_8$x$^5/_8$inch (16x16mm), creating a rabbet 1 $^1/_8$x$^5/_8$inch (29 x 16 mm). Insert a sheet of hardboard (HDF) into this rabbet and attach it with small nails. From above, add insulation, which can protrude a bit upwards (we use Styrofoam

* This is to accommodate a frame 17 $^1/_8$ inches long. If you want to make your hive compatible with US frame length standard (17 $^5/_8$ inches), increase the hive's length by $^1/_2$ inch. *Ed.*

with an aggregate thickness of 3–4 inches; 8–10 cm). It's best to cover the insulation from the top with Tyvek or roofing paper, but this is not absolutely mandatory.

8. The slopes of the roof consist of rafters (three per slope) with roof boards nailed to them. The rafters are 23 $^5/_8$ inches (60 mm) in length, made of any suitable stock (we use 1 $^1/_2$ x 1 $^3/_4$ inch; 40 x 45 mm). The roof boards should be $^3/_4$ to 1 inch (20–25 mm) thick, with any suitable length (we make them 54 inches; 137 cm).

9. The decorative elements are required, but their actual design is up to you.

10. The movable division board can be made in various ways. The simplest but least durable option is 2-inch-thick (50-mm) Styrofoam carefully wrapped in polyethylene film (sheet plastic). The more complicated is a solid wood or frame panel with strips of polypropylene foam stapled to its butt ends to make it fit snugly against the hive walls. So that bees can pass under it, leave a gap $^3/_8$–$^3/_4$ inch (10–20 mm) between the bottom of the division board and the screen separating the space under the frames.

11. The screen on the frame should be freely insertable through the removable panel and fixed in a horizontal position using any fasteners. Its dimensions are 17 $^1/_2$ x 36 $^{13}/_{16}$ inches (445 x 935 mm), with a frame thickness of $^3/_4$ inch (20 mm).

12. Any roofing material can be used; the cheapest is roll roofing—which is best added in two layers right away (giving it a useful life of up to 10 years).

A. Vertical cross-section

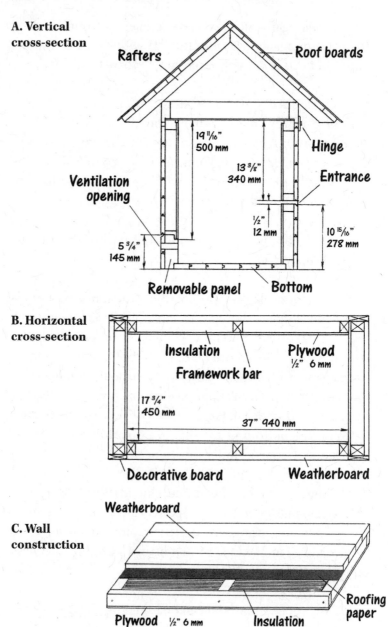

Rafters

Roof boards

19 ¹¹⁄₁₆"
500 mm

Hinge

13 ³⁄₈"
340 mm

Entrance

Ventilation opening

½"
12 mm

5 ³⁄₄"
145 mm

10 ¹⁵⁄₁₆"
278 mm

Removable panel

Bottom

B. Horizontal cross-section

Insulation

Plywood
½" 6 mm

Framework bar

17 ³⁄₄"
450 mm

37" 940 mm

Decorative board

Weatherboard

C. Wall construction

Weatherboard

Plywood ½" 6 mm

Insulation

Roofing paper

Figure 15. Hive plans (Version 2)

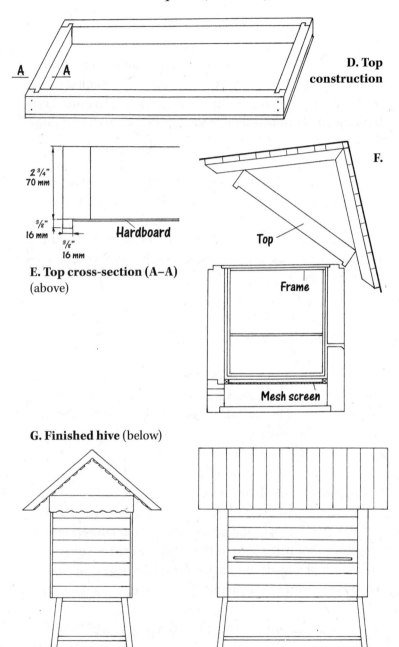

D. Top construction

F.

2 ¾"
70 mm

³/₈"
16 mm

³/₈"
16 mm

Hardboard

E. Top cross-section (A–A)
(above)

Top

Frame

Mesh screen

G. Finished hive (below)

Steps for building the walls:

1. The wall framework is made of bars measuring 2 inches or 50 mm (the thickness of the insulation) by about 2 inches or 40–50 mm (this figure can vary). Cut all the required rabbets ahead of time. Assemble the framework with butt joints using self-drilling 4-inch (100–110-mm) screws.

2. Line the framework's interior with $^1/_4$-inch (6-mm) plywood (this thickness has proven to work best).

3. Fill the framework with insulation (among synthetic insulation, polystyrene foam—or, simply put, Styrofoam—is the most suitable).

4. Cover the insulation with a layer of roofing paper or any other "breathing" moisture barrier such as Tyvek.

5. Nail siding—weatherboard at least $^5/_8$ inch (16 mm) thick (we use $^3/_4$ inch; 19 mm). Thin tongue-and-groove boards $^1/_2$ inch (12 mm) thick used for interior paneling are not suitable for siding.

Assembling the hive

1. Pre-drill holes in the side walls (4–6 per corner) and assemble the box using 5-inch (120-mm) self-drilling screws. The walls are best joined with a layer of insulation in between, such as jute or polypropylene foam ($^1/_{16}$ to $^1/_8$ inch thick; 2–3 mm).

2. Attach the bottom with 2-$^1/_2$-inch or 3-inch (60–70-mm) nails.

3. Insert the removable back panel and attach it using any suitable fasteners (screws or nails in pre-drilled holes).

3. Attach the roof slopes to the top using self-drilling screws.

4. Add the roofing material to the roof.

5. Install the hive at its new location, set the top and attach it to the front wall using two hinges.

Additional information

Are there other ways to build a hive? Of course there are. Personally, I build my hives exactly as described above. But if you decide to use some other technique, then be my guest! You need only make sure to preserve the interior dimensions and the basic overall layout of the hive, and thoroughly insulate the walls and especially the top, which is very important for wintering. If you decide to build the hive walls out of solid wood, try to make them as thick as possible. For outdoor wintering, the minimum is 2 inches (50 mm), but 3 inches (70–80 mm) is best. The problem with wooden walls is that they inevitably crack due to shifts in temperature and humidity, which negatively affects the insulating properties of the hive, not to mention its useful life. Therefore, it's a good idea to protect solid wood walls with some sort of siding, with a layer of extra insulation underneath it.

But if we place a layer of insulation between the inner wall and the siding, then we no longer need very thick inner walls, and once again we return from a solid-wood structure to a wooden framework. And this was the technique for building the best and longest-lasting hives both in the 19th

and now in the 21st century. The technique has remained all
but unchanged: a box with the necessary interior dimensions is assembled using inch-thick (20–25-mm) boards,
then a framework of wooden bars is nailed onto the inner
box, to support siding made from tongue-and-groove boards
$^3/_4$ to 1 inch (20–25 mm) thick. The framework is filled with
any form of insulation—moss, tow, or wood shavings. The
layer of insulation is typically 2 inches (50 mm) thick.

This technique for building hives may well be acknowl-
edged as the best, but there is one drawback: it is labor-
intensive and therefore expensive. Many craftsmen build
hives like these for their own use, but you're unlikely to find
them in stores. Modern hive manufacturers strive to simplify
and cheapen their products as much as possible, since they
know that even a slap-dash hive that is a bit cheaper will sell
much faster than an expensive, high-quality hive. For a very
long time now, hardly anyone has seen fit to invest much
money in beekeeping.

What other options are out there? In the "old days" hives
were hollowed out of solid logs, but today that doesn't sound
too realistic—nor does building hives out of pressed straw
with an internal layer of clay mixed with ash and manure. By
the way, I wouldn't consign the latter option to the history
books just yet, since straw is an excellent building material—
it's warm, long-lasting, and environmentally friendly. It may
well be that the "straw" technique of hive construction will
be reborn one day in some more technically advanced form.

There's also the modern Western technique for building
hives entirely out of high-density expanded polystyrene; however, I'm in no hurry to buy or build such hives. Beekeepers
who've worked with them say that they're quite fragile and
break easily, and that birds (especially woodpeckers) can
poke through them easily, and that wasps bite through them in

the summer. I also think that polystyrene is no obstacle for mice either. But then, that's just one man's opinion—some think differently.

Why am I open to using modern materials—plywood and Styrofoam (as insulation)—in building my hives? Because they currently allow us to simplify and cheapen hive construction as much as possible, even while maintaining the hive's high quality and excellent insulation properties. After all, our goal today is to bring about a renaissance in beekeeping by returning to natural beekeeping methods, and to restore the population of the local European dark bee.

But I do believe that the future belongs to sturdy, warm, stationary hives made from natural materials, built well and built to last, despite the amount of work required and consequently the cost. But we still have a great deal of thinking and doing ahead of us before we create a future in which stationary apiaries stand surrounded by mighty oaks and lindens, and people, freed from the rat race, meditate in peace about their life's purpose, amidst the friendly buzzing of bees (Photograph 31, p. 342). But that's another topic for another day.

Appendix 7
US Hive Plans (Version 3)

Beekeeping equipment standards and common building materials differ from one place to another.* The following US version of the horizontal hive with extra-deep frames accepts standard American frames (17 $^5/_8$ inches long with a 19-inch top bar) and utilizes dimensional lumber and materials commonly available from any hardware store. Besides, this model does not require any special woodworking equipment or advanced woodworking skills. You don't need to know how to cut a rabbet—or even to know what a rabbet is! If you've handled a hammer and a handsaw, you can build a hive like that!

Materials needed

• Framework stock: softwood "two-by-fours," untreated, 8 feet long, 6 pieces.
• Plywood for interior lining: $^3/_8$ inch thick, 4 x 8 feet, 1 sheet.
• Wood siding (thick exterior grade plywood, untreated, textured and grooved on one side): $^5/_8$ inch thick, 4 x 8 feet, 1 sheet.
• Rigid foam insulation: 1 $^1/_2$ inch thick, 4 x 8 feet, 1 sheet.

* This Appendix was prepared by the Editor. *Ed.*

- Roofing material: asphalt corrugated roof panel (usually 48 x 79 inches), 1 sheet.
- Roofing (asphalt) paper, 36 inches wide, 1 roll.
- Weather strip (the foam kind, with adhesive on one side), 11 feet.
- Mending plates (the type used in timber framing—perforated metal with spikes on one side—to connect the framework stock): 2 x 4 inches, 18 pieces.
- Screws (for assembling the roof framework), 3-inch, 8 screws.
- Screws (for assembling the hive box), 4-^{1}/$_2$-inch, 16 screws.
- Nails, 1-^{1}/$_2$-inch, 1 pound.
- Roofing nails or screws with rubber washers, 2- to 2-^{1}/$_2$-inch, 1 dozen.
- Hinges (to attach the top and the bottom to the hive body), 4 hinges total.
- Slide latches (to close and open the bottom), 2 pieces.
- Safety hook and eye (for the top), 1.
- Light-colored paint, 1 quart.

Tools needed

- Hand saw (alternatively, an electric jigsaw or circular saw).
- Miter box (if using a hand saw).
- Hammer.
- Drill with an assortment of wood bits.
- Screw driver.
- Staple gun (optional).
- Tape measure.
- Angle square.

- Knife (to cut insulation and roofing paper).
- Pencil.
- Paint brush.

Building instructions

Figure 16.A–D:

1. Measure, mark (F1, F2 etc.), and cut the plywood, siding board, insulation, and framework stock as shown.

Figure 16.E:

2. In parts F7 and F8, cut out the hive entrance slit as shown. In parts S7-1 and S7-2, cut out a strip as shown.

Figure 16.F:

3. Lay out the frame stock for the front wall, back wall, and two side walls as shown (the stock's wider side lies flat on the ground). Connect using mending plates (hammer them in). Align the top frame as shown (the stock "stands" on its narrower side). Pre-drill and assemble on screws (2 per corner).

4. Align the interior lining as shown and nail it to the frames. Then flip them over.

5. Fill the frames with insulation, then cover with roofing paper cut to size. Hold roofing paper in place with staples or glue.

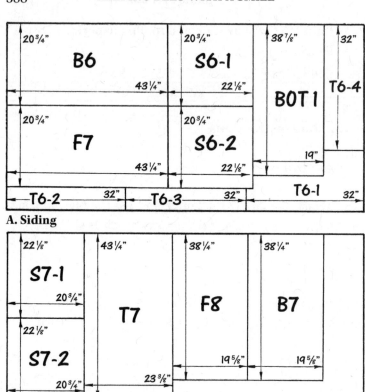

A. Siding

B. Lining

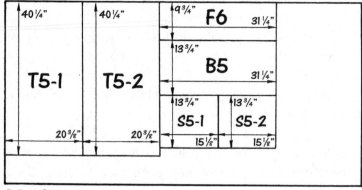

C. Insulation

Figure 16. US hive plans (Version 3)

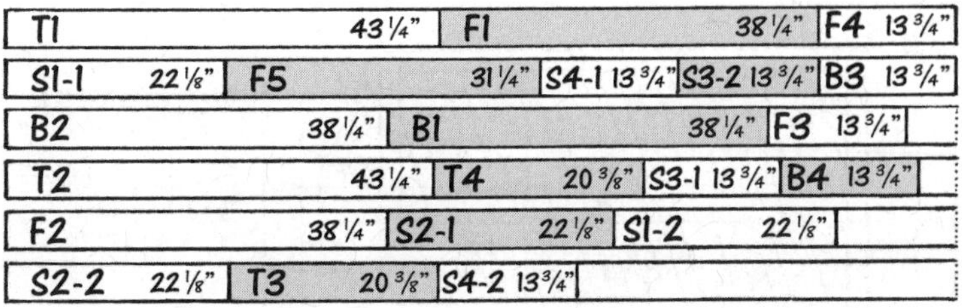

T1		43¼"	F1		38¼"	F4	13¾"
S1-1	22⅛"	F5		31¼"	S4-1 13¾"	S3-2 13¾"	B3 13¾"
B2		38¼"	B1		38¼"	F3	13¾"
T2		43¼"	T4	20⅜"	S3-1 13¾"	B4 13¾"	
F2		38¼"	S2-1	22⅛"	S1-2	22⅛"	
S2-2	22⅛"	T3	20⅜"	S4-2 13¾"			

D. Framework stock

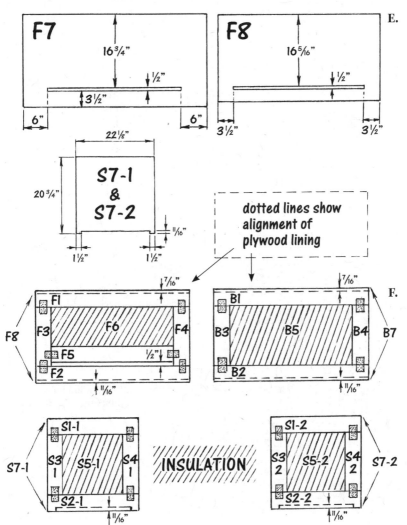

E.

F7
16¾"
½"
3½"
6"   6"

F8
16⁵⁄₁₆"
½"
3½"   3½"

22⅛"
S7-1 & S7-2
20¾"
¹¹⁄₁₆"
1½"   1½"

dotted lines show
alignment of
plywood lining

F.

⁷⁄₁₆"
F1
F8 F3   F6   F4   B7
F5   ½"
F2
¹¹⁄₁₆"

⁷⁄₁₆"
B1
B3   B5   B4
B2
¹¹⁄₁₆"

S1-1
S7-1   S3 1   S5-1   S4 1
S2-1
¹¹⁄₁₆"

INSULATION

S1-2
S3 2   S5-2   S4 2   S7-2
S2-2
¹¹⁄₁₆"

F.

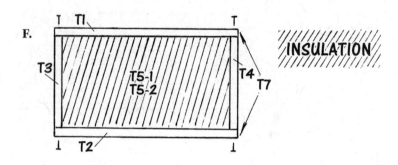

G.

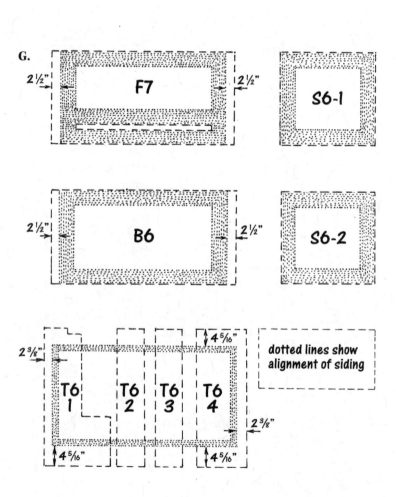

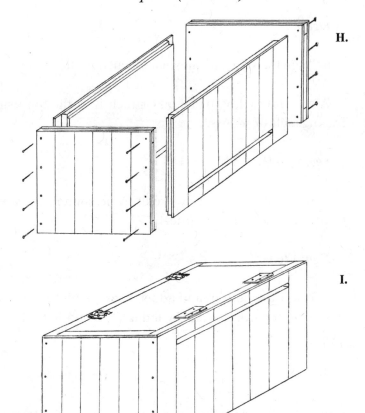

H.

I.

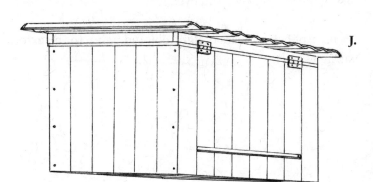

J.

Figure 16.G:

6. Align the siding as shown and nail it to the frames.

7. Cut the roofing panel and attach it to the top using roofing nails or screws.

Figure 16.H:

8. Assemble the hive box. Pre-drill and connect the walls as shown (4 screws per corner).

Figure 16.I:

9. Insert the bottom and attach it to the hive body with hinges on the front-wall side and latches on the back-wall side.

Figure 16.J:

10. Attach the weather strip along the entire perimeter of the top's underside (1 inch in from the edges). Attach the top to the front wall using hinges, and secure it to the back wall using the safety hook and eye.

11. Apply two coats of light-colored paint, to the exterior surfaces only.

Dimensions

Hive body internal dimensions
Depth (top of the top bar to the bottom)   20"
Length $18\,^3/_8$"
Width $38\,^1/_4$"

Hive body external dimensions
Depth $20\,^3/_4$"
Length $23\,^3/_8$"
Width $43\,^1/_4$"

Part list and dimensions

	Front wall	Back wall	Side wall, x2	Top
Frame, 2-by-4s, $3\,^1/_2$"x $1\,^1/_2$"	F1 $38\,^1/_4$" F2 $38\,^1/_4$" F3 $13\,^3/_4$" F4 $13\,^3/_4$" F5 $31\,^1/_4$"	B1 $38\,^1/_4$" B2 $38\,^1/_4$" B3 $13\,^3/_4$" B4 $13\,^3/_4$"	S1 $22\,^1/_8$" S2 $22\,^1/_8$" S3 $13\,^3/_4$" S4 $13\,^3/_4$"	T1 $43\,^1/_4$" T2 $43\,^1/_4$" T3 $20\,^3/_8$" T4 $20\,^3/_8$"
Lining, $^3/_8$" thick	F8 $38\,^1/_4$"x $19\,^5/_8$"	B7 $38\,^1/_4$"x $19\,^5/_8$"	S7 $22\,^1/_8$" x $20\,^3/_4$"	T7 $43\,^1/_4$"x $23\,^3/_8$"
Siding, $^5/_8$" thick	F7 $43\,^1/_4$"x $20\,^3/_4$"	B6 $43\,^1/_4$"x $20\,^3/_4$"	S6 $22\,^1/_8$" x $20\,^3/_4$"	T6 48" x 32"
Insulation, $1\,^1/_2$" thick	F6 $31\,^1/_4$" x $9\,^3/_4$"	B5 $31\,^1/_4$"x $13\,^3/_4$"	S5 $15\,^1/_8$" x $13\,^3/_4$"	T5 $40\,^1/_4$"x $20\,^3/_8$"
Roofing paper	F9 $38\,^1/_4$"x $20\,^3/_4$"	B8 $38\,^1/_4$"x $20\,^3/_4$"	S8 $22\,^1/_8$" x $20\,^3/_4$"	T8 $43\,^1/_4$"x $23\,^3/_8$"

Bottom: BOT1 $38\,^7/_8$" x 19"

Notes and observations

• You can fill this hive with extra-deep frames that you make yourself. Alternatively, you can make an extra-deep frame by connecting two standard deep frames (9 $1/4$ inches deep) obtained from any beekeeping supply company. This will result in a frame 18 $1/2$ inches deep. Cut off the top bar "shoulders" on the lower frame, then connect it to the upper frame with a mending plate on each side, using $3/8$-inch wood screws. (Use the furniture-type mending plate—a thin strip of metal about 3 inches long with four countersunk holes.) The resulting "double-deep" frame can be disconnected and extracted in a standard honey extractor.

• This hive model does not provide for a bee space above the top bars. If you use standard commercial frames with top bars that do not touch, cover them with a sheet of heavyweight cloth. Otherwise the bees will glue the frames to the hive's top. You do not need a cloth if you make your own frames with top bars that touch.

• If possible, build the hive as much in advance as possible, as bees may not like the smell of freshly cut lumber.

• This model can further be improved by using more eco-friendly materials (e.g., tongue-and-groove solid wood boards instead of plywood, etc.). With minor modification, it can also be made with a gable roof, with a bottom screen, or a removable back panel (see Appendix 6).

• The approximate material cost for this model, as of 2013, is $200. This figure can be substantially reduced by using reclaimed or substitute materials (e.g., used pallets for lumber stock, straw for insulation, etc.).

Glossary

Amitraz—a poisonous chemical used to treat bees for Varroa mite infestations.

Apiarist—a beekeeper.

Apiary—a beeyard, a place where bees are kept in manmade hives.

Apiculture—the practice and science of beekeeping.

Apis mellifera—the scientific species name for the European honeybee.

Afterswarm—a second, third, etc. swarm cast by a colony during one season. It contains a virgin queen.

Bait hive or **swarm trap**—a small hive or box hung in the tree to attract stray swarms. *Photos 15–18.*

Beebread—fermented pollen stored in comb cells and used to feed the brood and the queen. *Photo 8.*

Bee brush—a soft brush for swiping bees off the comb.

Bee gum or **log hive**—a hollowed section of a tree trunk serving as a hive, positioned horizontally or upright.

Bee space—a space between ¹/₄ and ³/₈ inch (6.4–9.5 mm) that allows for free passage of bees, but which they will not fill with comb or propolis. Discovery of bee space allowed the design of a hive from which frames with comb could be easily removed.

Beeswax—the substance secreted by worker bees to build comb.

Brace comb—strips of comb built to connect two adjacent honeycombs.

Brood—immature bees contained in comb cells: eggs, larvae, and pupae. *Photos 8–10.*

Body—in multi-story hives, the deep box containing the brood nest.

Bottom supering—in multi-story hive management, adding supers (shallow boxes) under the existing supers (i.e., under the lowest super and above the hive's body). *Figure 2, p. 79.*

Buildup, spring and **fall**—a rapid increase in the number of workers due to the queen's accelerated egg-laying activity.

Capped honey—comb honey sealed with a thin layer of wax. *Photo 23.*

Catalase—an enzyme secreted by the bees to prevent spoilage of their intestinal contents during wintering.

Cleansing flight—a mass flight of bees in early spring to purge their intestines.

Cluster, winter—a dense ball of bees formed to share and retain heat during winter. *Figure 1, p. 35.*

Colony—a bee family; a group of bees living together as one unit. Normally, a colony is composed of a queen, workers, drones, and brood, and occupies a tree hollow or a hive.

Comb—the wax structure that bees build to store honey and pollen, and to rear brood in. *Photos 8–10, 19, 23–26.*

Dadant, Charles (1817–1902)—a French-American beekeeper and inventor of the multi-story hive model that is now prevalent in Russia.

Dadant frame—as referred to in this book, a frame 17 $^1/_8$ inches (435 mm) long and 11 $^{13}/_{16}$ inches (300 mm) deep. In the United States, the standard Dadant brood frame dimensions are slightly different: 17 $^5/_8$ inches long by 11 $^1/_4$ inches deep.

Dearth—a period with no nectar flow in nature.

Deep frame—in this book, a Dadant standard-length frame that is 11 $^{13}/_{16}$ inches (300 mm) deep. In the United States today, "deep frames" are usually 9 $^1/_4$ inches deep.

Depth—the vertical dimension (height) of a hive or frame.

Division board—a board used to divide a horizontal hive into two parts: to separate the nest from the empty portion in winter and spring, or to separate two colonies occupying the same hive.

Drawing comb—building comb.

Drone—a male bee. Drones only serve for reproduction—to mate with virgin queens from other colonies. They die after their first mating. Drones still remaining in the colony in the fall are refused food and carried out of the hive, where they die.

Egg—the first stage of a bee's development, an elongated white capsule resembling a grain of rice. Eggs are laid almost exclusively by the queen. Fertilized eggs develop into female bees and unfertilized eggs into males (drones).

Emergency queen—a queen raised from an egg that was originally laid in a standard cell and intended to become a worker bee.

European dark bee (*Apis mellifera mellifera*)—the race (subspecies) of the European honeybee (*Apis mellifera*) native to central-northern Europe and farther east. It is darker in color and is better adapted to northern latitudes.

Extractor or **honey extractor**—a barrel or a large bucket in which frames containing honeycomb are spun to extract honey by centrifugal force.

Extra-deep frame—standard-length frame that is at least 17 ¹/₂ inches (450 mm) deep. *Photos 23–26.*

Feeder—a container with sugar syrup, honey, or other food for bees. The frame feeder described in this book is inserted into a hive like a frame and has an opening on one side for the bees to access the food. *Photo 21.*

Flow or **honeyflow**—the availability of nectar in nature.

Forager bee—a worker bee that flies out of the hive to collect nectar, pollen, water, and resin.

Foundation—a sheet of wax or plastic stamped with the bottoms of comb cells. Bees proceed to draw (build) comb from the foundation.

Frame—a rectangular enclosure for comb, usually made of wood. A frame with comb can be freely removed from and returned to the hive. A frame is composed of a top bar, two end bars (the vertical bars), and a bottom bar.

Hive tool—a tool resembling a small pry bar that is used for loosening frames glued with propolis, separating hive boxes, and for cleaning the hive.

Honeydew—the sweet liquid secreted by aphids and collected by bees if nectar is scarce.

Honeyflow or **flow**— the availability of nectar in nature.

Horizontal hive—a hive in which the nest can be expanded laterally rather than by adding boxes on top. The horizontal hive described in this book contains 25 frames that are 18 ¹/₂ inches (470 mm) deep. *Photos 1–2, 7, 22.*

Landing board—a board attached under the hive's entrance to assist bees with landing and entering the hive.

Langstroth hive—the multi-story movable-frame hive invented by L.L. Langstroth; currently the most widely used hive in the world.

Langstroth, Lorenzo Lorraine (1810–1895)—an American clergyman and prominent beekeeper; inventor of a movable-frame multistory hive that utilizes the correct bee space and is now the most widely used hive in the world.

Larva—"the little white worm," the second stage of immature bee development inside a comb cell, following an egg, and preceding a pupa. *Photo 8.*

Layens, Georges de (1834–1897)—a French botanist and apiculturist; inventor of one of the first horizontal hives with movable extra-deep frames. *Figures 3–4.*

Log hive or **bee gum**—a hollowed section of a tree trunk serving as a hive, positioned horizontally or upright.

Mating flight—a virgin queen flying out of the hive to mate with drones (male bees). The queen mates only once in her life, but with many drones. She then stores live sperm inside her body.

Nest—the interior of bees' home, especially the combs where brood is reared (the brood nest). *Photos 8–10.*

Nosema or **nosematosis**—a disease affecting adult honeybees. It is caused by a microscopic fungus, *Nosema*, and manifests with diarrhea, bees' inability to fly, and other symptoms.

Nucs or **nucleus colonies**—small colonies obtained by dividing a larger colony into several parts. Nucs are usually housed in smaller boxes containing three to six (usually five) frames.

Orientation flight—a bee flying in wide circles around the hive to remember its location and the environs before heading out into the field.

Primary swarm—the first swarm cast by a colony in the season. It contains a fertile old queen.

Proboscis—a bee's straw-like tongue, which she uses for sucking nectar.

Propolis—resins collected by bees from plants and used to seal cracks and smoothen surfaces inside the hive.

Pulling honey—collecting combs filled with honey from the hive.

Pupa—the final stage of immature bee development, following the larval stage. The pupa is enclosed in a cocoon spun by the larva inside the comb cell.

Rabbet—in woodworking, a groove cut in the wood. The top inner edge on the front and back walls of the hive has a rabbet cut into it to accept the frame rests—the protruding "shoulders" by which the frames are suspended inside the hive.

Races of bees—in beekeeping, honeybee subspecies, hybrids, or other groups that have similar characteristics.

Queen—the reproductive female bee.

Sealed brood—cells containing pupae undergoing the final metamorphosis before emerging as adult bees. *Photos 8–10.*

Skep—a dome-shaped basket used as a hive.

Smoker—a metal can with attached bellows, used for burning partially decayed wood or other fuel to generate smoke and deter bee attacks during hive inspections.

Split—part of a colony artificially separated from the mother colony to produce a new one.

Spring inspection—once the winter is over, examining the nest for the presence of brood (i.e., a live queen) and sufficient food reserves.

Super—a shallow box in a multi-story hive, used by bees for storing honey reserves.

Supersedure—a natural replacement of a colony's old queen with a new one. To perform supersedure, worker bees build special large queen cells, where the new queen is reared. Once she emerges, she kills the old queen.

Surplus honey—honey above what is required for the colony to winter and that can be pulled by the beekeeper.

Swarm—a large group of bees, including a queen, leaving the parental hive to establish a new colony. After emerging from the hive, the swarm congregates on an object (e.g., a tree branch) in a beard-like formation. Once the scout bees discover a suitable cavity for the new home, the swarm takes off and flies to occupy it. *Photo 12.*

Swarming—the natural process by which bees procreate. After raising a new queen, half the colony's workers and the existing queen leave to find a new home and start a new colony. The other half stay behind with the new queen. In a given season, a colony may cast none, one, or more swarms. Most swarms emerge in late spring and early summer.

Swarm box—any kind of box used for collecting swarms. *Photo 13.*

Swarm trap or **bait hive**—a small hive or box hung in the tree to attract stray swarms. Photos 15–18.

Thymol—a natural aromatic substance derived from thyme and used to treat bees for Varroa mite infestations.

Tree hive (Russian: *bort'*)—an artificial tree hollow in a living tree, often at considerable height, made for attracting and housing bee colonies. After natural tree hollows, tree hives are Russia's most ancient form of beekeeping and are still used today.

Top bar—the upper plank of a frame. Top bars can also be used without a frame, as bees will draw comb down from these. Top-bar hives were the first movable-comb hives and various models are still in use today.

Varroa—a parasitic mite, *Varroa destructor*, which attacks bees.

Virgin queen—a young queen bee that has not yet completed her mating flights and thus cannot lay fertilized eggs.

Wax moth—any of the species of moths that feed on bees' pollen, cocoons, and honeycomb, burrowing through wax and damaging the bee nest. They usually infest weaker bee colonies, abandoned hives, or honeycomb stored in a warm place. Wax moths include the lesser wax moth (*Achroia grisella*), the greater wax moth (*Galleria mellonella*), and, native to Europe, the bee moth (*Aphomia sociella*).

Winterizing—preparing bees for the winter, especially insulating the hives and rearranging nest frames to assure that they contain sufficient amounts of food.

Worker bees—infertile female bees that carry out all the work in the colony.

Index

MEDVINKA
Natural Beekeeping and Permaculture Center
Kaluga region, Russia (150 miles southwest of Moscow)

www.medvinka.ru

After years of working with bees and pondering the causes of their decline throughout the world, I realized the need to show that the natural approach to beekeeping is viable on a larger scale.

This led to the creation of a comprehensive Natural Beekeeping and Permaculture Center Medvinka that includes a model sustainable apiary, a European dark bee conservancy, and a nascent ecovillage—all in a place of amazing natural beauty.

With hundreds of local-race bee colonies housed in spacious horizontal hives, Medvinka offers plentiful volunteer opportunities, hands-on workshops, and a way to learn firsthand how to raise bees disease- and chemical-free while making our Earth beautiful and fostering strong communities. We build hives, catch and install swarms, plant trees and other nectar plants, construct off-grid eco-buildings, educate our children, and, of course, eat good honey—and much more!

We invite you to join us!

Fedor Lazutin
Author of *Keeping Bees With A Smile*

Growing Vegetables With A Smile
by Nikolay Kurdyumov

Unlock your creative abilities by understanding plants and the soil, and use your garden as a model for achieving success in life! Packed with practical advice on all aspects of natural growing, this uplifting volume makes the joy of a bountiful harvest accessible to all. It invites you to become a co-creator with your land, showing that gardening is as much about *you* as it is about cucumbers and tomatoes. You can *enjoy* it, dispense with hard work, and make plants happy and productive all at the same time. Nikolay Kurdyumov shares his gardening wisdom gained from a lifetime of experience and rediscovered permaculture texts of a hundred years ago. His humor and positive attitude are contagious. You will feel like running into your backyard, sticking seeds into the soil, and then... growing *with* your plants!

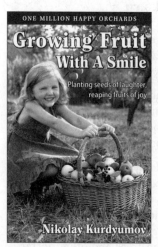

Growing Fruit With A Smile
by Nikolay Kurdyumov

Harvest tons of fabulous fruit and discover some of the Universe's most cherished secrets! A jaw-dropping read for both experienced fruit growers and backyard gardeners planting their first tree. Richly illustrated and chock-full of amazing information not found anywhere else. Immensely practical, thorough, and fun! Want to grow *five-pound* pears? That's easy! Ever thought it possible to get 20 tons of apples from your backyard, or to grow grapes in Manitoba? This book shows you how! You'll learn how to • Start an orchard from scratch *for free* with your own planting stock. • Prune with confidence—and discover tricks that make pruning unnecessary. • Graft like a pro and train trees into any shape for beauty and bumper crops. • Hoodwink pests and understand what trees want from you—and what you *really* want from them. • And *heaps* more. Totally eclipses all your Apple or Blackberry capabilities!

The Art of Soaring
by Vladimir Dolokhov & Vadim Gurangov

If bees can soar, so can you! When first published, *The Art of Soaring* stayed at the top of Russian bestseller lists for a whole *year*. Revealing potent ancient techniques for manifesting your reality through humor, the book became an instant favorite with over *one million* readers from all walks of life. Changing your life *on the spot* has never been so much *fun*! The theory section is followed by *dozens of* tantalizing real-life stories of healed personal relationships, financial success, miracle cures, and more. Simple and irresistibly positive, *The Art of Soaring* will make you feel *lighter*, and as you start applying these amazing techniques, get ready for miracles and laughter to enter your everyday life. Visit **www.DeepSnowPress.com** to find out more, and prepare for takeoff!

The Power of Luck: A User's Manual
by Vladimir Dolokhov & Vadim Gurangov

Building up the runaway success of their bestseller *The Art of Soaring*, the authors propel you into the stratosphere of light and laughter. With its hilarious real-life stories and a veritable avalanche of everyday magic, *The Power of Luck* unveils an ancient tradition of dissolving any problems in humor. It offers a path to laughter, freedom, and power. Put luck to work and let *your* results speak for themselves! Things you *never* believed possible are now within your reach. Have noisy neighbors? Use the mute button on your remote control to calm them down! Tomatoes not ripening on time? Walk your garden in a swimsuit, and they'll blush red! This book's mind-bending and efficient techniques expand our vision of what can be achieved in this life—and *how*. Please visit **www.DeepSnowPress.com** to discover this and our other outstanding titles.

www.HorizontalHive.com

More and more people begin to keep bees naturally in horizontal hives described in this book.

Horizontal Hive.com offers a place to learn more and to share your experiences.

Detailed plans and step-by-step instructions for making:
- swarm traps;
- horizontal hives;
- extra-deep frames.

How-to advice on:
- attracting local bee swarms;
- keeping bees in horizontal hives;
- preventing and solving problems.

Find suppliers of horizontal hives, swarm traps, extra-deep frames, and related equipment.

Natural beekeeping workshops, conferences, and field days.

And more! Happy keeping bees with a smile!

www.HorizontalHive.com